Date Due

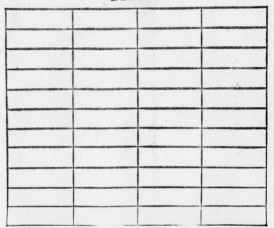

THE HISTORY OF
AMERICAN ORNITHOLOGY
BEFORE AUDUBON

Fig. 1. The Ivory-billed Woodpecker. From Mark Catesby's *Natural History of Carolina, Florida and the Bahama Islands* (1731–1743). Courtesy of the Trustees of the British Museum.

THE HISTORY OF
AMERICAN ORNITHOLOGY
BEFORE AUDUBON

ELSA GUERDRUM ALLEN

Research Associate in Ornithology
Cornell University

NEW YORK / RUSSELL & RUSSELL

TRANSACTIONS OF THE

AMERICAN PHILOSOPHICAL SOCIETY

NEW SERIES, VOL. 41, PART 3

FIRST PUBLISHED IN 1951

REISSUED, 1969, BY RUSSELL & RUSSELL

A DIVISION OF ATHENEUM PUBLISHERS, INC.

BY ARRANGEMENT WITH THE

AMERICAN PHILOSOPHICAL SOCIETY

L. C. CATALOG CARD NO: 68-27045

PRINTED IN THE UNITED STATES OF AMERICA

PREFACE

It is a pleasure to acknowledge the assistance of the many institutions which have made possible these studies and I gratefully express my appreciation to the following learned societies and libraries.

The American Council of Learned Societies for initial aid toward my studies of unpublished manuscripts and drawings of American birds in the British Museum and the Royal Society of London.

The American Philosophical Society for aid by which it was possible to undertake the study of Mark Catesby. Through two grants from the Penrose Fund it was possible to study letters and other source material of Catesby and his sponsors and thus integrate the whole group of botanical and zoological collectors in America in the mid-eighteenth century. I examined source material in the library of the American Philosophical Society.

The National Academy of Sciences for aid toward my study of John Abbot.

The United States National Museum for the privilege of republishing several illustrations of early naturalists.

The British Museum, Department of Manuscripts, for the privilege of consulting many sources relating to American ornithology especially Catesby and Abbot letters, accounts and drawings, and for permission to publish copies of drawings and excerpts from manuscripts, in particular to Mr. A. J. Watson for his assistance and kindness in several particular investigations. The Department of Prints and Drawings for the privilege of studying the John White Originals and to Mr. A. W. Aspital for indispensable aid in my study of John Abbot.

The Natural History Museum for the opportunity to examine unpublished drawings from the Cook Voyages and for permission to publish representative drawings of American birds, and in particular to Mr. F. C. Sawyer, Librarian of the Natural History Museum, and Miss Phyllis Thomas, Librarian at the Tring Museum of Zoology, now a part of the British Museum.

The Royal Society of London and Mr. H. M. Robinson, its Librarian, for permission to copy and publish the Mark Catesby letters in their files, and to examine other manuscripts and records having bearing on Catesby and other naturalists of his time.

Similar aid and courtesy were rendered by the Linnean Society of London, where I studied the correspondence of several naturalists who worked on American birds, the Victoria and Albert Museum Library, the Westminster Library, the Public Record Office, and the Indian Office. At Oxford in the Department of Botany and in the Hope Museum, new materials on Catesby and Abbot were found.

Chetham's Library, Manchester, for the privilege of studying their Abbot manuscripts in 1949 and again in 1950, when permission to make photographic copies of these drawings was given, and to Miss Hilda Lofthouse, Librarian, and her assistants.

The Paisley Public Library of Paisley, Scotland, and its Librarian, Miss Katherine McEwen, for assistance in the study of Alexander Wilson's early life, and Miss J. F. Hamilton for many notes sent me recently, since my time in Paisley was too short to cover all materials.

The Preussische Staatsbibliotek Handschriften Abteilung, Berlin, for permission to study the manuscripts and drawings from the Brazilian expedition of Johann Moritz von Nassau Siegen and George Marcgravius and for copies of selected North American plates to be used in this account.

The University of Upsala and its Library, the Carolina Rediviva, for the privilege of studying materials and manuscripts by and about Linnaeus and his predecessor, Olof Rudbeck. I was greatly aided by Dr. Arvid Uggla, Linnean Scholar at Upsala, and Baron Louis de Geer, the owner of the original Rudbeck drawings of birds which he kindly made available.

I express my appreciation to the following American libraries: Cornell University; the Academy of Natural Sciences of Philadelphia and its Librarian, Mrs. Venia Phillips; the American Museum of Natural History, New York, where Miss Hazel Gay, Librarian, has extended loans of books and checked bibliographical matters in books not available at Cornell; the Army Medical Library, History of Medicine Division, Cleveland, where Miss Dorothy Schullian, Curator of Rare Books, assisted in my study of Volcher Coiter, and arranged for the loan of Dutch books from the Library of the Surgeon General, Washington, and for the privilege of publishing Coiter's rare tract on the classification of birds; the Library of Congress, Washington, Manuscript Department for the privilege of examining Catesby and Jones Family Papers and Mark Catesby letters; and to the Boston Society of Natural History, now the New England Museum, for the privilege of studying their John Abbot drawings, now in the Houghton Collection of the Harvard Library, and to Mr. Philip Hofer and Miss Carolyn Jakeman for assistance in copying these drawings; Library of the University of Georgia, Athens, where is preserved another set of John Abbot bird drawings, and to Mr. W. W. De Renne for his interest and assistance in this project. Alpha Omicron Pi Society for the Ruth Capin Farmer Memorial Fellowship awarded toward a year of foreign study, which helped to make possible the study of Catesby and other naturalists in their home territory. The New-York Historical Society for recent aid.

I would also express grateful appreciation to the following persons: Dr. John T. Zimmer, Curator of Birds, American Museum of Natural History, Dr. Alexander Wetmore, Secretary, Smithsonian Institution, Dr. Herbert Friedmann, Curator of Birds, United States National Museum, and Mr. Rudyard Boulton, formerly Curator of Birds at the Field Museum, Chicago, for critical reading of the manuscript and helpful suggestions; Dr. Robert Cushman Murphy, Curator of Oceanic Birds, American Museum of Natural History, for long sustained interest in these studies; Professor Clark S. Northup, Professor of English, Emeritus at Cornell University, under whom these studies were begun; Dr. George Sarton, Professor of the History of Science, Harvard University, for long continued interest and introductions abroad; my husband, Dr. Arthur A. Allen, Professor of Ornithology, Cornell University, for constructive criticism and expert aid in elucidating many old accounts of birds and in identifying obscure plumages in old drawings.

Both here and abroad, I am indebted in numerous ways to many friends, of whom I would mention the following: Miss Ethel Davis, Bradford, Pa. for Latin translations; Mrs. Elizabeth van der Hoek, Ithaca, N. Y. for her translation of Dutch and old German letters; Mr. T. Catesby Jones, New York, N. Y. for information regarding Catesby source material; Drs. Friedrich Solmsen, Howard Adelmann, and Henry Guerlac, Cornell University; Mrs. Belle Gore, Principial Probate Registry, London; Mrs. Ulle Agrell, Vetenskaps Akademie, Stockholm, Sweden; Dr. Francis Harper, Bartram Association of Philadelphia; Dr. Leon A. Hausman, New Jersey College for Women; Mrs. Margaret Kennard, Washington, D. C.; Dr. Raymond Stearns, University of Illinois; Mr. Alexander Sprunt, Charleston, S. C.; Miss Margaret McKean, Johnstone, Renfrewshire, Scotland; Miss Elsa Lundell, Upsala, Sweden; Miss Sarah Tichenor, Elmira, N. Y.

I wish to acknowledge with appreciation the assistance of those persons who have helped in the typing, checking, and assembling of this manuscript, especially my daughters, Jean Frank Allen and Phebe Allen Travis; Mrs. B. E. Beasley for checking the bibliography and footnotes; Mrs. Florence Clark for many hours of typing.

Much of this book was written in the Laboratory of Ornithology where paintings of birds by Fuertes, Audubon, and other artists look down from the walls, ornithological books line the shelves, and interesting students of birds from many parts of the world provide stimulating associations.

E. G. A.

THE HISTORY OF AMERICAN ORNITHOLOGY BEFORE AUDUBON

ELSA G. ALLEN

CONTENTS

INTRODUCTION

In any field of study there comes a time when the story of its early growth and development should be told. Modern exact science in whatever branch of knowledge has not suddenly appeared, but by long labors of persons often unknown or forgotten has it reached its present important stature.

So it is with ornithology. But the historical background does not as a rule interest the average student who, in his effort to keep abreast of modern developments, regards the older period as obsolete and therefore unimportant.

Modern ornithologists, however, are deeply indebted for the vast stores of bird lore gradually assembled and made ready for them by their predecessors, and those who listen to the muse of history acquire not only the riches of information and a seasoned friendship with the past, but also a deepened and quickened ability to dispense their knowledge of birds to others.

It is the purpose of this book to look back on the pages of history and try to recapture the lives and studies of the principal workers on birds from Aristotle to Audubon. So vast a subject must, of necessity, omit a great many, but insofar as has seemed practicable, the book describes the development of the study of birds from the simple beliefs and cave drawings of primitive man to the science and finished plates of the nineteenth century.

Prehistoric bird lore of eight thousand years ago, with illustrations from the caves of southern Spain, is the introduction to this story. It then reviews the work of the ancients, giving a critical summary of Aristotle's studies of birds.

Evidence of the great philosopher's actual dissection of birds and many of his observations in the field are presented with some of his interpretations of migration, hibernation, and other life habits of birds.

The decline of natural philosophy after Aristotle and the lapse of learning in the early centuries of Christianity follow with examples of the use of birds in divination and magic.

The revival of learning under Moslem influence in Spain between the eighth and eleventh centuries prepared the way for the Renaissance of the twelfth century, under the brilliant leadership of Frederick II.

The account sets forth in some detail the progressive influence exercised by Frederick's court on the out-worn methods of scholasticism. Though busy with far-flung schemes of empire, this modern ruler understood the need for imparting the learning and culture of Greece to his peoples. Accordingly, he invited the most erudite thinkers and linguists of Europe to live at his court and devote their time to the translation of the works of the ancients, which had fallen into disuse.

Among other great scholars, Michael Scot (1175–1232) of Som, Scotland, who had spent years at the cultural centers of Spain, was called as being the greatest Aristotelian scholar of the time. When he had finished

the translation of Aristotle's *History of Animals* into Latin, however, Frederick found the great philosopher's knowledge of birds very limited, not only in his favorite subject of hawks and falconry, but also in the structure and habits of birds. The versatile Emperor, who all his life had indulged his passion for hawks, was inspired to set down his own ideas and discoveries, his experiments and interpretations in the realm of birds. His book, *De Arte Venandi cum Avibus,* though from the title it appears to be only a treatise on falconry, is a forthright account of birds, their structure, habits, and care. It was many centuries, however, before we could appreciate the extent of his ornithological knowledge, for not until 1942 was it possible for the Canadian scholar, Dr. Casey Wood, to assemble the many parts in several European languages, and render the whole into English.

The open spirit of enquiry and the searching method of experimentation that pervades Frederick II's work, foreshadows the new concept of direct observation of nature that finally dispelled that shackling belief in authority and gave the world an honest and normal interest in living things.

Frederick's progressive reign ended in 1250, but several factors and events continued to develop public interest in natural knowledge:

1. The rise of the universities which at first were aggregations of masters and students moving from place to place, as conditions prompted them.

2. The founding of the mendicant orders, the Dominicans, by the famous scholastic of Cologne, Albertus Magnus, and the Franciscans by the simple lover of nature, St. Francis of Assisi.

These selfless Christian organizations attracted the best teachers of Europe, who gave their services in the interest of learning and spreading the teachings of Christ.

3. The fall of Constantinople into Turkish possession in 1463, causing the Greek scholars resident there to be exiled to many parts of Europe.

4. The invention of movable type making possible the use of books by educated persons outside the Church.

5. The discovery of the New World.

All these epochal changes, which had their origin deep in the past, combined to produce the Renaissance, that general flowering of culture, in response to great world events. The world of nature, which hitherto had been but vaguely understood, became a fascinating empirical experience for all. Argosies set out to the far parts of the earth and returned, laden with riches and strange animals and plants. Science found many patrons among the noble and the wealthy, and menageries and collections of rarities were set up for the public enjoyment. Artists, too, were patronized by royalty and were engaged to live at the many courts and paint birds, mammals, fish, and reptiles from life. It is little wonder that some of the learned were inspired to name, describe and picture every bird known to them. These encyclopedists, however, understood nothing of the classification of birds according to true relationships.

The development of classification is traced from the unscientific lists of Conrad Gesner (1555), Pierre Belon (1555), and Ulysses Aldrovandus (1603) to the tables worked out by the English naturalists, John Ray and Francis Willughby, after their joint zoological collecting trips on the Continent (1672).

The study of birds by this time in Europe was reaching a high level of accuracy, but at this juncture in the evolution of ornithology, the story shifts to a consideration of early bird-lore in the Western World.

Nothing comparable to the work that had been done in Europe could be expected at this early date in America, but the account surveys the simple contributions of Spanish, French, and English travellers to the study of New World birds in early pre-colonial times.

Records of the Huguenot Colony of 1564 and the Roanoke Colony of 1585, both on our eastern coast, were found to hold references to unpublished ornithological materials in England. Reproductions of this work accompany this account while representative copies of American birds first painted by Captain Cook's artists on our Pacific coast also are included.

Up until 1730 the accounts of the natural history of this country were very incomplete, the labored and imperfect reports of almost any adventurer who spent a few months on these shores.

Something better could be expected of Mark Catesby who under British sponsors spent twelve years in the Colonies, returning to England in 1726. Although primarily a plant collector he produced a sumptuous two volume work, the *Natural History of Carolina Florida and the Bahama Islands,* which was the first publication on American birds. For this Mark Catesby is called the founder of American ornithology. His early life and scientific accomplishments in England have been worked out from British archives, and the story of his collecting, engraving and coloring one hundred American birds is an important chapter in this account of early development of ornithology in America.

Following Catesby, American birds were studied by eminent European compilers who did not visit the New World but their contributions to American descriptive ornithology were nevertheless great. Three British ornithologists, George Edwards, Thomas Pennant, and John Latham, fall into this group, while two continental systematists devoted considerable effort to classifying American birds according to the modern binomial system of nomenclature promulgated by Linnaeus. These workers were the French ornithologist, Brisson (1723–1806), and the German, Peter Simon Pallas (1741–1811).

Ornithological work actually done in America was resumed by another French scientist, Louis Jean Pierre Vieillot (1748–1831), who spent many months in the southern states in the first decade of the nineteenth century, and published his *Histoire des Oiseaux de l'Amérique Septentrionalis* with 131 plates (1807).

In order to clarify the progress that had been made in naming birds according to true relationships the account in connection with its review of these systematic workers sets forth the bearing of Linnaeus' system on the classification of American birds.

The closing chapters are concerned with the development of American ornithology under the influence of British naturalists who emigrated to America and remained here.

The first of these is John Bartram, who established his home on the west bank of the Schuylkill River near Philadelphia. He with his son William are founders of American natural science and William is the first truly American worker in American birds. Another contributor is John Abbot (1751–1840?) who but recently has been discovered as an ornithologist. Known to the great museums of Europe as a collector and painter of insects he nevertheless has done a vast work on American birds which is described from unpublished manuscripts and plates in the British museum and smaller collections of his art in America.

Lastly the book recounts the American career of the immigrant Scot, Alexander Wilson, who, after troubles at home, sought a fresh beginning in a new land (1794). All sources, including the archives of his native town, Paisley, have been brought to bear on this study. A reappraisal of the man and his work has seemed necessary in order to free his name from the unpleasant penumbra of inferiority that has surrounded him for more than a hundred years.

Wilson's death at forty-seven, just before he was to have finished his work, seems to have struck his distinguished friend George Ord with a sense of tragedy. In later years Ord championed Wilson's cause not only in writing his biography but in furthering financially and with friendly vigilance the erection of his long delayed monument in Paisley. Ord likewise brought out a less expensive edition of his works in the hope of building a public for Wilson's nine volume ornithology.

Alexander Wilson was soon superseded by John James Audubon, but his accuracy as an observer of detail and his thoroughness in learning the living bird in its natural environment have earned him the title of Father of American Ornithology. Had he lived his full span of years, he would undoubtedly have had some measure of the fame and popularity which came to his contemporary, Audubon.

It is hoped that this chronicle of bird study over the centuries will brighten many old lights in the ornithological firmament, and that new generations of ornithologists will appreciate the noble work of their predecessors, who often labored under great handicaps. Throughout the account, effort has been made to preserve the continuity of history, to evaluate the bird matter of each contribution in relation to the standards of the period in which it was written, and to present each writer with such details of his life as seem to have influenced his interest in birds.

I. ANCIENT BIRD LORE

It has long been known that southern Spain was a cradle of the human race; that here in the deep ravines gouged through the cork and Spanish oak forests, Neolithic man plied his simple existence. But not until 1913 did it come to light that birds in great variety were closely associated with the lives of these primitive cliff-dwelling people, and that pictures of them were drawn upon the walls of their crude shelters.

These hidden treasures pertaining to the genesis of ornithology remained for the British soldier, writer, and ornithologist, Colonel William Willoughby Verner, to uncover for us. After many campaigns in foreign wars, during which he was never without the panacea of bird-study, Colonel Verner having been wounded in battle, retired to southern Spain and there built a home close to the crags and marshes he had loved in his youth.

For many years he explored the strange caves and sepulchres of these mountains, which at first were interesting to him only as the retreats and nesting stations of the birds he was studying. He gave but little thought to the stories of the goatherds about pictures of animals, fish, men, and women said to be traced upon the walls of certain hidden recesses. But at last one day while riding with a faithful old peasant he questioned him about a distant crag that mounted above the surrounding country. This, he was told, was the "Tajo Segura," where many "relics of the Moors and pictures of animals" were to be found. Colonel Verner resolved to visit the place when his health should permit, for at this time (1901) he was suffering from wounds sustained in South Africa.

Years passed by with only sporadic visits to the Sierras, but in 1910 he took up the exploration of these mysterious mountains once more, and descended into an immense cavern near Ronda. There, wrapped in eternal darkness and safe from wind and rain, he beheld for the first time the tracings and crude script of ancient man upon the walls. Here too were many bones of a race of dwarfs which he presented to the Royal College of Surgeons.

From this point he worked out into other recesses in the mountains, penetrating sometimes five hundred metres into the rock, and he gradually came to realize that he had found treasures bearing upon the early history of man, his mode of living and the animals that sustained him.

He called upon his friend, the Abbé H. Breuil of the Institut de Paleontologie Humaine in Paris, a great authority on cave drawings, to help him decipher the meaning of his findings. Then the two friends photographed and copied and studied the figures of stags, ibex, wolves,

FIG. 2. Cave Drawings of Birds from southern Spain, 4000–6000 B.C. Courtesy *Country Life Magazine,* London.

fishes, and a number of birds, to all of which they assigned an age of from six to eight thousand years. The bird drawings depict a dozen recognizable kinds, among which are the bustard, crane, wild duck, goose, raven, spoonbill, gallinule, ibis, stork, eagle, and hawk. Especially interesting is a long flock of geese in exact formation, with heads up and necks stretched out ready to take off, in precisely the wary manner familiar to every hunter of today.

Such accurate rendering of the habits of birds some five or six thousand years ago may well cause us to reflect on primitive man's good understanding of the creatures round about him. Another similar and remarkable figure among these drawings is the flamingo pictured, according to its strange habit, with inverted bill for feeding in shallow water; clearly these prehistoric people not only knew birds as creatures of the chase on which they depended for food, but they observed them carefully for detail of habit in a way that most persons even today have not yet learned to do.

Lastly, the drawings are located in a cave that apparently served as a shrine. Its walls are worn and polished by the passage of myriad forms through the ages, and from this fact we may definitely connect birds with very early decorative art.

Undoubtedly, man's first relation to birds was as a hunter, because they were an important part of his food supply. In later history he acquired the husbandman's point of view, and soon began to formulate the beginnings of the laws of bird protection.

Moses, the great law-giver, says:

[Deuteronomy 20: 6] If a bird's nest chance to be before thee in the way, in any tree or on the ground, with young ones or eggs, and the dam sitting upon the young or upon the eggs, thou shalt not take the dam with the young: thou shalt in any wise let the dam go, but the young thou mayst take unto thyself; that it may be well with thee and that thou mayest prolong thy days.

The key-note of this decree is the protection of the mother-bird as breeding stock, but the taking of the young holds, in its phraseology, the age-old and moot principle that the hunter has a right to what he finds.

Other scriptural writers refer to birds especially as prognosticators of the seasons because of the regularity of their migrations. The Prophet Jeremiah, who lived on the Dead Sea, was accustomed to see cranes and storks going over and remarked to Judah "The stork in the heaven knoweth her appointed times and the turtle [dove] and the crane and the swallow observe the time of their coming." It is well known that the peasant folk of Palestine planted their crops according to the appearance of the birds in spring, and when the birds flew south in the fall it was time to harvest them.

Since ancient times birds in the popular mind have partaken of some guiding power and this also has further enshrined them in the heart of man and bred in him a reverence for them as well as many tenacious superstitions concerning their behavior, and medicinal properties.

Old travels and chronicles abound in the healing powers of liquors brewed from their bodies and feathers, and the charms cast by the wearing of their quills, claws, and bills.

But this is another story; our theme is the long gradual development of an exact knowledge of birds.

II. ARISTOTLE'S STUDIES OF BIRDS AND THE MIDDLE AGES

Nearly four hundred years before the Christian Era, Aristotle (384–322) was writing about the structure and habits of birds. He wrote also about mammals, fish, snakes, and invertebrates, and for his contributions our knowledge of living things he has come down through twenty-three centuries as the Father of Natural History.

The modern naturalist seldom turns to these zoological treatises, but despite their antiquity, he is usually surprised at their scope and substance. A search for bird matter through the *History of Animals* and the *Parts of Animals* yields a convincing impression of Aristotle's effort to explore the whole field of bird life for he presents a simple classification of birds, a good account of their external appearance, an elementary picture of their internal structure, and much about their habits.

Greek scholars through the centuries have tried to identify Aristotle's birds, to find out which hawks and waterfowl and small song birds were recognized by the great philosopher so long ago. But the identification of his birds in modern terms is not so indicative of Aristotle's ornithological acumen, as is his arrangement of all the birds that he knew according to a plan. The terms "genos" and "eidos" were used by him somewhat as we use "order" and "species," "genos" signifying a large group, while "eidos" was roughly comparable to the modern "species." "Animals of the same eidos generate animals like themselves," says Aristotle.

Birds, according to this writer, form the genos "Ornithes" of which there are 170 kinds and the whole genos is divided into five smaller groups: (1) Gamsonyches (the birds of prey); (2) Steganopodes (the swimming birds); (3) Peristeroide (the pigeons and doves); (4) Apodes (the swifts, martins and swallows); (5) all birds not included in the foregoing divisions.

In the last group, then, Aristotle placed the vast order of Passeriformes or Perching Birds except the swallows (assigned to the Apodes). Here, too, he must have included the very distinctive group of woodpeckers, although he was aware of some of their differences from the perching type.

Of the external appearance of birds, of shape and size, of bill and foot, and manner of flight Aristotle had observed a great deal. In addition to formulating their more obvious distinguishing characters, he understood that their wings were analogous to the forelegs of mammals, but he did not pursue the comparison far enough to realize the homology of these parts. As to the legs of a bird, he said: "Its haunch bone is long, like a thigh and is attached to the body as far as the middle of the belly." Here of course Aristotle mistook the "tarsus" or "shank" for the shin, not realizing that birds stand on their toes and that the foot and ankle bones are fused and elevated into the long tarso-metatarsus.

Aristotle realized that feathers are an essential characteristic of birds and that they correspond to the scales of reptiles. He was aware of the main details of feather structure, the rachis and barbs, and he knew that some feathers as in the ostrich and rhea have soft, hair-like barbs. Lacking instruments of magnification, however, he could not see the barbules that hold the barbs together and give the vanes of the feather their stiffness. He knew that birds change their colors by moulting their feathers, so that they vary with the seasons, and he warned inexperienced observers not to be deceived by these changes.

As to Aristotle's knowledge of dissection, there is always argument, but the critic Lones in his discussion of *Aristotle's Researches in Natural Science* (1913) points out that the various zoological texts show that he dissected parts of 110 kinds of animals and among them are the following birds: dove, duck, goose, owl, pigeon, partridge, quail, and swan. The absence of passerine birds here is notable and can probably be explained by the difficulty of observing, without the aid of instruments, the internal parts of such small subjects.

It is clear, then, that Aristotle opened and examined the principal organs of many birds. He paid particular attention to the alimentary tract; he knew that many birds have a crop for storing food and a glandular proventriculus lying between the crop and the ventriculus or gizzard. He knew that birds have caeca branching off from the alimentary canal, but he was not aware that nearly all birds have only two caeca. The liver, heart, lungs, kidney, spleen, pancreas, and gall bladder of many birds were observed by him, although he did not have a clear understanding of their functions. The determination of sex in species in which the male and female are alike in appearance is a question that has led even modern ornithologists into error, but Aristotle was able to recognize the birds' sex organs for he speaks of determining the sex of turtle doves and ring doves, in which the sexes are much alike, by "an examination of their interiors."

He examined also the brains of some birds but he did not understand that the brain is the nervous center of the organism. Rather did he believe that the brain served as a heat-regulating organ. He dissected out the brains of some birds and compared their weights with the brain-weights of larger animals. He likewise made some observations on the tongues of birds, believing that birds with broad tongues could talk. The tongue of the wryneck he knew to be long and protractile, while other woodpeckers, he said, had divided tongues like the serpents, and the whole tribe of woodpeckers had zygodactyl feet.

Closely allied to his knowledge of bird anatomy is his description of the bird embryo. He cannot be credited with a daily record of the chick embryo although his predecessor, Hippocrates (460–359 or 377), had recommended such a procedure,[1] but he was the first to put on record any accurate examinations of the developing embryo. He described the appearance of the embryo chick on the fourth day of incubation and again on the tenth and twentieth days, noting the progressive development of the heart appearing as a pulsating red spot on the white of the egg, the convoluted blood vessels, the embryonic membrane and finally the position of the bill, wing and claw with relation to the shell. In speaking of hatching pigeons he observed that the shell was damaged on the twentieth day although he did not appear to know whether the chick or the adult had broken it. It was Albertus Magnus (1193?–1280) some fifteen hundred years later who was the first to describe how the young bird breaks the shell with its bill.

We see that he reached also into the realm of the living bird. Field observation on almost every phase of the life history of birds can be found in Books VI, VIII, and IX of the *History of Animals*. Some of the topics that Aristotle discussed apparently from his personal [2] observation are the following: habitat; mating; nesting, including different types of nests; eggs, their color, shape, structure; food of birds; moult; voice and song; flight; sanitation; parasitism; brooding; hibernation; migration.

These subjects indicate that he attempted to present a complete account of birds. It is impossible that his views should be ours. But there is a substantial share of truth in all of his observations, except on those subjects that were steeped in folk belief.

A persistent legend about birds in ancient Greece was the belief that they hibernate in the bottom of ponds and spring holes. "Swallows, for instance, have been found in holes quite denuded of their feathers, and the kite on its first emergence from torpidity has been seen to fly from out some such hiding place," says Aristotle. This way of accounting for the fall disappearance of birds survived until modern times. Even such excellent observers as the great Linnaeus and Gilbert White could not be convinced of the fallacy of this myth. The American ornithologist, Dr. Elliott Coues [3] (1842–1899), was sufficiently interested in this subject to compile a bibliography of the hibernation of swallows and many of the entries are from the current literature of his time. It is not surprising, therefore, that an ancient writer should subscribe to this belief and use it to explain the apparent complete absence of some birds in all localities in winter. Says Aristotle, "We would defy anyone to assert that he had anywhere seen a turtle-dove in wintertime." [4]

Migration was resorted to by many birds but was apparently a matter of choice rather than an age-old instinct as we now know it to be. Of this Aristotle says, ". . . as men of great possessions spend their summer in cool places and their winter in sunny ones, so also all animals that can do so shift their habitat at various seasons." [5] He thought migration was primarily for the purpose of obtaining food or to escape cold, and if the bird were in poor condition, it made more haste to migrate. Equally credulous is his acceptance of the goatsucker legend, that these birds and other birds of the nighthawk and whip-poor-will type descend upon goats at night, attaching themselves to their udders causing the animals to go blind and often to die. But such occasional lapses into folk belief in this remote past should not detract from the great mass of ornithological information that he assembled. He has provided a large compendium of observations, much of which is still reliable.

Are there any circumstances in Aristotle's life that help to explain his unique interest in the crawling, prowling, and flying creatures about him?

His native city was Stagira lying on the northeast coast of Greece in the Gulf of Rendina, and here he was born in 384 B.C., the son of a skilled physician, Nichomachus, under whose guidance he had opportunity to observe animals which were used for dissection and sacrificial rites. As a youth he went with his father to the Court of Philip of Macedon (382–336 B.C.) and stayed several years, and his boyhood by the sea, together with

---

[1] Adelmann, 1935: 327–328. This notation refers to the bibliography where there is complete information concerning the source involved.

[2] Sarton, George, According to Jaeger (*Isis, Jour. Hist. Sci.,* **35** (100) : 181, 1944) he suggests the *Historia Animalium* shows traces of several authors and he thinks that the work of observation was distributed among several persons from the outset.

[3] Coues, 1878: 378–389.

[4] Aristotle, *History of animals*, Bk. 8, 16: 600a, Oxford, 1910.

[5] *Ibid.*, Bk. 8, 12: 596B.

the years in Macedonia, gave him ample opportunity to observe nature. His critic the late D'Arcy Wentworth Thompson, Professor of Natural History at University College, Dundee, sees these circumstances as potent factors in shaping his life for the study of natural science.[6]

Other travels also widened his knowledge of nature. He knew the islands of the Aegean Sea well. Here, wandering along the varied coastline, he learned the strange habits of marine animals. He was especially interested in the Island of Lesbos where his friend, Hermias (–344 B.C.) ruled, and where he and Xenocrates (396–314 B.C.), another disciple of Plato, (427–347 B.C.), spent two years following Plato's death. The people of Athens, fearing the political ambitions of Hermias, plotted his murder and this left Aristotle stranded in Lesbos with Hermias' adopted daughter, Pythias, and Xenocrates. Eventually Aristotle married this woman out of compassion, it is said, for her defenseless position, and after two years he was called to the court of Philip of Macedon to educate the young prince Alexander (356–323 B.C.), then about fourteen years of age (343 B.C.). During the four years that Aristotle acted as his tutor an enduring friendship was founded between master and pupil, a friendship which in later years furnished protection to Aristotle. This friendship, however, at the same time, furnished grounds for the Athenians to plot against him, for they feared nothing more than the growing power of Macedonia. At eighteen, Alexander, following the death of Philip, became Regent and entered upon his career of conquest.

Some writers have said that Aristotle accompanied Alexander on his campaigns, but this statement is doubted today; likewise the old tradition that specimens were sent to him from these conquered territories. Instead, Aristotle, after twelve years' absence, returned to Athens, and under the protection of Macedonia, continued his teachings which he had begun when he left Plato's school about 347 B.C. He did a great deal of writing during this period, but he had many political enemies who sought to ruin him because of his association with Alexander. It became necessary for him to leave Athens, and he retired to Chalcis in Euboea, was deprived of citizenship on the pretext of impiety for erecting a statue to his friend Hermias, and, because he refused to return for trial, he was sentenced to death. Frail health and excessive study, however, had already marked him, and he died at sixty-two in 322 B.C.

There seems to be little in addition to Aristotle's travels, which after all were not extensive, to account for his interest in animal life. We are left with the conviction that he in truth was born a naturalist and some of the events of his life served to strengthen an already determined leaning toward zoology.

If Aristotle's work in the study of animals could have been continued by disciples of his example, there probably would not have been the great lapse in natural phi-

losophy that marks the next several centuries. But many factors brought about the gradual cessation of the study of animal life. Aristotle's successor in the Peripatetic School was his personal friend Theophrastus (382–287 B.C.), a man with a primary interest in plant study, whose work on classification and physiology is considered as important to botany as was Aristotle's *History of Animals* to zoology. Theophrastus contemplated, also, a work on animal life, in which he planned to study more closely many of Aristotle's promulgations, but if he ever wrote this book, it has been lost. Straton, a physicist, after thirty-seven years, succeeded Theophrastus as president of the school. He served for eighteen years and is known for his theories of color and sound, and for studies of the embryo, week by week, but nothing comparable to Aristotle's forthright investigation of living creatures was done. The study of nature in Greece was giving way to less original fields such as ethics and rhetoric and we must look to Italy for such small contribution to animal study as was made.

A popular form of literature in Rome prior to the Christian Era was the general encyclopaedia made up of epitomized accounts of the various branches of knowledge. These contained little or no direct observation but had a bookish tone showing that the compilers had read widely. Varro (–216 B.C.), Verrius Flaccus (*ca.* 75), Tranquillus Suetonius (70?–140) and the Elder Pliny were all encyclopaedists, the last of whom was the most important to natural science. His full name was Gaius Plinius Segundus (A.D. 23–79).

Pliny began his writing as a young man, and while engaged in the Germanic wars as a cavalry officer he wrote copious notes and stories that he heard about birds and animals. Unfortunately he had not the ability to organize and weed out his material, but put the whole heterogeneous mass into his *Natural History*. Thus was compiled the principal review of knowledge of the first century and the *Historia Naturalis* is the best index to the then current Roman attitude toward the animate world. In addition to its discussion of the natural history of the various animal groups—birds, mammals, fish, serpents, and shell animals, it treats of physics, astronomy, agriculture, metals, and art. Pliny attempted to cover all fields in which the educated Roman might be interested, and he assembled a prodigious amount of fact, hearsay, and legend. But there is little that has stood the test of time.

The whole work occupies thirty-seven "books," a thick tome which was rendered into English by Philemon Holland (1552–1637), and published in London in 1601. Book X is devoted to "Fowles and Flying Creatures," with a few pages on vipers, salamanders, and the sleep of animals at the end of the chapter. At the conclusion of the bird matter, he put a paragraph on the "bat, the only bird which suckles its young."

Pliny took the obvious character of the feet as the basis of his arrangement of birds and divided them into

---

[6] Thompson, 1913.

"those with wide hooked talons as hawkes; or round long clawes as Hennes; or else they be broad, flat and whole footed as geese and all the sort in manner of water-fowle." But he failed to proceed with the discussion of them in any orderly manner, and incorporated folk belief and accurate comment indiscriminately as it crossed his mind.

For example, the fights of the Pygmies with the Cranes made a popular tale, which he describes as follows:

The Pygmies, a pretty people three times nine inches high, are much troubled with cranes and in spring they (the Pygmies) all set out mounted on the backs of rams and goats armed with bowes and arrowes and so down to the seaside they march where they make foule work among the egges and cranelings newly hatched which they destroy without all pity.

Another famous passage in more serious vein is his effusion on the nightingale's song.

In attempting to describe the intricate singing of this bird, Pliny states that, if another nightingale obtrude, the original singer will continue until it dies of exhaustion rather than renounce the stage to its opponent. Some critics have used this description in attempting to infuse Pliny's nature writing with feeling, but on close reading of the passage, it seems only a long dilation upon a popular belief that struck his fancy.

Vanity and industry seem to have been combined in Pliny to give him an omnivorous appetite for learning. He counted all time not spent in study as wasted, and even while eating or bathing he wished to be read to. Occasionally a brilliant idea came to him, and the story is told that in pondering the age which animals attain, he marked a dolphin's tail, thinking this would help him to learn its life-span. This was probably the first attempt at bird and animal marking, but Pliny never knew the success of his experiment, for the dolphin is said to have lived for three hundred years before it was captured.[7]

Pliny lived in the time when magic and divination were rife in Rome. Birds, parts of birds, and even their excreta were distilled into foul liquors, or their entrails were exposed upon the sacrificial altars, in order that divine wishes might be revealed. Naturally, these beliefs find a place in Pliny's writing, and he does not neglect the efficacy of swallow feathers hung about the neck as a cure for throat trouble, nor the owl's heart placed upon a woman's breast as she sleeps to make her divulge her secrets.

Nevertheless, despite the great amount of unreliable compilation in Pliny's *Natural History,* the reader can find a few statements on birds which appear to be the author's own and accurate observation. He knew the cuckoo's parasitic habit and described it well. He knew, likewise, the climbing habit of the woodpeckers and asserts that they know by the sound of the wood, as they

---

[7] Thorndyke, 1923: **1**: 55.

drill, whether there be food within. He also had observed a great deal on domestic fowls and cage birds.

Pliny was the son of a Roman knight and a senator's daughter. He was born A.D. 23 at Comum and at twelve years of age was taken to Rome by his father to be educated under the poet and military commander, P. Pomponius Segundus. From this preceptor Pliny acquired a great love of learning. He studied philosophy and rhetoric under Lucius Seneca (3 B.C.–A.D. 65) and he learned botany in the garden of Antonius Castor. His zoology was based mostly on Aristotle but he drew also upon the writings of Juba (–46), King of Mauretania in North Africa.

Under the Emperor Vespasian (9–79), who became his personal friend, Pliny was governor of Spain in 70 and later went as an emissary to the Belgian Province and to Africa. These travels gave opportunity to acquire wider knowledge of birds, animals, and plant life as well as an insight into the resources and customs of the far-flung Roman Empire. He wrote several treatises on military and philosophical subjects but the *Naturalis Historia* is the only one of his books that survives.

In the year 77 Vespasian gave him command of the Roman fleet at Misenum, and two years later he perished in the eruption of Vesuvius that destroyed Pompeii.

THE DARK AGES

With the coming of Christianity the feeling toward secular knowledge radically changed. The pursuit of learning came to be considered ungodly and incompatible with virtue. Gradually Aristotle was laid aside and his dynamic investigation of nature no longer discussed nor emulated.

Medicine alone, of the sciences, was given opportunity to progress especially under Galen of Pergamos (129–200) who expressed enough orthodox belief in God and the sanctity of the body to be compatible with Christian teachings.

It was during the early Christian Era, probably the second century, that a new kind of animal story took form. Alexander's conquests had brought certain oriental influences to the Mediterranean, and Alexandria, the great city in Egypt named after him, became the seat and meeting place of Greek and oriental culture. From the Orient came magic and sorcery; from Greece the sublimated theology of the early Christian Fathers many of whom were Greeks who had moved to Alexandria. The confluence of these two powerful forces gave to early Christianity its mysticism and symbolism.

In a world which previously had been pagan it was difficult for people to revamp their lives and live according to Christian teaching. The hidden meanings of the Bible had to be expounded for men were struck with fear at the Christian conception of original sin and the imminent danger of the fires of hell. It is no wonder that the teachers of such a doctrine sought ways by which to mediate these difficulties and symbolism offered a channel through which scriptural dogma could be rationalized. Instead of seeing God in the wonders of nature, men were taught to believe that natural phenomena were manifestations of Holy Writ. As W. Dampier Whetham in his *History of Science* (1930) words this thought: "What in the Scriptures or in the world of nature conforms to the Christian Scheme as interpreted by each Father, may be received as fact; what does not so agree is to be accepted only in a symbolic sense."

Thus it was that the *Physiologus,*[8] a collection of fabulous bird and animal stories in allegorical dress, came to be written by a group of Christian teachers probably in the second century at Alexandria. It was written in Greek and its function was to point the lessons of the Bible in imagery that people could understand.

Many birds figured in these symbolical tales among them the pelican, the owl, the hoopoe, the crow, the turtle dove, the swallow, the pigeon, and the ostrich. Mammals, reptiles, and even precious stones were endowed with magic properties which simple folk accepted as true, and by thus conditioning themselves to the supernatural they were able to take in unquestioningly many of the doctrines of the Scriptures. For example, one of these allegories tells that the lion brings forth its young still-born but on the third day the male lion breathes upon them and they receive life. This was regarded as an elucidation of the Resurrection. There was little or no zoology in these pronouncements but they served to keep alive a popular conception of bird and beast. Through retelling they changed considerably from their original form, becoming still more colored with fancy but also somewhat tinctured with fact, so that in time they were denounced as impious and worldly and were censored by Pope Gelasius in 496. However, by this time, the *Physiologus* had been translated into several Eastern and European languages and another similar group of allegories called the Bestiaries had been written. Both of these ancient books with new material added from time to time, continued to be read and were the principal source of animal lore during the Dark Ages.

Direct observation of birds was little practiced though vast migrant flocks passed twice a year just as they do now, between Europe and Africa. Aristotle was forgotten except by the patient monks who labored in their cells copying on parchment the things that the great philosopher had said nearly a thousand years ago. This benighted picture was further darkened a few years later by Justinian I (483–565), of the Eastern Roman Empire. In 529 he closed all the Greek philosophical schools in order to suppress competition with the official church schools of his realm.

The outlook for natural science could not have been less auspicious. Education thus went entirely into the hands of the Church, but there was no standard to be maintained either in the cathedral schools or in the monasteries. Many of the clergy were illiterate but this was not regarded seriously since it was necessary to curb the desire for secular learning because it was firmly believed that study of earthly things would unfit the student for meditation on God and the Scriptures.

Cassiodorus (468–568), a statesman, monk and writer of the time of the Ostrogoth king, Theodoric (497–524), had attempted to improve the educational situation by founding two monasteries where the inmates would be adequately instructed and would spend part of their time in copying useful manuscripts. He emphasized the need of perpetuating and transmitting both sacred and "profane" knowledge but of course greater emphasis was put upon sacred than profane or secular knowledge. There is one manuscript of this period in which birds are included. It is a résumé of the *Ornithiaka*[9] of Dionysius Exiguus (fl. sixth cen.), a learned friend of Cassiodorus and it deals mainly with the various ways of trapping birds. This manuscript, assigned to the year 512 contains 48 pictures of birds and several good descriptions. This Codex, containing several manuscripts on natural history, was prepared for Anicia Juliana (*ca.* 463–*ca.* 527), a patrician woman who lived in Constantinople. When this great city fell in 1453, the Codex[10] passed into Turkish possession and, after additions in Arabic and Hebrew, it was bought in 1569 by Augier Gheslin (1522–1592) of Bousebecque for the library of the Austrian Emperor, Maximilian II (1527–1576).

In the Western Province of Spain, by reason of its geographical position, the first real concern for the lax education then prevalent was manifested, and certain enactments of the council of Toledo point to a general stiffening of the requirements of those who were to become priests.[11] A product of this forward looking movement was Isidore (*ca.* 560–636), the Bishop of Seville, a Spanish scholar who preserved for the future the small remnant of secular learning that survived the heavy bans which Christian teaching placed upon the pursuit of knowledge.

Isidore, in a sort of encyclopedia, compiled the secular knowledge on all subjects considered suitable for the Spanish student of the seventh century. The title of the work is *Etymologies sive origines* but it is usually referred to as the *"Etymologies"* in reference to the great importance the author attaches to the derivations of words. His idea was that the road to knowledge was by way of words, and further that they were to be elucidated by reference to their origin rather than the things they stood for. Thus the word "aves" had reference to the fact that birds were creatures that travel by pathless ways or roads (viae).

---

[8] *Ibid.,* 501. Thorndyke argues against the allegorical character of the *Physiologus* and maintains that even in that day the common man was interested in a childish way in nature; this then was the fount from which sprang the *Physiologus,* written perhaps by several.

[9] Anker, 1938: 5.
[10] Wiener Nationalbibliothek (Cod. Med. Gr. 1), folio 474–485.
[11] Brehaut, 1912.

Chapter 7 of Isidore's Book XII on animals is occupied with birds. What he has to say on the swan's voice is still seen to color modern interpretation of the voice of this bird.

The swan (cygnus) is so called from singing, because it pours forth sweet song in modulated tones. And it sings sweetly for the reason that it has a long curving neck and it must needs be that the voice, struggling out by a long and winding way, should utter various notes.

The crow [says Isidore] is a bird full of years and augurs say it increases a man's anxieties by the tokens it gives, that it reveals ambushes, and foretells the future. But it is great wickedness to believe that God entrusts his counsels to crows.

Of the cuckoo he says that these "have a time for coming, perched on the shoulders of kites because of their short weak flights in order that they may not grow weary and fail in the long spaces of the air." He apparently knew that the cuckoo lays its eggs in other birds' nests and credited the intruder with first devouring the eggs that it finds there. The saliva of cuckoos produces grasshoppers, he solemnly concludes.

This gives some indication of the stagnating condition of the natural sciences in the early Christian Era. Though Aristotle had in a sense discovered for us the true animal world and put the torch of inductive method into our hands, the light was put out by the storm winds of political and religious dissent, and birds and animals and plants and all creeping things waited in comparative darkness for several centuries.

But a revival of learning was at hand and it came into Europe by way of Spain. Spain, as we know, was invaded by Moslems from North Africa in the eighth century and gradually Arabic culture flowered forth in several Spanish centers, principally Cordova, Seville, and Toledo, and in the writing of the great thinker, Averroes (1126–1198), a native of Cordova, the ground work for the renewed study of nature was laid.

But we should go back and trace briefly the way in which this was possible. We recall that in the sixth century the Greek philosophical schools were closed and that Aristotle was falling more and more into disuse. However, he had survived in the commentaries of various Roman and Syrian writers. The first of these was Boetius (480–524) a Roman with a passion for Greek literature who translated several of Aristotle's treatises into Latin. These were a principal source from which the Middle Ages derived their knowledge of the great philosopher. Another of these commentators was Porphyry (233–ca. 304), a Syrian who wrote on Aristotle in the form of questions and answers. His work also was used extensively in the Middle Ages. Through Porphyry and other Syrian scholars, Aristotle's scientific and philosophical works were translated into Syriac and from Syriac they were rendered into Arabic. For three centuries between 800 and 1100 fresh translations and commentaries on Aristotle were produced under the Arabian scholars who worked principally in Bagdad

where several schools for the study of Greek science and philosophy had been founded. So eager were students and scholars for these writings that the Arabic school of culture is said to be responsible for the "deification" of Aristotle, that super estimation of his accomplishment that was out of all proportion to his actual knowledge.

But it was necessary to produce Aristotle in some other language than Arabic if his influence in science and thought was to be felt in the western world. It is in this process of what is called the "rediscovery of Aristotle" that Averroes is so important a link, for it was his commentaries, freshly turned into Latin, that were read by educated Europeans in the later Middle Ages. In this way fresh vigor was introduced into the long dormant study of nature.

Averroes' two fundamental doctrines were: (1) the eternity of matter and of the world; (2) the oneness of the active intellect in all men.

Both of these concepts are of Aristotelian origin and led him to teach that man is made to discover truth. From this he reasoned that the serious study of God and his works is the noblest form of worship. God to Averroes was a supreme abstraction while to the Moslem world he was an intensely personal being. Averroes was therefore persecuted for heresy and banished for two years because he would not espouse the fanatical religion of his day. But by good fortune he was recalled and introduced to the progressive Kalif Abn Yakub Yusuf (1163–1184) as one qualified to expound Aristotle. Averroes became his private physician and spent much time under his protection.

With Averroes' more modern interpretation of Aristotle's writings, this philosopher exercised a great influence at Oxford, Paris and Padua. It was before the organization of the university on modern lines but it was customary in this later scholastic period for students and scholars to gather round the great personalities of the day, or their disciples, there to garner wisdom and exchange ideas with men from far and near.

Thus it was that the translator Michael Scot (1175–1232) of Som, Scotland, became acquainted with Averroes. After studying at Oxford, Paris, Palermo and Bologna he came to Toledo where he learned Arabic and read the works of both Avicenna (980–1037) and Averroes in their original form.

FREDERICK II OF HOHENSTAUFEN: FIRST ORNITHOLOGIST OF EUROPE

It was Michael Scot's knowledge of Aristotle that secured for him an invitation to live at the court of Frederick II (1194–1250). This monarch has been called the "first modern man upon a throne," and his brilliant court gave rise to a revival of learning that is known as the Renaissance of the twelfth century.[12] Because of his versatility and his particular knowledge of birds it seems appropriate to give some account of his background and his ornithological accomplishment.

---

[12] Haskins, 1927.

He was the son of the Roman Emperor Henry VI (1165–1197), a wise ruler whose greatest delights were hunting, and the lyrical poets of Germany known as Minnisingers. Frederick's mother was Constance of Sicily, the daughter of Roger I (1031–1101) one of the Norman kings under whose rule this beautiful island of several races and creeds was peacefully engaged in agriculture and architecture. Roger was famous for his masculine beauty and tolerance, and he kept the Greeks and Arabs, the Christians and Moslems of his kingdom at peace with each other thus building a rich and varied culture.

Perhaps we can see in this parentage, Henry VI and Constance of Sicily, the seeds of some of their son's versatility. Frederick II had his love of learning from the Arabs and his tolerance and industry from the Normans who were of Scandinavian origin. He was adroit without being unprincipled in his diplomatic dealings and he was as ambitious as his father had been, and much more clever.

We cannot go into his political career punctuated with battles with the Lombard states of Northern Italy, his disputes with the Pope over Sicily and his far-flung schemes to make Jerusalem a part of his empire. The translator of his book *De Arte venandi cum Avibus*, Dr. Casey Wood (1856–1942),[13] likens him to a stormy petrel, coursing back and forth across central Europe and the Near East, welding together and enlightening his heterogeneous realm.

How he became so fascinated with the study of birds we cannot know but we have his own words that "for thirty years" he had been planning to set down his ornithological observations. He approached the subject from the standpoint of falconry but his knowledge of birds was by no means limited to the birds of prey. After Michael Scot had completed the translation of Aristotle's *Historia Animalium* Frederick found it inadequate not only on falconry but in its general account of birds, and he set to work, probably about 1228, to write about birds and particularly falconry, gathering new material and working over his old material for some ten or fifteen years.

It was at this time that he returned from the Sixth Crusade by which he became Lord of Jerusalem, and it is probable that his love of falconry was fired anew by contacts with the orientals with whom the training of falcons had been an art since very ancient times. He brought back many of the finest falconers of the East and learned the secrets of their skill at first hand, while he built many castles and hunting lodges especially in Italy in order to indulge his passion for this kingly sport.

It is unfortunate that the journals that he kept have been lost but a fragment of one is extant from which we can gain some idea of the grand scale on which he pursued his favorite study.

This is an entry covering a few months of 1239–1240

in which over fifty of the Emperor's falconers are mentioned by name. He speaks of hawks captured in Malta; of the care of buildings and mews for hawks in several parts of Italy and Sicily; and of wages and equipment for falconers. In May he speaks of sending nineteen falconers to Malta for capturing more hawks and he orders all sparrow hawks in the County of Molise to be brought together under a special keeper.

These are but glimpses from his diary but they indicate the feverish activity of his mind which could render such solicitous care for his beloved birds while affairs of state pressed hard upon him.

Although the title of Frederick's fascinating mediaeval work *De Arte venandi cum Avibus* mentions only the art of hunting with birds, a substantial part of the text is a clear account of structure and classification. The translator, Dr. Casey Wood, worked from several manuscripts deposited in Europe—at Bologna, Paris, Nantes, Oxford, Rome, the Vatican Library, Vienna, Geneva, and Stuttgart. Some conception of the manuscript material to be covered may be had from the fact that in the Bologna Library alone there is a parchment of 144 folios, each of which is 200 mm. × 270 mm. and each folio has two closely written columns of 47 lines. It is entirely written by hand in Latin.

It is interesting that Frederick after first planning to dedicate his book to the Sultan of Egypt inscribed his work in its final form to Manfred (*ca.* 1232–1266), his young illegitimate son by the beloved noblewoman Bianca whom he married on his deathbed.[14] Manfred had long been his companion on his hunting trips and Frederick gave him all the notes for the completion of the book. Manfred added some of his own observations to the material and also had executed the illustrations, the directions for which his father had given him. Dr. Wood regards these drawings as of great importance indicating the quality of scientific observation and artistic skill at the time of the writing. The human figures are Byzantine but the birds are so lifelike and so brilliant in coloring as to seem almost photographic. The whole book is pervaded with a spirit of enquiry and experiment as may be judged by these incidents:[15] Frederick, who spent much time in Apulia, had experts come from Africa to test the incubation of ostrich eggs by the sun's heat, and on another occasion, in trying to learn how vultures find their food, he sealed their eyes in order to test their sense of smell.

As a further mark of his scientific acumen some of his fully verified observations may be cited:

The arrangement and function of the different types of feathers.
The sequence of the moult of birds.
The structure of the leg and foot.
The number of joints in each of the bird's toes.
The explanation for "hard" and "soft" bills.

[13] Wood, 1942.

[14] Not fully authenticated.
[15] Haskins, 1921: **36**: 334–355.

These and hundreds of other observations on birds, their structure, and their habits he made himself, but when confronted with the strange mating display of the bustard he said: "The male bustard's neck swells to great size to induce admiration in the beholder. The reason why it remains always the same size in the female, others may decide."

Frederick's early death in 1250, and that of Manfred in 1266 at the age of only thirty-four, together with the scattered and unfinished condition of the various manuscripts, have combined to keep the world largely in ignorance of this interesting work on birds. At first, parts of it were circulated in codex form but it was published in Augsburg in 1596, about one hundred years after the invention of printing. Other editions came out in 1756, in 1788, and in 1896 but the complete monumental volume, based on all necessary source material, was not available until 1942 and unfortunately Dr. Wood did not live to see his printed work but died on January 26, 1942, a few months previous to the publication.

The seasoned ornithologist will enjoy this mediaeval account of ornithology not only for the revelation it gives of bird lore seven hundred years ago, but also for its picture of one of the great figures of history.

As said earlier in these pages, the contemplation and study of the phenomena of nature were believed to detract from the uplifting influence of the contemplation of God. In the words of Charles Singer,[16] "the world was God's footstool" and therefore religion was all-important. But under many influences from the Orient and Byzantium, as Turkey was called in ancient times, there grew up in Western Europe the belief that man, called the microcosm, reflected the vast universe or the macrocosm that lay around him. Plato had expounded such a system in his Timaeus, and Aristotle in his philosophical dissertations had visualized the universe as a system of concentric circles in which "the fixed stars, moving regularly in a circle, controlled the ordered course of nature, the events that proceeded in recurring manifest and unalterable rounds, such as winter and summer, night and day, growth and decay."[17]

With these doctrines as matters of common belief, it was not difficult to regard the planets, those variable heavenly bodies, as having some influence on man's uncertain earthly life. Thus it was that man took his place at the center of the universe while around him circled the seven planets each of which was believed to have definite influence over certain organs and parts of his body. The twelve constellations of the zodiac formed the outer circle around the planets and these being connected with the planets, acted through them on the various regions of the human body. Such a conception of the universe offered endless comfort to the uneducated and even the most learned believed in astrology and the power of the heavens with their myriad stars to make or break their lives.

Arabian influence greatly strengthened these mystical beliefs and for several centuries more and more elaborate schemes based on the doctrines of microcosm and macrocosm were set forth. Isidore of Seville accepted them in rather simple form; the Abbess Hildegard of Bingen (1099–1180) and Bernard Sylvestres (ca. 1150) enlarged upon them adding for each relationship a spiritual and highly sublimated interpretation designed to bring the human being in ever closer contact with God. The greatest interpreter of this mystical philosophy was Dante Alighieri (1265–1321) who described his scheme of the universe in the Divine Comedy (1472).

These religious conceptions were much more of a hindrance than a help to science and served to keep it largely static during the scholastic period which lasted through the Middle Ages. The scholastic thinker viewed all knowledge as a whole, was not interested in speculating on what lay outside the primum mobile or the outermost circle of the universe, while for the structure and meaning of the material world about him, he was provided with a definite plan that had been used by countless workers before him. In short he had not discovered the value of observing for himself and it was mostly through the teachings of Averroes and his interpretation of Aristotle's biologic writings that the scholastics broke loose from the trammels of old method or as it was called, "authority."

It is interesting that it was one of the most prominent scholastic writers who was the first to become familiar with Aristotle's natural philosophy even to the point of translating his Historia Animalium and interpolating some of his own observations on nature. This was Albertus Magnus (1206–1280), a contemporary of Frederick II, and one who belonged to the Dominican Order of Friars. He was at the same time a teacher at Cologne. His treatise on animals is characterized by direct observation and general caution. He uses such expressions as "I have tested this," "this is not true," "I have not experienced this," and he definitely doubts what the ancients said of whales. In regard to birds he was inclined to believe what he heard, and quoted without question that a "trustworthy person" told of an eagle's nest containing 300 ducks, 100 geese, 40 hares, and many large fish for the young birds.[18]

Albertus Magnus is also the author of a treatise De Animalibus, the birds of which a German, S. Killermann, has treated of in Die Vogelkunde des Albertus Magnus, Regensburg, 1910.

A disciple of Albertus, Thomas de Cantimpré (fl. 1233–1247),[19] in his De Naturis Rerum goes a step farther and prefixes all experiments with "experimentator" and calls upon diligent investigators of nature to testify to the virtue of words, herbs, and stones, "which have been demonstrated by most certain experience." He thus shows a long forward step in advocating direct observation but is still something of a believer in magic.

[16] Singer, 1928: 84.
[17] Ibid., 83.

[18] Thorndyke, 1914: 23: 285.
[19] Called also Thomas Contimpratensis.

This work contains mention of 114 birds, with, however, the bat included.[20]

This is a remarkable number of birds to be recognized at such an early date. Thomas de Cantimpré is said to have written twenty other treatises on nature but he was primarily a hagiographer having written the lives of several saints. He was born of a noble family probably in 1301 at Leuv-Saint-Pierre near Brussels and joined the order of Saint Augustine in Abbaye de Cantimpré when he was only seventeen. He was a particular friend of the French Cardinal Jacques de Vitry and at the request of Thomas Aquinas (1225?–1274) was asked, because of his knowledge of Greek, to translate parts of Aristotle. He died according to some authorities in 1263, though others state 1270 and 1274.

His book, the complete title of which is *De Natura Rerum Segundum Diversos Philosophos* (in edit), was translated into German by Conrad von Megenberg (*ca.* 1309–1374) (Conradus del Monte Puellarum) in the late fifteenth century under the title *Das Buch der Natur* and with twelve full page wood cuts was published in Augsburg in 1475. It had six printings before 1500, was the first natural history book in the German language, and had wide use up to the Revival of Learning. Thus Thomas de Cantimpré and Conrad von Megenberg are important figures in the evolution of ornithology, helping through their common work to spread a more or less accurate knowledge of birds. Their accounts of birds represent an intermediate stage between those of Albertus Magnus a true scholastic, and those of Conrad Gesner one of the great encyclopedists.

We should not attempt to pass from the age of scholasticism to the Revival of Learning, however, without realizing some of the main helps in this transition. Though Albertus Magnus had presented the Aristotelian writings in somewhat westernized form, it was necessary to adjust them to ecclesiastical doctrine and this was done in large part by his pupil another Dominican Friar, St. Thomas Aquinas. He it was who succeeded in separating philosophy so that theology or the "mysteries of religion (which cannot be proved by reason)" were recognized in a department called "faith." This is the teaching of his *Summa Theologia* and Aquinas is hailed as the liberator of scientific thought from the straight-jacket of theology.

Another important factor contributing to the transition out of scholasticism and into modernism was the rise of the universities. At first they were aggregations of masters and scholars formed into guilds, and Paris and Bologna were the first centers to attract such groups from far and near to take up the new studies which the translations of Greek and Arabic masterpieces made available. In Salerno, Italy, even earlier, probably about 1230, a medical school was founded where the teachings of Hippocrates and Galen were expounded, and from this school went out many enlightened physicians who laid the ground work for the great advances in medicine and surgery during the Renaissance. The Mendicant Orders also were a help in this transition for they attracted the best trained minds of the day, men who gave their services as teachers. St. Francis of Assisi (1182–1226), famous for his love of nature, founded the Order of Franciscans, and this group addressed itself especially to science. All members were pledged to own nothing, to give their lives to study and by unselfish teaching to bring Christ into the lives of even the most humble.

Many great men belonged to this order two of the most famous and influential being Robert Grosseteste (*ca.* 1175–1253) the Bishop of Lincoln who worked on optics, and Roger Bacon, (1214–1294) who contributed to several branches of learning notably astronomy, ancient languages, chemistry, geography, and mathematics. One student of Bacon, Charles Singer, in his book *From Magic to Science* (1928) on page 93 sums up Bacon's contribution to thought as "accuracy of method, criticism of authority, and reliance on experiment—the pillars of modern science."

With these principles of science recognized, the world was ready, indeed, it could not fail to experience a great awakening and so with the roots of a potential revival reaching far into the past, the Renaissance sprang into flower beginning in Italy in the fourteenth century and reaching into all Western Europe through the fifteenth and sixteenth centuries.

III. CONTINENTAL BIRD LORE AND THE ENCYCLOPEDISTS

Several world events of the fifteenth century were powerful forces in the spread of the Renaissance. Chief among them were the fall of Constantinople in 1463 causing many Greek scholars to be exiled all over Europe, the inventions of printing and paper making, and the discovery of the New World.

Until the invention of movable type, books had not been available to the ordinary man. They were written by hand on parchment and were not reproducible except by long labor. They were therefore scarce and costly.

Hence it is easy to understand the quickening effect that book making had upon a world eager to learn. Even more stimulating were the discovery of America, the rounding of the Cape of Good Hope and many travels into the Far Eastern countries all of which were made possible by the recently acquired mariner's compass. This global exploration not only brought fabulous wealth to the powerful people; it fired the imaginations of the common people who drank in the fantastic stories of adventure which the returning travellers had to tell. Many accounts of these expeditions were published and often birds and animals and other curiosities from far across the sea were exhibited. Thus the world of nature hitherto so poorly understood became a fascinating empirical adventure for all.

---

[20] Aiken, 1947: 205–224.

In addition to these changes, greater freedom of thought was fostered by the contemporaneous spread of the Reformation. The Bible for many centuries had been available to Europeans only in Greek, Latin, and Hebrew but in 1525 it was rendered into understandable English by William Tyndall (1492–1536). For this "heresy" he suffered martyrdom by strangling, and countless other people were burned at the stake for independent thinking. The battle for intellectual freedom was not to be abandoned.

Gradually the unquestioning acceptance of the conventional and vitiated writings of old authorities waned and died; people, spurred by the enlightening invention of books, began to read, to think, and to observe for themselves, and the world of affairs and of living things was within the reach of all.

There are three men especially important in the study of birds during the period of the Revival of Learning. They are the Swiss-German doctor, Conrad Gesner, (1516–1565), the Italian naturalist, Professor Ulysses Aldrovandus (1522–1607), and the French zoologist, Pierre Belon (1517?–1564). All these men were born within the same decade and all produced important books on birds. A Dutch anatomist, Volcher Coiter (1534–1576) of Gröningen, also contributed with drawings and text on the structure, anatomy, and embryology of birds, as well as a tract on their classification.

CONRAD GESNER

The first of these authorities, Conrad Gesner, was born in Zurich in 1516 the son of a poor furrier, Ursus Gesner. The father was killed in the battle of Zug in 1531 and the family being large had to be divided. Conrad was sent to live with an uncle who awakened in him a love of plants.

Through the help of his teacher, Oswald Myconius (1488–1552), a Zwinglian divine and classical scholar, Gesner was able to continue school in Zurich during his boyhood. Later through subsidies provided by the scholastic senate of Zurich, and the kind patronage of Heinrich Bullinger (1504–1575), the famous Protestant writer, he studied at the Universities of Strassbourg and Brouges. For three years he taught Greek at the newly opened Academy of Lausanne and one year he spent at the great medical university at Montpellier where he met Guillaume Rondelet (1507–1566) the French ichthyologist and professor of anatomy. During his travels and training abroad Gesner made many friends and correspondents on whom he called for aid when compiling his writings. Two of his intimate friends were Rondelet and Johannes Fries the great Latin scholar.

After receiving his medical degree at Basle in 1541, he returned to Zurich as a physician but his practice was never great. An insatiable desire for learning was his dominating characteristic as may be seen from his books on widely different subjects. Most of his botanical works came out after his death, but in 1541 and 1542 he

FIG. 3. Conrad Gesner (1516–1565), Learned Swiss Encyclopedist. From Jardine's Naturalist's Library.

published the *Enchiridion historiae plantarum* and the *Catalogus plantarum*. For several years he was busy amassing the vast materials for his *Bibliotheca universalis* for which he is called the Father of Bibliography.[1] This great work published in 1545 preserved for posterity the record of the literary world in that all-important first century of printing and publishing. Compendia of knowledge were greatly in demand, and many beautiful illuminated books were brought out. Another contribution by Gesner that shows his consuming love of knowledge is his *Mithridates de differentiis Linguis,* an account of 130 known languages with the Lord's Prayer in 22 tongues (1555). Yet with all this close application to writing, Gesner continued his field studies and botanized and collected up and down the Alps and along the Adriatic, often bringing home his favorite alpine plants or strange zoological specimens.

The bulk of his zoological work is embodied in the *Historia Animalium.* This is a vast storehouse of information on the animal world, divided into five parts, and it presents an encyclopedic account of all the forms of the animal kingdom known at that time. For convenience it is arranged alphabetically because classification according to true relationships was then but poorly understood. This monumental work was published between 1551 and 1558, exclusive of the fifth part on snakes which was issued posthumously in 1587.

---

[1] Bay, 1916: 53–86.

The third part on birds was published in 1555, and contains 217 accounts of birds illustrated with a woodcut for each species. The text covers external and anatomical descriptions, distribution, habits, and something about each bird's place in literature and mythology.

Fabulous birds likewise are described but Gesner made it clear that he gave them no credence. Since, however, he was writing a book for public consumption he thought they should be included. Apparently Gesner was anxious to engage public interest for he went to great trouble to make the accounts complete and to secure numerous illustrations. Lucas Shan [2] was the artist for most of the illustrations but Johan Thomann (*ca.* 1555) and Hans Asper (1499–1571) probably executed some of the bird drawings.

Gesner's *Historia Animalium* is said to be the starting point of modern zoology and Liber III marks an important step in the development of ornithology.

As an encyclopedia of birds it is somewhat outranked by Aldrovandus' *Ornithologia* which followed about half a century later, but it is noteworthy that in the mid-sixteenth century Gesner saw the need for a book on birds for the people, and to this end he surveyed all sources going back to the writers of early times as well as to those of his own epoch who understood this department of knowledge. It is interesting that the bird pictures with short explanations under the title *Icones Avium* were also published separately in 1555.

Despite the handicaps of poverty and poor health and an invalid wife, Gesner's love of learning bore him successfully into the fields of the sciences and the humanities alike, and for his distinguished attainments he attracted the attention of Emperor Ferdinand and was ennobled in 1564. Though one of the most renowned men of his time, he remained devoted to his native city, ever ready to help others, his home though simple being always open to visiting scholars and scientists. His botanical garden was known all over Europe and as soon as his means permitted he built a small museum in which to house his collections. Fifteen large windows on which he painted a series of fish were a striking feature, and many shelves were arranged to hold his metals, stones, and fossils, as well as plants and occasional birds.

Gesner found his greatest satisfaction in working at this museum. Here he studied and wrote, but it was often necessary for him to visit the Baden Baths in Germany for his health. Whenever he improved sufficiently, he seized the opportunity to complete some literary or scientific work. After 1560 he was seldom well; yet he gave much time to the alleviation of the suffering caused by the plague which was sweeping Europe at this time. The loss of his mother in 1564 greatly affected him and he had little hope of long surviving. In December 1565 he realized his condition and asked to be taken into his museum where he had ordered a bed made

ready for him. He died on December 13, lacking three months of fifty years, and was buried in the Munster next to the grave of his friend, Johannes Fries, who likewise died of the plague. His library and manuscripts were turned over to his one-time pupil and colleague, Caspar Wolf, who, among other writings by Gesner, published two hundred and twenty-six letters in 1577. It is thought that there are many more of Gesner's letters in various European libraries.

ULYSSES ALDROVANDUS

Ulysses Aldrovandus was the second writer of the Renaissance who made important contributions to the study of birds. A native of Bologna, he was born within the same decade as Gesner, in 1522, and spent nearly all of his long life in his home city. He was the son of a noble family, but lost his father when he was still a child, and his mother sent him to be a page in a wealthy bishopric at the age of six. At twelve he was apprenticed to a merchant in Brescia but he disliked this commercial work and went to travel in Spain.

His later training was received at the Universities of Bologna and Padua. In these centers of learning he studied first law and later medicine, and received his medical degree in 1553 from Bologna. He studied botany under the Italian botanist Lucas Ghinas and anatomy under Gabriello Fallopius (1523–1562) at Padua. During his student years he met the great French anatomist and ichthyologist, Guillaume Rondelet (1507–1566) in Rome. These contacts with the leading scientists of the day no doubt helped to determine Aldrovandus' career in natural science. Indeed Rondelet is said to have influenced him to devote his main studies to zoology and botany.

In 1554, the year after he received his degree, he was made Professor of Philosophy at the University of Bologna with a lectureship also in botany. In 1560 he was given the Chair of Botany but the breadth of his learning caused the University to bestow upon him the title of Professor of Natural History. This appears to be one of the earliest departures from the title of "natural philosophy" and signalizes the more experimental trend in science, for which the succeeding seventeenth century is noted.

In this field of empiric philosophy, based on actual observation, Aldrovandus made a great name for himself. He conceived the plan of a natural history covering all departments of nature. In summer and autumn he took to the fields and woods in order to study the living creatures in natural conditions. Draughtsmen and amanuenses accompanied him to make drawings and write down his descriptions, while collectors prepared specimens which were brought back to the University. In 1568 so great had grown the public interest in Aldrovandus' teachings that the Senate of Bologna established the Botanical Garden of that city, and Aldrovandus as its first director developed friendly relations with the citizenry by lectures and demonstrations either at his

---

[2] This artist is sometimes erroneously called Shron or Shon. Some of Shan's original bird pictures are in the collection of Felix Platter (1536–1614), who was a professor at Basle.

FIG. 4. Ulysses Aldrovandus (1522–1605 or 7), First Professor of Natural History. From Jardine's Naturalist's Library.

home or in the public gardens. At this time he was also inspector of drugs and in this position he made enemies among the apothecaries who objected to some of his regulations of the drug business. Aldrovandus then sought the aid of Pope Gregory XIII who supported him staunchly, and as a result of his experience as inspector he wrote a treatise on drugs, *Antidotii Bononiensis epitome* (1574), which has served as the model for many later books on pharmacy. His main interest, however, was descriptive zoology with apparently a particular interest in birds. Of the study of birds he expressed himself in these words:

The subject of ornithology is indeed an arduous one, whose very difficulty provokes investigation for here an aspiring mind may try its strength and if it succeed the triumph is neither low nor grovelling, but splendid and honourable; and should failure ensue the very attempt is noble and commendable.

It is significant that he prepared first his books on ornithology, but so exacting and time-consuming was this task that he was seventy-seven when he began to publish them. Under such a weight of years it is not surprising that he described his labors as follows:

I could wish you to judge how much toil and trouble has been given to this work. I have supplied the names of birds not only in Greek and Latin but also in Hebrew, Arabic and Italian, and in short in all known languages. I have described the birds and figured those I have had an opportunity of drawing. I have illustrated their nature and habits, have dwelt upon their food, the manner in which they are cap-

tured, and how they may be best preserved: likewise the nourishment they afford, their use as medicine, their employment upon emblems, symbols, and images and in sacred and profane mythology, and on coins, in proverbs and hieroglyphics. Whatever can be usefully said upon birds may be found here.

The bird matter is divided into twelve parts beginning with the rapacious birds (hawks and owls), then those of a mixed nature (the bats and the ostriches), then fabulous birds, then parrots and crows. Many anatomical studies also are to be found in Aldrovandus' work such as the following: the bones and muscles of eagles, the nictitating membrane, the controlling muscles of the movable upper mandible in parrots, the tongue of the magpie, progress in incubation, the skeleton of the starling, the windpipe of the lapwing.

He seems to have had a deep interest in all phases of ornithology and he furnishes another example of the true naturalist who is impelled by a clear love of study and cares little for the emoluments of rank and position. Had Aldrovandus followed the life to which he was born, the easy way of the nobility, or even jurisprudence at which he spent seven years, he would probably have remained wealthy but he would have left no monument of his labor. He spent his fortune on his studies. His extensive travels as well as the vast amount of art work were paid for in large measure from private funds although the Senate of Bologna aided him somewhat during his life time and, after his death, appropriated large sums for the publication of his writings.

Some accounts of Aldrovandus refer to a solitary old age of poverty and blindness but although his arduous labors greatly depleted his income, and caused him to go blind three years before he died, he could not have been destitute for he knew the ministering care of a devoted wife who was conversant with all his work, and instrumental in obtaining the support of the Senate for his publications.

Only four volumes of his work were published before his death. Three of these were his *Ornithologia* containing 2,600 folio pages published in 1599, 1600 and 1603 and the fourth on insects which was published in 1602. After his death which occurred on May 10, 1605,[3] the remaining volumes of his fourteen published works were completed and edited on the advice of the Senate by several of Aldrovandus' pupils, chief among whom was Corneille Uterverus, his successor at the University.

By his contemporaries Aldrovandus was revered as a great leader in natural history because of the breadth of his researches that covered all the zoological groups. It would be impossible for anyone to execute such a work without culling from previous writers. For this reason he has been accused of plagiarizing from Gesner and others, but certainly he added a vast amount of new material by hard personal effort.

[3] Some sources say that he died in the public hospital of Bologna in 1607.

It is more difficult perhaps to evaluate fairly his illustrations. Accustomed as we are, to the exquisite accuracy of present day zoological illustration, we find most of his wood cuts little short of grotesque and ridiculous: Here is a stupid looking crow, the proverbial thief of grain solemnly holding a sheaf of wheat in his huge bill; here a murderous hawk feebly grasping with weak talons a helpless dormouse which looks on unperturbed without even laying back his ears; and here an eagle with yards of snake wrapped round its legs and neck. Although Aldrovandus engaged artists of distinguished reputation, few of their illustrations reveal any skill in portraying the living bird. An exception to this, however, is the woodcut of the Virginia nightingale (*Richmondena cardinalis*) the beloved cardinal of southern and central

drawings executed by some of the best artists of Europe were transferred by Napoleon in the heyday of his conquests to the Jardin des Plantes, where they remained until 1814.

Aldrovandus' renown rests mainly on his ability to do extensive and patient research and on his large following of students at Bologna's famous university. His position as one of the great encyclopedists is assured but his writings show but little understanding of relationships in the various groups of animals that he described. His name is perpetuated in the genus of plants, Aldrovanda,[6] one of the six genera of the family Droseraceae or Sundews named by his compatriot, Guiseppi Monti.

Gesner and Aldrovandus may be said to mark the peak of encyclopedic writing on birds but as L. C. Miall

Fig. 5. Hawk with snake from Aldrovandus' *Ornithologiae* (1599–1603).

United States. Aldrovandus tells in his text that he received this bird (unquestionably alive) from the keeper of the Pisa gardens, Franciseus Malocchius[4] who sent it with an account of its habits including its bellicose behavior when confronted with its own image in a mirror. The cardinal was a popular cage bird at this time. A few other American birds are included in Aldrovandus' work, the turkey (*Meleagris gallopavo*), the mourning dove, (*Zenaidura macroura*), and the tufted titmouse (*Parus bicolor*), the latter two being open to question according to the late Mr. Bayard Christy.[5]

Aldrovandus' manuscripts and collections of specimens, paintings, and carvings were left to the city of Bologna and by decision of the Senate formed the nucleus of the Bologna Museum. Many of the original colored

says in his book:[7] "The encyclopedic naturalists were far more eager to amass information than to sift it."

It remained for the seventeenth and eighteenth centuries to screen out much of the merely "curious" information of these early writers and delve more basically into the truly scientific study of birds.

Some of this fundamental study of birds, however, began with the late sixteenth century and was accomplished by two of Aldronvandus' contemporaries, Volcher Coiter and Pierre Belon, both of whom worked on the structure of birds.

VOLCHER COITER

Volcher Coiter (1534–1576) was a student of the famous Italian professor and, in 1564 at his mentor's sug-

[4] Christy, 1942: 177.
[5] *The Auk*, 1933: 278 and note.

[6] Chatin, 1858: 580–582.
[7] Miall, 1912.

FIG. 6. Volcher Coiter (1534–1576), Dutch anatomist and author of the earliest classification of birds. Courtesy of the Army Medical Library.

gestion, entered upon a series of daily examinations of incubated eggs, writing descriptions and making drawings of the daily advance in development.

Not since Aristotle, more than 1800 years before, had similar work been done, although Hippocrates (*ca.* 420 B.C.) had advocated such studies and Aldrovandus had contemplated making them himself. But as a busy professor, he wisely delegated some of his cherished plans to his more promising students, and Coiter no doubt more than fulfilled his professor's expectations. His study outranks Aldronvandus' embryological account of the chick, which was published twenty-eight years later, when he brought out his three-volume *Ornithologia.*

Coiter's account of the developing chick was incorporated in a longer paper whose title rendered into English is, *Tables of the Principal External and Internal Parts of the Human Body and Various Anatomical Exercises*

and *Observations Illustrated with New, Diverse and Very Ingenious Figures, Extremely Useful Especially* to *Those Devoted to Anatomical Study.* It was published at Nuremberg in 1572. We are indebted to Dr. Howard B. Adelmann of Cornell University for a skillful annotated translation of this paper from the original Latin. Dr. Adelmann includes in his translation a list of this writer's other scientific papers among which is one describing the anatomy of birds, *De Anatomia Avium Nuremberg* (1573). There is no mention, however, of Coiter's *De Differentiis Avium* which sets forth his conception of the bird world according to structure and habit, which is the earliest attempt at a system for the arrangement and classification of birds.

This treatise has remained practically unknown because it is part of a larger work, the *De Avium Sceletis et Praecipuis Musculis.* This whole tract also is little known because it is bound with that rare work by Coiter, the *Lectiones Gabrielis Fallopii de Partibus Similaribus Humani Corporis* (1575). There is nothing on the title page of this work, however, to indicate the presence of the ornithological tract, the *De Avium Sceletis et Praecipuis Musculis* in the same volume.

My first knowledge of the *De Differentiis Avium* I owe to a cursory mention of it in Dr. Alfred Newton's *Dictionary of Birds.* A footnote referred to a copy in the Library of the Surgeon General, Washington. On my next trip to Washington, therefore, I enquired whether I might see it but owing to restrictions in effect during the Second World War this was not permitted. Three years later on December 26, 1947, it was possible to see the book at the Army Medical Library in Cleveland where it was temporarily being held. Through the courtesy of Miss Dorothy Schullian, Curator of Rare Books at this library, I arranged for the *De Differentiis Avium* to be microfilmed together with some of Coiter's bird skeleton drawings. Miss Schullian has kindly informed me of the whereabouts of other copies of the *Lectiones Fallopii,* as follows:

Bibliothèque Nationale; British Museum (two copies); Yale Medical Library; and the New York Academy of Medicine. With the copy belonging to the Library of the Surgeon General, there are, therefore, six copies in public institutions; three in Europe and three in the United States; but there may be others belonging to private persons.

DESCRIPTION OF THE LECTIONES GABRIELIS FALLOPII

This work is a group of lecture notes assembled by Volcher Coiter while he was attending Fallopius' course in anatomy at the University of Padua. It is bound in light leather, stained and mended, and the upper and lower edges are tied with leather thongs. It is, apparently, the original binding.

The treatise, bearing number 38,147, is divided into twelve chapters, occupying fourteen pages and is illustrated with four tablets—three of which 1, 2, and 4, contain drawings appertaining to birds. It is written in

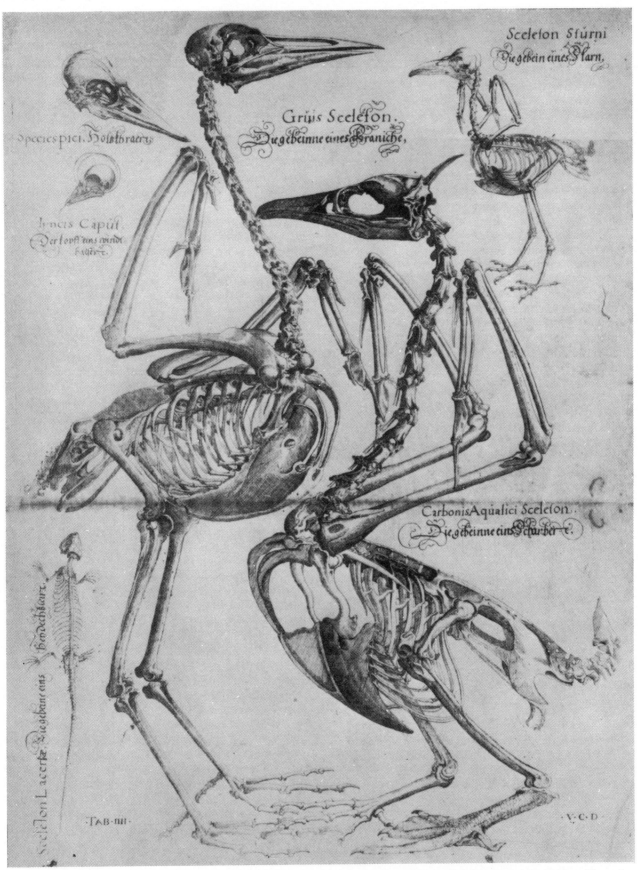

FIG. 7. A study of bird skeletons by Volcher Coiter from *Lectiones Gabrielis Fallopii de Partibus Similaribus Humani Corporis* (1575).

the Latin of the sixteeth century and was published at Nuremberg in 1575.

An interesting feature of this copy is the hand-written lines on the title page, on which Miss Schullian has a paper now in press.

The twelve chapters of the *De Avium Sceletis Praecipuis* are divided as follows: (1) Discussion of the skeletons of birds in general with some remarks on Aristotle's interpretations of the structure of birds; (2) De Differentiis Avium; (3) the bird's cranium; (4) neck; (5) forebreast; (6) clavicle; (7) scapula; (8) sternum; (9) ribs; (10) lumbar bones, the sacrum, ilium, ishium, and pubis; (11) bones of the wing and the method of flying; (12) bones of the shin or shank, and foot bones.

The text on all of these headings is proof that Volcher Coiter knew and understood the way of a bird's skeleton functions, and the drawings of several types of bird skeletons attest this, also. These skeletons are the crane, the starling, the cormorant, the parrot and in addition to these entire skeletons there are the skull of a woodpecker, showing the hyoid bones encircling the skull, and the tongue of the parrot. In the drawing of the cormorant skeleton Coiter shows the peculiar apophysis on the skull which projects backward from the cranium and also the podothecum and the webbing and tarsal sheath on one leg.

Let us look for a moment at the second chapter of Coiter's treatise—the *De Differentiis Avium*. I am indebted to my friend Miss Ethel Davis, an excellent linguist for rendering this chapter into English. It cannot be called a classification in the modern, scientific sense of the word, but it is a tabulation in outlined, bracketed form and presents at a glance a synopsis of Coiter's knowledge of birds, showing that he had studied them both in the laboratory and in the field.

Let us consider a few of his more discerning observations.

1. Birds that are wont to change their positions. Here he is referring to mimicry which many birds practice instinctively in order to make themselves resemble their immediate environment and thereby escape their enemies.

2. Birds that have long legs use them as a rudder.

3. Birds with slender necks "fold" them in flight because a long slender neck can be easily broken when shaken (i.e.) if the neck be slender in proportion to its width.

In Coiter's tabulation of environment he proves himself a good observer of the adaptations of birds to their surroundings. For example, birds that live in the marshes have elongated toes but they are only slightly webbed in order to fit them for walking in slippery, soft and wet places.

As to the parts of birds, Coiter gives an outline of the different types of beaks and points out the kind of food suited to each: (1) the straight beak for seizing; (2)

the hooked beak for tearing flesh; (3) the broad beak for those of placid habits like foraging in the grass; (4) beaks with saw-like edges in place of teeth, as in the ducks; (5) beaks that are neat and delicate for collecting vegetable matter and catching small animals, such as insects.

Coiter, likewise, takes up the neck structure of birds with some detail, and makes this generalization: "It is not possible for a [bird with] short neck with long legs, nor a [bird with] long neck with short legs to manage feeding from the ground, and no bird with hooked claws has a long neck."

In his discussion of the feet of birds Coiter departs from his own observation, and follows Pliny, thus falling into the error of thinking that certain birds are without feet. These he calls the Apodes, and assigns to this group the Birds of Paradise which, until modern times, were thought to be footless because the native collectors never saved the legs.

He recognizes that most birds have three toes in front and one behind, but makes the erroneous statement that the hind toe takes the place of a spur, there being no homology between a toe and a spur.

Some birds, Coiter says, have only three toes and some have two toes directed forward and two backward, as in the parrots, and in their case, the inner toes are shorter than the outer.

Lastly, in his tabulation, Coiter takes up the "flat-footed" birds, by which odd term he seems to mean the seabirds, such as the auks and murres which rest on the whole tarsus. He discusses the different types of membrane or webbing between the toes, which may be whole, as in ducks, divided as in some gulls, joined to the rear toe, as in the cormorants, or fluted, as in the coots.

When we consider Coiter's dates of the latter sixteenth century, a time when civilization was little directed toward the animate world, it is surprising that he knew so accurately the details of bird structure, and also so much of their life habits.

Little has been learned about Coiter during the four hundred years since he was born. Recently, however, there is a growing interest in him, stimulated by the excellent biographical account of him, published by the late Dr. G. W. Th. Nuijens [8] (d. 1945). Again I am indebted to my friend, Miss Davis, for rendering Dr. Nuijens' Dutch articles into English.

Volcher Coiter was born in Gröningen in 1534, the son of a lawyer. Nothing is known of his childhood, but as a young man, he received his training at St. Martin's School at Gröningen, where Regnerus Praedinius was rector. He showed particular ability in medical science and was awarded a scholarship or subsidy by the Town Council to continue for five years until he should have finished his studies. He left his home city at twenty-one years of age in 1555, and apparently never returned, but spent his time going from place to place on the Continent in order to study under the leading pro-

[8] Nuijens, 1933–1934: 251–269.

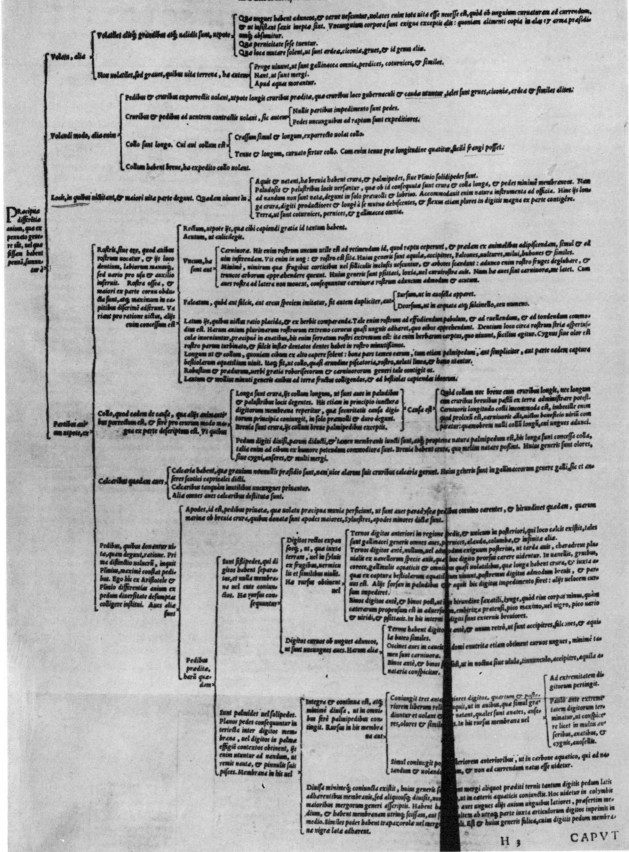

FIG. 8. The *De Differentiis Auium* (1575) of Volcher Coiter. Courtesy of the Army Medical Library.

409

fessors in his field. He met, and studied under, Fallopius at the University of Padua. At Montpellier he met, and became a good friend of, Rondelet; and at Bologna, where he came in 1559, he was one of Aldrovandus' most able students. At Rome he studied under Eustachius at the Hospital of the Holy Ghost. In 1563 he returned to Bologna and this time studied surgery under Julius Caesar Arantius, but gave instruction, himself, in anatomy, and in 1564 was given the position of Professor of Surgery and Anatomy, although he was then only thirty years old and several years the junior of other members of the staff. Apparently, he was gifted in the art of teaching, but two years later in 1566 his name disappears from among the faculty. Others, jealous of his success, plotted against him and hampered his work. He was fearless in the fight against quackery and barber surgeons, and this, too, made enemies for him. But most basic of all to Coiter's loss of popularity was his conversion to Protestantism, which automatically would close any prominent position in Italy to him.

At this point in Coiter's career, the German historian J. A. Schelhorn aids the student by his description of university conditions in Bologna and Padua at this precise time:

It was not safe for foreigners in Italy, and Coiter, after a street fight by students, was taken prisoner, bound, and sent to Rome. He was returned to Bologna, but was held there in the Prison of the Dominicans for a year. Through unknown help, he obtained his release in 1567. This forced him to leave Italy, and he set out for Bavaria, where his friend, a man named Camererius, aided him in getting a post as physician to Ludwig, the Duke of Bavaria.

Here he rested from persecution for a few years, but Coiter was a broken man, unhappy and humbled by cruel experience. We may judge of this by a document discovered in the Archives of Nuremberg. This is written in Old-German, and I am indebted to my friend, Mrs. Elizabeth Van der Hoek, for its translation. Its substance is Coiter's five-year agreement with the city of Nuremberg as town physician, a position to which he was appointed in 1569. Though the duties were heavy and poorly paid, Coiter was able to devote himself to his writing, and during the next six years wrote several of his principal works; the last of which was the *Lectiones Gabrielis Fallopii*.

In 1576 he went with Johann Casimer, a fiery Calvinist, as army physician in the Huguenot Wars. He did not return from this expedition, but died just as peace was declared and the army was returning on June 2, 1576.

It is unfortunate that Volcher Coiter never returned to his native country. He lies buried on foreign soil, but his writings are assembled in the Natural History Museum in Leyden and his portrait [9] hangs on the wall.

PIERRE BELON

Pierre Belon, another contributor to the structure and anatomy of birds, was contemporary with the two encyclopedists, Gesner and Aldrovandus, and also with Volcher Coiter.

His studies in zoology were confined mostly to birds and fish, but he devoted himself considerably also to botany, particularly in naturalizing exotic trees and shrubs in France.

Nothing definite is known of his parentage but he was born in Souletière in the parish of Oise in Le Mans (Sarthe) in 1517 and he tells us that as a boy he spent the year 1532 in Brittany, living with the peasants and roaming the woods and fields in search of birds and plants.

Although Belon was of humble origin and could have had little reason to think he would ever acquire great learning, it is interesting to see how fortunate he was in falling in with persons of wealth and influence who could further his ambition to study.

In his youth he was patronized by the Chancellor of France and later by the Bishop of Clermont and two Cardinals, Tournon and Lorraine. It was, however, not without long periods of dire need and adventure that these strokes of luck came to him. He entered the service of the Cardinal de Tournon as a servant but so clever and trustworthy was Belon that the Cardinal sent him on a diplomatic mission to Switzerland. Again when arrested on the suspicion of heresy, Belon's good fortune brought him release. He met a gentleman named Dehamna and, because of their mutual admiration for the contemporary poet Pierre De Ronsard (1524–1585), M. Dehamna was moved to pay for Belon's freedom. Thus aided first by one and then another, he led an exciting life and finally through various patrons gained a university education, taking a medical degree at the Collège de France in Paris. He studied also at the famous Protestant center Wittemburg where he became a friend of the Professor of Botany, Valerius Cordus (1515–1544), and subsequently travelled with him.

Between 1546 and 1549 Belon was exploring the countries of the Near East including Greece, Palestine, Turkey, Syria, Egypt, Crete, Corfu, and other Mediterranean islands. His account of these travels was published in Paris in 1553 in the form of a small illustrated book [10] in which plants, birds, animals, serpents, buildings, and menageries are described very informally. The book was popular and was translated by the French naturalist, Clusius (1526–1609), into Latin and German.

Belon's next journey took him to England where he met the Venetian Ambassador, Daniel Barbaro, who permitted him to copy some three hundred drawings of fishes of the Adriatic in his possession. No doubt this opportunity did much to fix Belon's interest on fishes and was the inspiration for his book on fishes the *Histoire Naturelle des Éstranges Poissons Marins*.

[9] De Liut, 1934: 2486–2487.

[10] Belon, 1553.

Fig. 9. Pierre Belon (1517?–1564), Pioneer in Comparative Anatomy. From Jardine's Naturalist's Library.

His best work, and the one on which rests his ornithological fame, is his *Histoire de la Nature des Oyseaux,* a 400 page folio published in Paris in 1555. It lists about two hundred birds, mostly European, but the author recognized some preserved specimens brought from America. It is divided as follows into seven livres or parts on rather unscientific grounds but at least he made more than an alphabetical arrangement:

1. De la Nature des Oyseaux
2. Vivant de Rapine
3. Qui ont le pied plat et nagent sur les eaux
4. Qui n'ont le pied plat
5. De Campagne, qui font leurs nids sur terre
6. Qui Habitent Indifferemment en touts lieux, et paissent de toutes sortes de viandes
7. Des Oysillons que Hantent Les Hayes buschettes, et buissons

Nearly every bird is illustrated with a hand colored woodcut and Belon claims to be the first to include portraits of his subjects, but he shares this honor with his contemporary, Conrad Gesner. He claims also to be the first one to devise a method of preserving specimens of birds in his collection. Although this method cannot have been successful, since prepared birds are not known until about a hundred years later, Belon certainly did

considerable dissection of birds which led him to an understanding of their anatomy and skeletal structure.

A striking feature of his *History of Birds* is his account of the homology between the human and avian skeletons. This had not been worked out by other writers and was an important contribution to comparative anatomy and morphology. The human and bird skeletons are pictured on opposite pages and the functions of the component parts, with the bird's modifications for flight, are clearly set forth. Belon thus proved himself a practical investigator by the direct method. He was always eager to describe from actual experience and it is related that when he was living in Padua, he took the boat every Thursday night over to Venice in order to be able to handle the birds and fish in the markets and to talk with the fowlers and fishermen on the quays. Travelling home Sunday nights he was back at the University Monday mornings.

In addition to his zoological interests Belon had a love of plants and trees and one of his ambitions was to establish at some university a sort of experimental garden where he could study the naturalization of exotic species. He interested King Henry II (1519–1559) in this project which he planned to pursue at the University of Paris. Here there had been a botanical garden since 1506, and the king proposed to award him a pension of 600 livres for his studies.

While waiting for the pension to materialize Belon travelled extensively in Provence and Italy, studying botanical gardens at Venice, Pisa, Florence, and Salerno, which last named city had a garden founded in 1317. The pension, however, was never paid and Belon continued his studies under the uncertain protection of various patrons.

In 1561 we find him a protégé of the French Admiral, Gaspard de Coligny (1517–1572). At this time the religious strife between Catholics and Protestants was at its height but although Belon had met the famous Luther (1483–1546) and had lost many of his friends to Protestantism he remained a true Catholic. When Coligny definitely renounced the Catholic religion and became the leader of the Huguenots, Belon was struck with sorrow and felt nearly friendless. He had as well his literary enemies who accused him of plagiarism from Gesner and Aldrovandus and finally in April 1564 as he was walking home one night through the Bois de Boulogne he was attacked and slain by an unknown assassin. At the time of his death he was at work on a translation of Theophrastus (382–287), Aristotle's successor in the Peripatetic School and the author of an important botanical work, the *History of Plants.* This and another translation of Dioscorides (fl. 1st century) the Greek medical writer and physician to Nero (37–68) were never finished.

These translations of the ancient classics show Belon to have been a scholar as well as an investigator of nature. He was much esteemed by the learned Gesner whom he met in 1557 but Belon was more a man of ac-

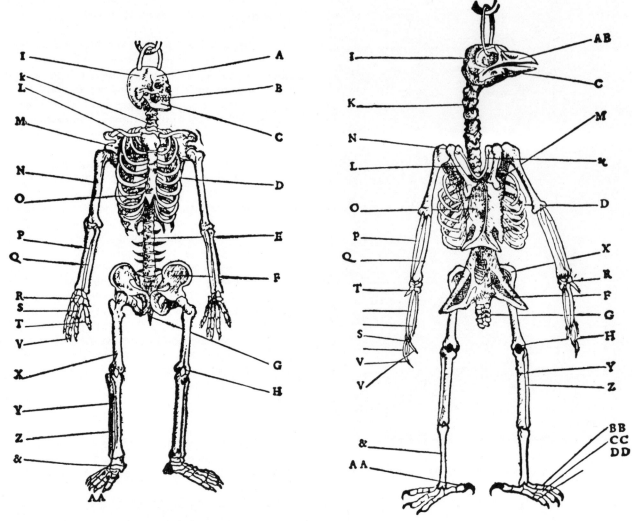

FIG. 10. Comparative Study of Man and Bird Skeletons. *L'Histoire de la nature des Oyseaux* (1555).

tion than Gesner, and being dependent upon royal favor and the protection of his patrons he never built himself into the life of his home city as did Gesner in Zurich. However, he is revered in the history of science for his contributions to experimental philosophy both in zoology and in botany. In France he is particularly remembered for naturalizing many beautiful trees and shrubs that now grow in the public gardens.

A monument was erected to Belon in his home city Le Mans in 1885.

COLLECTIONS OF RARITIES

In addition to these forthright studies of the structure and embryology of birds, and the amassing of encyclopedic accounts by Gesner and Aldrovandus there were certain other more popular trends in this branch of study. It was a vital interest among most of the scientific men of the sixteenth century to make "collections of rarities." Now a rarity was an elastic term signifying anything from a fossil plant to a large and ill-prepared

bird or mammal. Such perishable specimens could not exist long in the cabinets of the earliest collectors, for moths and other vermin soon destroyed them. At first, only bills and feet of birds and occasional dried bones were displayed; but Belon is said to have prepared a few complete birds and to have published a method of preserving them. However, no bird specimens of such antiquity have come down to us and the method was probably not imitated by others.

The first successfully made stuffed birds were apparently those in the collection of Olaf Worm, better known as Ole Worm (1588–1654), who was an archaeologist and Professor of Medicine at the University of Copenhagen. His collection was famous throughout Europe. Large birds, great sea dwellers like the shark and the sturgeon hung from the ceiling, dried crocodiles and tortoises climbed the walls while gigantic bones of sea mammals cluttered up the floor. In this setting of fearsome creatures, a few birds perched here and there, among them, the stuffed effigy of a famous American or rather Holarctic bird, a great auk (*Penguinus impennis*). This bird had been sent to Ole Worm from the Faroe Islands and became a pet in the Worm household—even to wearing a white collar about its neck. Worm included this collar in his drawing of the bird and this feature caused much speculation about the bird's plumage, some saying it was a remnant of the winter plumage. Finally, however, Professor J. Steenstrup in the *Edinburgh Philosophical Journal* (10 : 97, 1885) declared the white ring to be artificial. "Et Beidrag till Geirfuglens."

This once incredibly abundant bird is now extinct. It was circumpolar in distribution but was always more abundant on American shores and waters than on those of the Eastern Hemisphere. It underwent the more relentless persecution on the American side of the Atlantic because of the constant reconnoitering expeditions sent over by European nations. Funk Island and the coast lines of Labrador and Newfoundland were three of the great auk's last strongholds. It seems certain that the last member of this fine race disappeared about 1844. The auk was one of the most striking of Ole Worm's birds but he had many others.

A catalogue of his museum was published at Leyden the year after his death in 1655. Pages 290–312 with copper plate portraits of ten species of birds were devoted to the avian material. This catalogue is now very rare but the fact that twenty-two pages were given to birds indicates a fairly large number of specimens in his collection. Some bird specimens were on exhibition at this time in the Museum of Drottningholm, Sweden.

Another sign of greater popular interest in natural history was the keeping of birds and animals in captivity. Menageries had been popular in the ancient world and the conquistadores had found them well established in Mexico and South America. But in Europe, only rarely were strange exotic animals exhibited. We read of Charlemagne's (742–814) elephant presented to him by the Caliph Haroun al Raschid (766–809) of Bagdad and of Frederick II's giraffe, but these are merely bits of curious personal history. During the period of frequent expeditions to Asia, to Africa, to the island world of the Pacific, and to the Americas there were vast new stores of knowledge fairly inundating the eager people at home. Practically every argosy that set sail carried artists and collectors whose duty it was to bring back drawings and specimens of birds, animals, and plants. Many of these poor creatures perished on the long voyages for lack of proper care, but such as survived were provided for by royal command or by the patrons of art and travel. It became customary for princes and titled persons to support these ventures for they realized their prestige was enhanced by their interest in science.

People flocked to see these strange captive creatures and artists were engaged to paint them from life. Thus as the public became more familiar with living things, which formerly they had but vaguely visualized, books with improved illustrations came into demand. It was natural that birds with their multifarious colors should appeal as a subject to write about and to illustrate with colored engravings.

The wood cut had long been used by the early writers on birds and had been found satisfactory because it could be reproduced in the printing process, but during the seventeenth century great progress was made in the art of bookmaking and many authors and publishers deemed it advisable to include engravings or plates in their books.

One of the first books to contain bird illustrations of this new type was a compilation from several encyclopedic books, by John Johnstone (1603–1675), a physician of Scottish ancestry but Polish by birth who practiced medicine in Leyden. The book under the title *Historiae Naturalis de Avibus* was published in 1650 at Frankfurt and contained engravings executed by the two sons of the famous publisher, Matthaeus Merian (?–1650), and colored by hand. Part six is devoted to birds, the other nine parts having to do with sky, elements, meteors, fossils (minerals), plants, quadrupeds, invertebrates, fishes, and man. This book was widely read in several languages and was even mentioned by Linnaeus a hundred years later in his *Systema Naturae*. An English translation by "a person of quality" appeared in London in 1657. An interesting but archaic feature of this work is its inclusion of several fabulous birds such as the harpy, the phoenix, and the griffin although at this time few believed in such myths. The book in the same form was issued again in Heilbronn in 1765 and in 1772–1774 a French translation came out, considerably enlarged in text and in the number of illustrations. It was divided into three parts the first of which treated of, and was illustrated by, the birds in the Menagerie du Roi which had been painted and engraved by the French artist Nicholas Robert (1610–1685). Parts two and three were the original material of Johnstone. This book thus had a long popularity and was the forerunner of many elaborate ornithological works such as Buffon and Naumann on the Continent, and Edwards and Pennant in England.

We have seen that the spread of the Renaissance through western Europe affected ornithology in several ways. Exploration into all parts of the world vastly increased the knowledge of birds and presented a fascinating array of new kinds to be captured for the menageries, to be stuffed for the museums and to be painted by the artists. The invention of the microscope in 1590 enabled students to probe beyond what the unaided eye could see, while the discovery of the preserving properties of alcohol, made the shipping and storing of specimens for display or future reference much simpler.

The collections of rarities then became so large and unwieldy that they had to be better housed and then systematized. Gradually the few parts of birds or the few mounted birds that some scientists had were superseded by whole cabinets of birds. These were the forerunners of the modern museum collection, and in the realm of living creatures the menagerie, which at first had been a few poorly housed unhappy animals, became the modern zoological garden where wild creatures were commodiously caged and scientifically fed.

It was natural that the devotees of these various activities in the furtherance of natural history should be drawn together by their common interest,[11] and thus it was that academies of science and other learned bodies had their genesis. One of the first of these, the Accademia del Cimento, sprang up in Florence and was sponsored by the two Medici brothers, the Grand Duke Ferdinand II and Leopold.[12] A condition of membership of its nine scientists was that each one should communicate some unknown discovery in natural science. This was in deference to its "spiritual father," Galileo (1564–1642), who had toured Italy at the height of his fame in the interest of experimental research.

It was a period when several momentous zoological discoveries were made. Vesalius (1515–1564) had revolutionized anatomy by insisting on human dissection and thus he proved that the Galen (A.D. 130) code of anatomy was not compatible with what was demonstrated on the dissecting table. Harvey (1578–1657) studied the motion of the heart and observed the heart action in fishes, frogs, birds, and various embryos, arriving at last at an understanding of the circular course of the blood. Harvey's Professor, Fabricius of Aquependente (1537–1619), at Padua came forward with an explanation of the valves of the heart, and in addition contributed much new material to Coiter's embryological studies of the chick. Other important discoveries in human anatomy were made by Cesalpinus (1509–1603), Fallopius (1523–1562), and Eustachius while Leopold pursued further studies of avian embryology. In these experiments which involved artificial incubation, Leopold employed two Egyptian scientists who worked in his laboratory and garden.

All this scientific activity in Italy was prompt to be echoed in Switzerland, France, and England, and somewhat later in Germany. The advantages of cooperative effort were definitely felt not only because of the expense of individual equipment but also because of the stimulating effect of brotherhood in research. Some of the members of the Accademia del Cimento were interested in physics, others in botany. With a microscope built by Galileo, F. Stelluti (1577–1646) first studied the morphology of bees and the Society published his work[13] in 1625. Its most important publication and one that turned the eyes of Europe to the New World was the *Thesaurus Mexicanus,* an account of the plant and animal life of Mexico. After this, however, the Society's main patron Leopold, who had worked as hard as any

of its members, was made Cardinal and the Accademia del Cimento soon languished and ceased to exist in 1657.

We might with profit follow the spread of the scientific movement into other cities and countries of western Europe and find other ornithological experiments and publications but we must turn now to England from which country, primarily, American ornithology took its origin.

IV. EARLY BIRD LORE IN ENGLAND

William Turner (d. 1568) was the moving spirit of early bird study in England but a few curious treatises preceded him, which, though not very reliable, are quaint and typical of their time.

Giraldus Cambrensis (1146–1223) wrote the topography of Ireland published in 1587 and devoted ten short chapters to an account of birds. Hawks and game are treated of in the *Boke of St. Albans,* the work of a woman, perhaps the first feminine ornithologist of Christendom, one Dame Juliana Berners or Barnes (b. 1388?) a sportswoman but also the prioress of Sopwell nunnery. Her book contained also a *Treatyse on Fysshynge with an Angle* and was published in 1486.

England has always been a game-loving country and it is natural that many of the early records about birds should deal with hunting, and the prices of game. Thus is shown the people's interest in keeping track of the choice large birds such as cranes, herons, bustards, and spoonbills which furnished out the banquet tables on state occasions. But paradoxically enough some of the most prodigal despoilers of bird life had also a warm protective thought about them. Henry VIII (1491–1547), bluebeard and epicure though he was, imposed a check upon the slaughter. This was an act to stop the destruction of wild-fowl. Section four of the Act of 1534 prohibits

the taking of the eggs of any kind of wild-fowl from the first of March [1533], and the last day of June, and so on yearly under pain of punishment besides having to forfeit for every egg of any crane or Bustard twenty pence, of a Bittour (Bittern), Heroune, or Shoellard (spoonbill) eight pence, and for every egg of mallard, teal, or any other wildfowl, except crows, Ravens, Bosards (Buzzards) and other fowl not used to be eaten, a penny.

This law proved to be oppressive and parts of it were repealed in 1550,[1] but the penalties for taking eggs remained. This restriction, while a step in the right direction, was of small avail to save the larger birds, and cranes and bustards completely disappeared from the English countryside about 1700 because of the unrelenting ravages upon them by hunters. Some birds like the black headed gull were taken from the various gulleries in Nórfolk, Essex, and Staffordshire and fattened in captivity on kitchen refuse and liver, while thousands of winders (widgeon), rumors (rails), grows (Black grouse), and peions (pigeons) were netted, shot, and

[11] Ornstein, 1928.

[12] The earliest of these societies was the Accademia secretorum naturae, founded in Naples in 1560, and the next, Accademia dei Lincei in Rome in 1603.

[13] Stelluti, 1625.

[1] Gurney, 1921: 167.

cudgeled for food. Nor was it only the water and marsh loving species that were taken as food. In many of the old writings one finds mention of larks, thrushes, wagtails, finches, and "small birds" as food and in Joseph Strutt [2] the prices (beyond whch no poulterer could charge) for some of these birds in the market are given as follows:

	sh.	d.
Swan	4	0
Teal		2
Snipe		1
Woodcock		3
13 Thrushes		6
13 small birds		1

On the other hand, some of England's most beloved writers displayed a love of animals and especially of birds. A notable account of birds which strikes sympathetic response in the modern student is Chaucer's (1340?–1400) famous *Parlement of Briddis* in which thirty-seven species are mentioned with well chosen allusion to their salient characteristics—the occasion of the parliament being Saint Valentine's Day when all the birds come together to choose their mates under the friendly counsel of the Goddess of Nature. An interesting paper in a current magazine discusses Chaucer's ornithological attainments.[3] Though Chaucer was primarily a business man he showed one of the essentials of the master of literary expression, a personally acquired knowledge of natural history.

England indeed during the period of the Revival of Learning presented a mixed picture of waste and protection of its bird life. Also should be mentioned as characteristic of this time, her preoccupation with the ancient sport of falconry, that practice of training certain of the swiftest birds of prey to come to the lure and to strike the game for their masters. Among the royalty it was really more than a sport. It came to be regarded as a symbol of royalty to such an extent that every king's retinue carried several kinds of hawks in its processions and, when not being flown or displayed as a mark of the king's grandeur and importance, the falcons were fed and cared for in commodious enclosures called hawk mews. One such stood near Charing Cross in London about where the National Portrait Gallery now stands.

We have already discussed Frederick II's passion for falconry in the twelfth century. It is of signal interest that five hundred years later it was still a favorite "sport of kings" [4] and even today it has its votaries among young men who find pleasure in training these noble birds.

Falconry at best, however, is but a romantic off-shoot of the science of ornithology and though it has gathered unto itself a wealth of picturesque literature it cannot be said to be an integral part of the study of birds.

It was necessary that birds should acquire a true en-

tity, that they should captivate the interest not as delicacies to please the jaded epicure, not as mediaeval concoctions to cure the love-lorn but just as elusive songsters of the gardens or as queer croaking denizens of the fens and swales.

William Turner, Dean of Wells, became known as a writer on birds when he published in 1544 an interpretation of the birds mentioned by Aristotle and Pliny under the title, *Avium Praecipuarum, quarum apud Plinium et Aristotelem mentio est, brevis et sucincta historia.* This was reprinted in 1823, and again in 1903 by Mr. A. H. Evans who added many notes that help the reader to appreciate Turner's first-hand knowledge of birds.

Turner, the son of a tanner, was born about 1500 in Morpeth in Northumberland. Nothing is known of his early education but he became a member of Pembroke Hall, Cambridge through the influence of Thomas, Lord Wentworth. He was graduated in 1529 or 1530, became a Fellow in 1531, was studying for the M.A. in 1533, was Senior Treasurer in 1538 and finally became Dean of Wells in 1550. While at Cambridge, Turner became acquainted with John Caius (1510–1573), founder of the college named after himself, who also was a writer on natural history subjects.[5] Under his influence to some extent, Turner took up the study of birds. At Cambridge also he was an intimate friend of Nicholas Ridley,[6] famous agitator for reformed opinions on religion, and Turner never renounced his non-conformist beliefs although they caused him to lose his Deanery and his writings to be banned. After leaving Cambridge, Turner travelled on the Continent, visiting at Zurich the famous Professor Conrad Gesner with whom he kept up a correspondence for many years.

Under Queen Elizabeth (1553–1603), Turner was recalled to his Deanery for a time but in 1564 was again dismissed for non-conformity and went to live in London. Only four more years were allotted to him, however, for he died on July 7, 1568, and was buried in the Church of St. Olave Crutched Friars where his widow, Jane Turner, daughter of George Ander an alderman of Cambridge, erected a memorial tablet for him.

Turner became seriously interested in field observation of birds while he was a student at Cambridge because he speaks of not having seen "so common a thing as the nest of the water ousel," before he went to the university. He was distressed over the gross ignorance of both the educated in the university and the simple folk of the countryside and seems to have applied himself with real zeal despite his interrupted and checkered career, to the study of plants and animals largely by

---

[2] Strutt, 1776: **3**: 113.

[3] Bombardier, 1944: **256**: 120–125.

[4] Fuertes, 1920: 429–460.

[5] Caius, 1570 and 1729. He describes thirteen birds, including a puffin which he kept alive in his house for eight months—a small list but done with detail. It is thought this was part of a larger list intended for Gesner but on account of his early death not sent to him.

[6] Condemned for heresy and burnt alive Oct. 16, 1555.

the direct method.[7] We are indebted to Turner also for his publication of the posthumous work, *Dialogus De Avibus,*[8] of his Belgian friend Gybertus Longalius (1507–1543) one of the oldest and rarest books on birds.

In conclusion about Turner it is noteworthy that he furnished Gesner in Zurich with much information on British fishes. His fame was still bright a hundred years later, for John Ray praised his solid learning and justice.

Between Turner and the cooperative work of John Ray (1628–1705) and Francis Willughby (1635–1672) soon to be discussed in these pages, there were no outstanding ornithological books published.

But early in the seventeenth century there were a few county histories in which birds are included, while in the decade of 1660–1670 two books of some importance appeared. One, the *Natural Rarities of England, Scotland and Wales* by Joshua Childrey (1623–1670) in 1661, and the other the *Pinax Rerum Naturalium Britannicarum* by Christopher Merrett (1614–1695) published in 1667. This latter book is a land mark in British ornithology because it is the first printed list of British birds. However, it is not commendable either for number of species or what the author says of them. In fact it contains only thirty-seven birds, and Merrett had very little field experience. John Ray a few years later referred to it as "Merrett's bungling Pinax" but others appeared to think well of it probably because, though not well executed, it was a unique piece of work.

More useful to one seeking information on British birds was Richard Carew's (1555–1620), *Survey of Cornwall* (1602) which gives a picture of the birds of Southern England. First the game species, then the hawks, and lastly the singing birds of which he mentions lynets, goldfinches, ruddockes (robins), canarie birds, black-birds, thrushes and divers others. He remarks the great scarcity of nightingales and wondered whether some antipathy of the species to the soil were the cause. Crossbills with their destructiveness to apples, and the old fable about the hibernation of swallows are next given as taken from the Swedish Prelate Olaus Magnus (1490–1557). This seemed difficult for Carew to believe but he was "induced to give it a place in his mind" and quoted thus: ". . . in the North parts of the world, as summer weareth out, they [the swallows] clap mouth to mouth, wing to wing, and legge to legge, and so after a sweet singing fall downe into certain great lakes or pooles among the Canes from whence next Spring they receive a new resurrection. . . ." Notwithstanding this astounding credulousness, Carew was a keen agriculturist, bee-keeper, and general observer of Nature. He was likewise an antiquary and the high sheriff of Cornwall. His survey of that county is the best one

of several county histories [9] each of which included special accounts of the local birds. George Owen (1552–1613) a native of Wales appeared the next year with his *Description of Pembrokeshire* (1603) in which he furnished reliable evidence on the breeding of spoonbills (*Platalea leucorodia*) in that part of Wales. His account of the woodcock netting is a distressing example of one-time abundance in contrast to present day scarcity of these fine birds, but it is significant as another instance of real field observation. Likewise his remarks on the purchase price of some birds point to great abundance of certain species as shown by these words: "I have heard a gentleman of good sort and credytte report that he hath bought in St. Davids, ij woodcockes, iij snipes, and certayne teales and blackbyrdes for a penny, . . ." He concludes his account with the oft-repeated story of the generation of the barnacle goose from driftwood, as persistent a bit of folk belief about birds as the hibernation of swallows.

Many other county histories with more or less matter on birds, were eventually written, of which I would mention only those by Dr. Robert Plot (1641–1696) published in the latter seventeenth century. His *Natural History of Oxfordshire* with sixteen plates was published in 1677 but is of little value as far as birds are concerned. His *Natural History of Staffordshire* on the other hand represents much more observation on the author's part and is particularly interesting for its account of the nesting of the pewits or black-headed gulls. His bird observations occupy twelve pages and Plot seems to have aspired to do other county natural history books but no doubt his many duties as keeper of the Ashmolean Museum at Oxford, as Professor of Chemistry and as practicing physician left little time for outdoor studies.

Of superior quality again and more in the nature of Turner's work with definite field observation is the diversified work on birds done by Sir Thomas Browne (1605–1682). Philosopher, writer, physician, and naturalist was he; a modest but exceedingly erudite resident of Norwich, who maintained at his home a considerable museum of curios. Of it Sir John Evelyn (1620–1706), probably the main author of the Royal Society, at the time of his visit to Sir Thomas Browne on October 7, 1672 remarked: ". . . his whole house and garden being a paradise and cabinet of Rarities. . . ." Amongst other curiosities, Sir Thomas had a collection of the eggs of all the fowl and birds he could procure in that country (especially the promontory of Norwich) which was frequented (as he said) by several birds which seldom or never go farther into the land, as cranes, storks, eagles, and a variety of waterfowl. All of Sir Thomas Browne's writings on birds and fishes were extracted from his manuscripts in the British Museum and

---

[7] One of the early publications on English birds which Turner is thought to have made use of is a poem by John Skelton (1460?–1529), *The book of Phylyp Sparowe* (1508). This poem mentions sixty-nine birds.

[8] An excellent copy of this work is in the Emma Shearer Wood Libr. of Ornithology at McGill Univ.

[9] Another county history of this period is by John Aubrey (1626–1697), *The natural history of Wiltshire,* ed. by J. Britton, 1847, London, Wiltshire Topog. Soc.

edited by Thomas Southwell,[10] noted authority on seals and whales, in 1902. Mr. Southwell was likewise an ornithologist, a member of the British Ornithologists' Union and well qualified to estimate Sir Thomas Browne's knowledge of birds. Though Browne was a good observer and sketcher of birds Mr. Southwell points out that he appears to have preferred to turn his findings over to more professional naturalists, rather than to rush them into print himself.

Browne is interesting as one of the early observers of birds by the direct method. He was definite in his views on migration when most persons were still believing in hibernation and he deduced that the birds which come in the spring are from the south while the fall migrants come from the north. He enjoyed the birds of prey particularly and wrote a discourse on falconry;[11] he engaged in sketching birds and in collecting birds' eggs, and also kept some dried specimens of unusual species. His total list of birds in Southwell's edition numbered eighty-nine species with some conspicuous omissions such as the owl, pheasant, snipe, wood pigeon, and various common small birds. Professor Alfred Newton (1829–1907) of Cambridge, who assisted Southwell in the preparation of Browne's *Notes and Letters,* thinks his list was not intended to be complete (else such obvious omissions would not have been made), but was probably compiled for Sir Nicolas Bacon, a fellow resident of Norfolk, who also was interested in birds.

Sir Thomas Browne furnishes another proof of the appeal which birds make to persons of widely varying interests. He is described as a great scholar and thinker but a reading of his *Religio Medici* (the Religion of a Doctor) reveals his doctrine of unity and accord with all nature, and though some of his writings suggest a mystical response to the physical world, he was likewise strongly empirical and engaged in extensive travels in order to acquire correct knowledge and the unbiased point of view. His travels on the Continent the same year that Ray and Willughby were studying and collecting together, and their meeting at Montpellier, resulted in Browne's transmitting to Ray and Willughby certain drawings of birds for use in their proposed cooperative work. The drawings, nearly life size, bearing Sir Thomas Browne's name and pronounced "creditable" by J. H. Gurney, are in the British Museum (Bibl. Sloane 5266) and one of them represents the Manx shearwater[12] (*Puffinus puffinus puffinus*), a member of the American Check-List of birds. This was reproduced in Willughby's *Ornithology,* pl. 78,[13] and was duly ac-

knowledge by Willughby but apparently these drawings were intended only for a loan and Browne in a letter to his son Dr. Edward Browne regrets that Ray and Sir Philip Skippon, both of whom promised to return them, never did so.[14]

Browne belongs to a period of great change of attitude toward natural science. Fettered for a thousand years by blind faith in the writings of a few accepted authorities the world now began to think on nature with unafraid determination to find the truth. Though Browne's writings on birds are by no means full, he studied and wrote on many phases of ornithology and the quality is consistently good.

He was born in London in 1605 and in 1636 after his training at Oxford, and some years' residence and travel on the Continent, he established his home in Norwich where he practiced medicine and enjoyed his gardens and collections amid a happy family life with his wife[15] and ten children. He died on October 19, 1672, upon the completion of his seventy-sixth year and was buried in the Church of St. Peter, Mancroft Norwich.[16]

Browne's natural history observations might have been produced as a survey of Norfolk as this was the period in English literature when many county histories were published. But Browne's published writings were mostly of a humanistic nature.

JOHN RAY AND FRANCIS WILLUGHBY

The way had gradually been prepared for the two scientists, John Ray (1627–1705) and Francis Willughby (1635–1672), who represent a new type of natural history work. England, worn with religious and political strife, was beginning to turn to the world of nature for correction of her atrophied system of education, and experimental science, which had been struggling some two thousand years for recognition, found one of its greatest champions in the English statesman, Francis Bacon (1561–1626). Although he cannot be called a contributor to natural knowledge it was he who sensed his country's need for new standards and who with fearless eloquence laid bare the outmoded practices of university life. Disputation, dialectics, and the stultifying tradition of Latin as the language of culture, were some of the evils he sought to correct.

Said Bacon in his *Advancement of Learning* (1605) "as . . . usages and orders of the universities were derived from more obscure time, it is the more requisite they be re-examined." Again in the *Novum Organum*

[10] Thomas Southwell was a resident of Norwich and wrote on the birds of Norwich, continuing a work started by H. Stevenson, and published in 1866.

[11] Gurney, 1921: 205.

[12] Found in northeastern Atlantic Ocean but accidental on Long Island and in Maine.

[13] I am indebted to Miss Hazel Gay, librarian of the Amer. Mus. Nat. Hist. N. Y., for checking this information from the Museum's copy of Willughby.

[14] Wilkin, *Sir Thomas Browne's collected works,* 337, 1835; also Appendix E. London, H. G. Bohn, 1852.

[15] Dorothy, fourth daughter of Edward Mileham of Burlingham, St. Peter, said to have been a woman of classical beauty. Only three daughters and one son, Dr. Edward Browne (1644–1708), president of Royal Col. of Physicians (1704), survived the parents.

[16] See *Proc. Archaeol. Soc. 1847* for details of damage to Sir Thomas Browne's mortal remains by excavators. His skull, according to the Dict. of Nat. Biog., is now kept under glass at a Norwich hospital.

FIG. 11. John Ray (1627–1705), English Botanist and Ornithologist. Courtesy of the Trustees of the British Museum.

XC (1620), referring to the restrictions imposed upon students:

For the studies of men in these places [the colleges, academies, etc.] are confined and, as it were, imprisoned in the writings of certain authors, from whom if any man dissent, he is straightway arraigned as a turbulent person or innovator.

It is said that Bacon conceived the idea of founding two lectureships [17] in natural philosophy at Cambridge and Oxford "with science in general thereunto belonging" but, since Bacon was always in trouble financially, it is not surprising that the funds he bequeathed were inadequate.

He is credited also with having inspired the foundation of the Royal Society of London for the Improvement of Natural Knowledge but he did not live to see this plan realized, for he died in 1626 twenty years before any concrete organization of such a society took place. It is certain, however, that he influenced such liberal trends not only by his philosophical writings but also by the way in which he lived. Though a man vain and luxury-loving he had an abounding interest in nature and kept beautful gardens of flowers and a representative aviary at a cost of three hundred pounds at his home. A phrase from his *House of Solomon* is significant: "the enlarging of the bounds of Human Empire" and in his all-inclusive description of the activities of

------

[17] Ornstein, 1913: 279 and note.

man in sounding the depths of his capabilities he has this to say of birds:

We have also parks and enclosures of all sorts of beasts and birds which we use not only for view or rareness but likewise for dissection and trials; that thereby we may take light what may be wrought upon the body of man.

The founding of the Royal Society was indeed an event of far-reaching importance in conservative England. It differed from the Accademia del Cimento in Florence and the Academie des Sciences of France in not being sponsored by royalty or men of wealth; it was merely a group of progressive scientists devoted to the experimental method who met informally beginning in 1645 at each others' lodgings and later at Gresham College. Doctors, astronomers, and mathematicians comprised a large part of the group but it is interesting to know that Dr. Christopher Merrett (1614–1695), the botanist and the author of the first catalogue of British birds, described above, was among the initial group that later became the Royal Society.

Another ornithological note is sounded in the fact that one of the first papers of the Society presented by the President, Sir Robert Moray (d. 1673), was on barnacles and told the old familiar story of the generation of birds from tiny shells adhering to trees on an island of West Scotland. Unfortunately this is not a high order of ornithology but at least it indicates a lively interest in birds in the early years of this society which became so powerful an influence in natural science.

Of much greater importance to ornithology is the fact that the learned young nobleman, Sir Francis Willughby, who was primarily devoted to birds was one of the eight leading members when Charles II (1630–1685) presented the charter on July 15, 1662.

Willughby had entered Cambridge in 1652 and soon became acquainted with John Ray who had already been there several years. Despite their difference in age and upbringing these two scientists present a noble example of partnership in research, and it was their love of study and of nature that set them on common ground. Ray was a blacksmith's son and had his early education in a grammar school that held its classes in the Braintree Church. His tutor was a Mr. Love who grounded him well in his studies leading to his entry into Catherine Hall, Cambridge, at only sixteen years of age. He remained there only a year and three quarters and then removed to Trinity College where he said "the polite arts and sciences were principally minded and cultivated." A Doctor Duport (1606–1679), noted Greek scholar and Master of Magdalene College was his tutor, and Ray became a learned and fluent orator at the same time that he was perfecting his grasp of Natural Philosophy. He was chosen Minor Fellow of Trinity in 1649 and Major Fellow in 1650, and until 1660 when he was dismissed because of his religious views he held many offices of honor and trust. Despite his change of worldly position, however, he preserved his salient characteristic of modest devotion to study. Erudition, piety, and scientific acumen combined to make Ray a great scientist and one of England's most famous preachers. The Archbishop of Canterbury, Thomas Tenison (1636–1715), philanthropist and founder of London's first public library, remarked of him: "Mr. Ray was much celebrated for his preaching of solid and useful divinity instead of that enthusiastic stuff which the sermons of that time were generally filled with." He really lived his religion.

Discussions of Ray's life and accomplishments can be read in many biographical dictionaries and works on botany and an exhaustive work [18] has lately been published, but a more personal touch is lent in the old manuscript on John Ray by his friend, George Dale of Braintree, a village lying a short distance from Ray's home at Black Notley.

This manuscript came to light in the Bodleian Library in 1916 and the *Essex Review* for October 1916 at last published it under the authorship of Andrew Clark whose tutor, Dr. W. Warde Fowler, discovered it.[19] From this short account occupying a few sheets of foolscap paper, we learn that Ray began his botanical travels August 9, 1658 when he started off on horseback from Cambridge, going to Northampton Coventry and Buxton, and as far north as Lancashire in quest of herbs. At this time he was thirty-one years of age and so far had distinguished himself mostly in Greek and mathematics, as shown by his election as Greek and mathematical lecturer to Trinity College. The love of plants, however, lay deep in his heart and he devoted himself on this first "simpling" journey to the study and collection of herbs. The publication resulting therefrom, *Catalogus Plantarum circa Cantabrigiam,* was the beginning of a long series of successful botanical papers.

Ray's second journey of July and August 1661 shows more interest in birds and furnishes an early account of the solan goose, a bird famous in English and American literature. This is the gannet which breeds in almost countless thousands in the Gulf of St. Lawrence and winters along our Atlantic Coast. It is likewise abundant on the Scottish Coast and Iceland.

The following year Ray invited Willughby to accompany him and together they went through England going from Cambridge over to Bangor whence they followed the coast line to Gloucester and Bristol; thence through the southern peninsula to Lands End and back to Eton near London. The account of the ornithological findings is incorporated in the *Ornithology* and we may reasonably assume that the two naturalists were congenial and found their joint efforts satisfactory.

The next year, in 1663–1664, Ray and Willughby carried out an ambitious plan of travelling through Western Europe with the idea of producing eventually a comprehensive description of the whole animal kingdom. They were accompanied by Nathaniel Bacon (1642–

1676), a lawyer, and Philip Skippon of Blythburg in Suffolk, who later fell heir to a Suffolk knighthood but who at this time was a promising student of Ray. They visited Holland, Germany, Switzerland, France, and Italy, having crossed to Calais on April 18, 1663, so that the migration and nesting seasons of the birds were at hand. This afforded the best opportunity for seeing a wide variety of species. One account of the expedition may be read in Ray's *Travels through the Low Countries* (1738), but the ornithological findings of the expedition are best presented in the pages of *Willughby's Ornithology* (1678), which Ray completed after Willughby's death.

THE ILLUSTRATIONS FOR THE PROPOSED COOPERATIVE WORK BY RAY AND WILLUGHBY

Ray and Willughby, in addition to studying and collecting birds on their Continental expedition were also gathering numerous illustrations because they did not intend to attempt a large collection of specimens.

They secured drawings both plain and colored as follows:

1. A group of drawings by Sir Thomas Browne whom they met at Montpellier. These were intended as a loan but were not returned.
2. A group of Aldrovandus' printed figures which they inspected in Bologna in February 1664.
3. A group of the full-plate illustrations from the Italian work Uccelliera by Giovanni Pietro Olina (*ca.* 1622).[20]
4. A few from the French writer Carolus Clusius (1526–1609).
5. Some of Willem Piso's (1611–1678) the Dutch physician, a member of the Dutch expedition to Brazil in 1660.

All these various drawings were selected with thought for their resemblance to life and with due regard to their fitness to be copied by Ray's engravers.

A stroke of good luck awaited the travelling naturalists when they arrived at Strasbourg for here they procured some excellent illustrative material with descriptive text from a picturesque old German hunter and collector of Strasbourg, named Leonhard Baldner (1612–1694). This self-made naturalist came from a long line of fisherfolk and he devoted his life to studying the fauna of his region. He says in the introduction to his book: [21]

To the end that God Almighty be praised and acknowledged by us, we must not forget the benefits of the three Rivers

---

[18] Raven, 1942.

[19] Boulger, 1916: 57–71.

[20] Olina's work is important because, from the point of view of illustration, it is intermediate between the text figures such as Gesner used and the more pleasing "plates" of the eighteenth century. His work contains 63 full-page engravings of birds and directions for catching birds, for retaining them in captivity and information on their diseases.

[21] A manuscript on birds (56), fish (40), mammals, amphibia, worms, etc., dated 1653, purchased by Willughby in 1663. Now in the Brit. Mus., Add'l MSS. 6485–6486.

which we, God be Blessed, do here at Strassburg enjoy, viz., the Rhine, the Ill and the Breusch; in which there is no want of Fishes, Crabfishes and Fowls and all other things that live in the water, which we are abundantly blessed with. In consideration of this and the delight I took therein, I was led to procure among these wonderful works themselves all fishes, crabfishes, waterfowls, four-footed water beasts, insects, worms, and chafers and all living things that move in the water, as many as I could get which are found about Strassburg in fresh waters, and all of which I had in my own hands. I caused them to be painted in lively colors and every one called by its name; and as much as I could learn by diligent examination I described briefly every one according to my own experience.

Baldner did not intend to make a book of fishes and fowls, much less of insects but because in 1649 he had shot some strange birds that he did not recognize he caused them to be painted and so delightful were his reflections and contemplations about them that for thirty years he cast his net and shot his gun, examining, drawing, and cherishing all his trophies with the true naturalist's ardor.

Though Baldner was a humble man he must have had some aptitude for what might be called simple conservational work. It is well known that Europeans began to legislate in behalf of their wildlife while America was prodigally exploiting her own, and even in the mid-sixteenth century European countries imposed restrictions upon the taking of game. Baldner was made warden of fisheries and forests before the Rhine and its banks had been turned to commercial uses. He regarded this home territory as the garden spot of the world more blessed with wild creatures than any other part of Europe, and he strove to convey the story of its multiform charms by means of a "Bird-Fish- and Animal-Book."

He employed a man in Strasbourg to draw and paint for him. However, he wrote the brief and quaint accounts of color, size, habitat, and gustatory merits of each bird himself. He also practiced the anatomist's art and carefully measured the length and thickness of the gut of the birds he collected and he examined the contents of the stomach and the size and color of the liver. Sometimes he pondered these findings and came to some rational conclusion about the meaning of it all. Of the osprey he wrote as follows:

The gut of an Osprey has a length of six ells, but is scarcely half as thick as a quill pen, while the stomach is small, because it is the nature of this bird to digest its food slowly and be able to fast a long time.

Baldner pronounced the bittern as of no use and took no exception to its being barred as food by the Jews, for said he, "it is no delicacy and of no use whatever except for its claws especially the hind claws which makes a good tooth pick." These were sometimes mounted in silver and flashed in the best society.

In describing the voice of the bittern Baldner showed himself keener than many ornithologists of a much later period. He declared the booming noise of the bittern, which can be heard for two miles, to be produced through the long nostrils while the beak is closed and lifted up.

Of night herons he said they were rare, causing him to drive twenty miles on one occasion and to wait eleven hours to hear and see them, but in vain.

He definitely discredited the widely accepted fable of a barnacle goose which was supposed to be generated by a tree. Conrad Gesner only a hundred years before him affirmed that in Scotland there was a tree that produced them as its fruit. Wishing to be doubly sure of this matter, Baldner kept two geese of this kind which he got on February 27, 1649, and fed them on fruit until December 19, 1651, but, as nothing happened he "dined on them." He tells also of keeping three more of them and never could discover that they either paired or laid eggs. This was in accord with the popular belief that these birds do not copulate but Baldner persisting in the enquiry finally discovered a "male bird with testes."

Baldner described over seventy birds—mostly aquatic species, and he showed an astuteness, an intelligence and an open-mindedness far ahead of the average professional zoologist of that day but since he was uneducated in the usual formal way of his time, no one hearkened to his findings until two hundred and fifty years after his death.

Then a German professor, Robert Lauterhorn,[22] of the University of Heidelberg in 1901 brought his work to public attention with an historical introduction and hundreds of notes on Baldner's specimens. Mr. Lauterhorn attempts to do justice to this pioneer work, declaring that if it had been written on the Thames instead of on the Rhine, it would have been widely read like the *Natural History of Selborne* by Gilbert White.

This may be called Baldner's formal introduction to ornithologists but Ray and Willughby "discovered" him when on July 23, 1663, they stopped to visit him on their southward course into Italy. It is interesting to read in Ray's preface to the *Ornithology of Willughby,* his own feeling about this plain naturalist. Says Ray:

For my part, I must needs acknowledge that I have received much light and information from the Work of this poor man, and have been thereby inabled to clear many difficulties, and rectify some mistakes in Gesner.

In Strasbourg they bought a large number of water bird paintings and a written description of them by the old river fisherman, and at Nuremberg Willughby had bought another collection of paintings which are still in the Willughby family among other treasures at Wollaton Hall. The drawings secured at Strasbourg are dated December 31, 1653 and represent the first copy, but the original drawings were destroyed in the bombardment of Strasbourg in August 1870. Willughby's copy (for he was the sponsor of the expedition and defrayed such costs himself) contained 159 pages of text and colored plates of fifty-six birds, a few mammals, mollusks, worms, amphibias, etc. Before Ray and Willughby

---

[22] Lauterhorn, 1901: 432–437.

used the text it was translated by Frederick Slare, M.D., as stated in their *Historia Piscium*. Both the original copy purchased by Willughby and the translation are in the British Museum Manuscript Department, numbers 6485 and 6486 mentioned above. There were six copies of the original Baldner manuscript according to Hans Gadow (1855–1927).[23] In addition to those in the British Museum, there is one in the Town Library of Strasbourg. It contains 114 pages and is described as badly written and the text is placed either beneath the drawings or on the back of them. The drawings themselves are uncouth and painted as with "ground bricks." This is explained and the set takes unto itself new charm by Baldner's note added to his original manuscript as follows: "My son Andreas Baldner has written and painted this book from my Bird-and-Fish-Book in the twelfth year of his age; therefore the work shall be his own."

The twentieth of January, 1687, Leonhard Baldner as father certified as above. Much paternal pride is evinced in this note that his twelve-year-old boy was following in his footsteps among the birds and beasts.

A de luxe edition was made for the Elector Karl at Heidelberg and from him it went to Cassel in 1686. This is now in the Landes Bibliotek. It contains 122 pages, 129 illustrations, and a beautiful title page.

I have dwelt at some length on Leonhard Baldner, his writings and pictures because two collections of his work appear to have found their way to the United States. One of these is the set owned by the late Dr. John C. Phillips[24] of Wenham, Massachusetts. It was not known to the previous describers of Baldner's work, Robert Lauterhorn (1903), Hans Gadow (1907), and J. H. Gurney (1921). It came to Dr. Phillips through an English dealer. In 1748 it was in the possession of one Phillip Henry Zollman[25] the translator of the Baldner manuscript and apparently a publisher in London.

Dr. Phillips' copy of Baldner's work is said to be nearly identical with the British Museum copy except that it contains an elaborate title page and a portrait of the author.

The other set that has come to this country is that described by Mr. Albert C. Lownes of Providence, R. I. Writing in the *Auk* for October 1940 (pp. 532–535), he tells of a copy in his possession which gives every indication of being the exact collection from which Ray and Willughby worked. In substantiation of the authenticity of the manuscript Mr. Lownes refers to the notation "Picturam transmisit Th: Browne, M. D." which appears on one of the drawings, and he quotes also a passage from Ray's preface to Willughby's *Or-*

nithology (English Translation 1678, sixth page), in which Thomas Browne's contributions in drawings, notes, etc. to the collection that Willughby was assembling from various sources, are mentioned.

Yet the fact remains undisputed that the Baldner manuscript in the British Museum is authentic and another one referred to by J. H. Gurney in his *Early Annals of Ornithology*[26] as the "Nuremberg Volume" is still (i.e. in 1921) in the hands of Willughby's descendants.[27]

It is necessary to read both Mr. Phillips' article and that of Mr. Lownes in order fully to appreciate this interesting problem in early ornithological iconography, but suffice it to quote here Mr. Lowne's explanation as follows:

Two possible explanations occur to me. Willughby might have bought two copies of Baldner's manuscript, although Ray mentions but one; or Baldner may have presented a second copy to Ray. Baldner does not seem to have had any connections with the other naturalists of his time and the meeting with Willughby must have been an important event in his life. The fact that both copies bear identical dates suggests a connection between them. The Museum copy has two pictures to a page, while the present has but one in all but a few instances. My copy, too, has a picture of Baldner. Without making more direct comparisons than I have been able to make, it is impossible to reach a direct conclusion, but it seems to me that the Museum copy might have been a "working copy" which Ray used. In any event, this collection of pictures, with the Baldner manuscript in the British Museum and the "Nurenberg" volume, which Ray mentions in the preface to the *Ornithology* quoted above, seems to be the principal original source used by the outstanding English naturalists of the seventeenth century.

We should take particular interest in Baldner and his work also for the reason that several birds of the American Check-List were in the lot of paintings purchased by Willughby.

They are as follows: red-breasted merganser, *Mergus serrator*; golden-eye duck, *Glaucionetta clangula*; mallard, *Anas platyrhynchos*; osprey, *Pandion haliaetus*; Caspian tern, *Hydroprogne caspia*; common tern, *Sterna hirundo*.

In these years of travel on the Continent, the naturalists touched at most of the leading cities and universities of Holland, Germany, Italy, and France. Ray at least, attended lectures on anatomy at the University of Padua, but he always assisted in the collecting of plants and animals which was of major importance to the expedition. It is pointed out by Charles Raven, however, that Willughby having parted from the group in Naples and having gone to Spain in 1663 was not contributing to the labor of the most fruitful part of the journey and that most of the credit for the findings should go to Ray and Skippon.

[23] Gadow, 1907: 765.

[24] Phillips, 1925: 332–341.

[25] This name was quoted as "Tollman" by Phillips (*Auk,* July, 1925), but Lownes (*Auk,* Oct., 1940) points out this error, adding that it was not known whether Zollman actually owned the manuscript or merely translated it. Zollman was a member of the Roy. Soc. and its Sec. of For'n Corresp. from the establishment of this office until his death in 1748. To judge by his publications, he was a physicist.

[26] Gurney, 1921: 211.

[27] Willughby's eldest son, Francis, died at nineteen years; his daughter, Cassandra, in the late seventeenth century married the Duke of Chandos, who was Mark Catesby's patron in 1719; the second son, Thomas, was one of the ten peers created by Queen Anne, and called Lord Middleton.

We should remember that Willughby carried most of the financial burden and perhaps considered himself less bound by the collector's obligation and more concerned with the advantage of travelling extensively thus broadening his horizon. So he went to Spain, observing the life of rich and poor, but his account yields little nature lore. Of birds he said naught except that the red-legged partridge was abundantly used for food. While Willughby was in Spain, Ray and Skippon spent a few months in Rome where they were distressed over the slaughter of birds for the market. Says Ray:

Plenty there is of wild fowl of all sorts . . . of small birds the greatest plenty I have anywhere seen . . . one would think that in a short time they should destroy all the birds of these kinds in the country. They spare not the least and most innocent birds e.g. robin-redbreasts, finches, titmice, wagtails, wrens.

The original party had become separated when the King of France ordered all Englishmen out of the country by May 1, 1666. Ray met other friends and made many new ones ere he returned to England on April 8, 1666. He had been away three years and had gathered vast new stores of information, quantities of new materials and a reputation for learning that raised him from the modest position of a learner to a world-travelled authority on plants, fish, birds, reptiles, and mammals.

We have the feeling that the benefits and learning accruing to Willughby from these three years were considerably less. He was brilliant and versatile; he described specimens and made dissections, but his methods of work were unsystematic and desultory. In addition to these handicaps, Willughby's health was not good, perhaps it was even frail, and he was further worried by the illness of his father during the Continental sojourn. Soon after he returned from Spain his father, Sir Francis Willughby, died leaving his son two large estates, Wollaton Hall in Nottinghamshire and Middleton Hall in Warwickshire. Francis then settled down for a brief space of time to work over his collections at Middleton Hall, and Ray assisted him. Indeed Ray spent a great deal of time with him as we may judge from a letter to Dr. Lister dated June 18, 1667:

The most part of the winter I spent in reviewing and helping to put in order Mr. Willughby's collection of Birds, Fishes, Shells, Stones, and other Fossils, Seeds, Dried Plants, Coins, etc.

This partnership in work was interrupted in 1668 when Willughby married Emma the second daughter and co-heiress of Sir Henry Barnard. In 1669, however, Ray and his friend were at work again experimenting on the motion of sap in trees and other botanical problems. Entomological studies likewise engaged Willughby, and his observations on the strange life histories of Ichneumon wasps were presented to the Royal Society. He gathered material also on Hemiptera, Neuroptera, and Diptera as well as descriptions of worms and leeches. These findings were used by Ray when he came to write his *History of Insects*, a subject which

Fig. 12. Francis Willughby, A Founder of Modern Ornithology, from Jardine's Naturalist's Library.

at that time included, as his biographer remarks, "anything from an amoeba to an earthworm."

But the years allotted to Willughby now were few. He was contemplating a trip to the New World in 1671, but recurrent alarming illness forced him to lay down his many interests and unfinished writings, and he died of pleurisy on July 3, 1672, leaving his widow and three young children, Francis, Cassandra, and Thomas.

As would be expected, Ray was one of the executors of Willughby's will and since he was to be responsible for the guidance and tutoring of Willughby's children he received an annuity of £60 annually, nearly his sole support after he lost his fellowship at Oxford for refusing to conform to the Bartholomew Act (1662).[28]

Ray had discussed with Willughby shortly before he died the ultimate disposition of his scientific writings and materials, and Ray knew that his friend thought them too unfinished to be worthy of publication. Nevertheless Ray resolved to express his friendship in the labor of preparing Willughby's ornithology for the world. He did it modestly and generously without a word to indicate the prodigious job it proved to be. Perhaps once in a personal letter to his friend, Peter Courthope, he made an admission of what he had un-

---

[28] Raven, 1942: 60.

dertaken: "The death of Mr. Willughby hath cast more business upon me than I would willingly have undertook."

Ray therefore continued to live some five years at Middleton Hall where he could more conveniently devote himself to the study and preparation of Willughby's collections and manuscripts. This likewise kept him in touch with the Willughby children but they were at this time too young to need his tutoring and were under the care of a governess. Ray's position after Willughby died was one of great loneliness, for Lady Willughby had no appreciation of her husband's scientific pursuits nor was she understanding of Ray's plan to publish his manuscripts. It seems incredible that Ray with his native reticence and forty-six years could see the remedy for his situation but, after painful weighing of the matter, he proposed marriage to the children's governess, one Margaret Oakley, a girl less than half his age. She accepted, and they were married on June 5, 1673 about eleven months after Willughby's death. Apparently they continued to live at Middleton Hall under the same roof with Willughby's mother, Lady Cassandra, as well as his widow, until fate took a hand and relieved the situation. Lady Cassandra died on July 25, 1675 and the widow soon afterwards married the affluent but notorious Sir Joshua Child (1630–1699), and took the children from Ray's tutelage. It became necessary for Ray and his wife to leave Middleton, and, after a stay in Coleshill, they went to live in the house lent him by his friend, Edward Bullock, a short distance from Black Notley.

About this time Ray was offered the secretaryship of the Royal Society, of which he had been a member since 1668. He was in London at the time but no persuasions would avail to make him accept the post. He was barred from it both by his position and by his conscience, for he felt it his duty to support himself without recourse to secular employment, either by writing scientific treatises or by preaching the gospel. He had no worldly ambitions and found his cup full of contentment in the house he built for his mother at Dewlawns [29] in Black Notley. To this simple three-room retreat with its barn and outbuildings Ray brought his wife in 1679 and for the next quarter century he lived a life of study with his kind and efficient consort and four daughters.

The *Ornithology* had been published in the previous year by the Royal Society. We cannot go into the heated controversy over the relative shares of Ray and Willughby in bringing this great work to completion. We know that Willughby died six years before it was published and, after viewing all the evidence, it is clear that the greater credit must go to Ray. It is probable too that he took this method of discharging a debt to a dear friend who had made his studies and travels possible, and who took him into his home when misfortune beset him. We should not lose sight of the fact, however, that Willughby furnished much of the inspiration for their joint labors. His vital enthusiasm for birds, his scientific curiosity about their behavior and the minutiae of their structure both external and internal are of a different order and complement very well Ray's systematic and somewhat plodding method of work.

When they set out on this enterprise, they were striving for a work quite different from the dry compilations such as had been done by the encyclopedists. They refused to contract and epitomize the contents of bulky accounts by writing abbreviated ones to take their place, "lest," says Ray, "they should tempt students to gratify their sloth" by taking up with such shortcuts instead of reading the authors themselves. They scorned the fabulous birds and the marvel-loving descriptions that filled the old books, and they were not interested in coining new names, but in general were satisfied to take those used by their predecessors. Says Ray: "To what purpose is it eternally to wrangle about things which certainly to determine is either absolutely impossible or next door to it?"

In this attitude Ray was far from the modern systematist's point of view. He often thought that Willughby was too meticulous in his descriptions, contend-

Fig. 13. A plate from Willughby's *Ornithologia* (1676). The Virginia Nightingale (upper right) is the American Cardinal. Courtesy of the Trustees of the British Museum.

[29] Spelled "Dewlands" in some publications.

ing that in nature two individuals seldom have the same spots and streaks, and that it is difficult to word descriptions concerned with such minutiae intelligibly.

It is commonly conceded that the Willughby *Ornithology* marks the beginning of scientific ornithology in Europe. It presents the best classification of birds to date, making use of structural characteristics and avoiding the combination of ecological factors such as habitat with those of structure, as Belon and Coiter had done.

The question of the author of the classification can be studied at length in Raven's scholarly biography of Ray, and the modern student should consult this and other recent works in order to avoid the pitfalls of articles written under prejudice and without sufficient study of the facts.

Suffice it to say here that Ray was not one to mitigate his indebtedness nor was he one to belittle his own assistance to the work. He tells us plainly that Willughby had not made any arrangement of the birds in his manuscript, but had placed widely different ones in juxtaposition. Says Ray:

Viewing his Mss. after his death, I found the several animals in every kind, both birds and beasts and fishes and insects, digested into a method of his own contriving, but few of their descriptions or histories, so full and perfect as he intended them;

Therefore it must be true that Ray is the author of the systematic arrangement of birds in Willughby's *Ornithology* in three books. These are bound in one large volume which contains a lengthy preface by John Ray, an appendix to the History of Birds, a summary of falconry and other ornithological matter.

I. *Of Birds in General* occupies only the first twentyfive pages, concluding with a Catalogus avium Britannicum, pp. 1–23, which is followed by a table giving the classification of the main groups of birds.
II. *Of Land Birds.*
   a. Of such as have hooked Beaks and Talons.
      1. Of Rapacious Diurnal Birds.
      2. Of Nocturnal Rapacious Birds.
   b. Of birds with straight or less-hooked Bills.
      1. Small birds with thick short Strong Bills commonly called Hard-billed Birds.
III. *Of Water Fowl.*
   a. Of cloven-footed Water Fowl wading in water or frequenting water places.
   b. Birds of a middle nature between swimmers and waders that do both swim and wade.
     i. Cloven-footed birds that swim in the water.
     ii. Whole-footed, long legged birds.
     iii. Whole-footed birds having the back toe loose, with a narrow bill hooked at one end and not toothed.
     iv. Of whole-footed birds with the back toe loose (i.e. not joined in the web), having a narrow bill hooked at the end and toothed, called Divers, in Latine *Mergi.*

     v. Of Douckers or Loons, called in Latine *Colymbi.*
     vi. Of Sea Gulls, called in Latine *Lari.*
     vii. Of whole-footed birds with broad bills: (1) The Goose-kind, (2) Broad-billed birds of the Duck Kind.

Following this classification of birds, there is an appendix giving a discussion of birds culled mostly from F. Hernandez' (1514–1578) work, and a summary of falconry,[30] collected out of several authors. This discussion of the ancient sport of falconry is another of the more complete accounts in literature, giving a glossary of terms, and rules for managing and feeding. Since this is a reviving sport today, hawk fanciers would do well to consult Willughby.

An alphabetical index is next interpolated, followed by seventy-eight plates. The British Museum copy of Willughby from which this description was made contains several hand-colored plates. There are three other more interesting copies of Willughby in the Emma Shearer Wood Library of Ornithology at McGill University, Montreal, Canada; one in Latin bearing the Willughby arms and the words "Sumptus in Calgographos fecit Illustriss D. Emma Willughby Vidua," indicating that it was one of the widow's edition.[31] The remaining two are in English, one containing ninety colored figures of birds and ninety-seven colored backgrounds; the other bearing all the necessary proofs of having belonged to the famous diarist, Samuel Pepys (1633–1703). The late Doctor Casey Wood points out that this was probably a specially prepared copy [32] given by Ray when Pepys was President of the Royal Society.

There is another printing of the *Ornithology* of Francis Willughby, also dated 1678, but the text is somewhat enlarged and revised. It contains eighty plates, two of which show netting and trapping scenes.[33] The bird plates (two signed F. H. Van Houe, *ca.* 1676, and one W. Faithorne, 1616–1691) show two to nine engravings on a plate and a number of American species are represented, notably the Canada goose (Tab. LXX), old squaw (swallow-tailed sheldrake) (Tab. LXXVIII), golden-eye (Tab. LXXIII) with a drawing of the trachea to the left of the bird, the Virginian nightingale

---

[30] A more intimate discussion of falconry is provided in the old treatise by Edmund Bert, *Gentleman, Hawks and Hawking,* reprint (100 copies) from the original of 1619, by Quaritch, London, 1891. Introduction by J. E. Harting, librarian of the Linnean Society.

[31] Lady Willughby financed the plates for one edition.

[32] Wood, 1931: 629.

[33] It should be pointed out that this feature is not present in all printings. The American Museum of Natural History possesses two copies of Willughby, both of 1678, but only one copy, that bearing the name of Edgar A. Mearns, has the two pages of illustrations of bird traps. These devices seem sufficiently ingenious and operable to be valuable for present-day use to control injurious flocks of birds such as starlings. The description of the working of these devices in the text is both clear and amusing, with many suggestions on camouflage to outwit the luckless birds.

(cardinal) (Tab. XLIIII), and the great auk (penguin)—obviously made from Ole Worm's pet, the great auk with a white collar. Many of the plates and much of the text of the *Three Considerable Discourses* are extracted from Gesner and Aldrovandus, from Markham's *Hunger Prevention* and other works, so that the whole book tends to have an encyclopedic flavor which, had Ray composed a work truly his own, would probably not have been present. In fact, it was Dr. Martin Lister (1638?–1712) who influenced Ray to include the section on falconry.

Ray had a great deal of experience with birds and was much better qualified for the task of completing Willughby's work than is generally believed. Some of the leading works on birds, such as Merret's *Pinax* (1667) and Johnstone's *Historia Naturalis De Avibus* (1652) and the *Onomasticon Zoicon* (1668), which was an attempt to list the animals of the encyclopedists and compare them with the birds and animals of St. James Park and the Museum of the Royal Society, he already held in contempt. The author of the *Onomasticon Zoicon,* Walter Charleton (1619–1707), was physician to Charles I and an Oxford graduate reputed to be learned in natural history, but Ray regarded him as a mere imitator, if not a plagiarist.

The secret of Ray's vast learning even in the fields that he was not cultivating must be found in his quiet alertness to all things in nature. He never as a student missed an opportunity to dissect birds, and tells of studying four birds, a bittern, a curlew, a yarwhelp (godwit), and a duck-like bird, in John Nedd's chamber in Trinity College. Also at Padua when he was studying anatomy under Pietro Marchetti in 1663–1664 he dissected a Capercaillie (*Gallina montana*) and often bought birds in the markets for the purpose of describing and dissecting them. In a letter written to Lister he explains the woodpecker's barbed tongue as a tool for extracting larvae. Says Ray, "I once got out from the crops of these birds [spotted woodpeckers and wrynecks] *on dissection* larvae as big as my small finger."

There are numerous drawings of dissections in the *Ornithology* of Francis Willughby but it is difficult to know which ones are attributable to Willughby and which to Ray. It would appear, however, that Willughby and Ray together had examined the lungs of many birds and thereby had come to some knowledge of the birds' system of air sacs. They were familiar with the change in the size of the gonads of birds at different seasons, and apparently correlated this to some extent with migration; they understood the birds' excretory system and how it differed from that of mammals; and they made a careful study of the "vessel," as they called it, of the windpipe or labyrinth or syrinx of the broad-billed divers. Says the Willughby text:

In some birds this vessel is made up wholly of bone, as in Wild Ducks, without any void spaces to be filled and closed up with membranes.

What the use thereof is, whether to increase the force of the voice or for a receptacle to contain air which may serve them while they dive, to enable them to remain longer under water, or to perform both of these offices, I know not.

Apparently after Ray had written his opinion, Mr. Dent, apothecary at Cambridge informed Ray that this structure is proper only to the broad-billed duck kind. This strange syrinx is depicted in the plate with the golden-eye duck (Tab. LXXVIII). Another (Tab. XXI) presents the head of a woodpecker showing the long slender hyoid apparatus curving up the back of the skull, while Tab. LXII presents the leg bone of a diver to show its very posterior attachment to the body.

There can be no doubt that Ray and Willughby worked together over many problems in the structure and anatomy of birds, that they labored together at making a workable classification and that they, especially in England, engaged in real field work. It is manifest from the finished volume, however, that Ray was the exact and searching scientist familiar with the literature of natural science and very conversant with the physiological and embryological researches of Malpighius (1628–1694), Fabricius of Aquapendente (1537–1619), and William Harvey (1578–1657).

On the other hand, Willughby could outdo his learned friend in ornithological curiosity and propounded to Ray certain questions of minute detail, for him to try to answer. Willughby no doubt realized that he was laying down his fascinating pursuit of birds, and Ray in meticulous loyalty to his friend grouped these under a separate heading:

Containing some particulars which Mr. Willughby propounded to myself to enquire out, observe, and experiment in Birds.

For example,

whether the parrot only moves the upper clap of its bill, as Aldronvandus affirms; Whether birds, when ready to lay, can detain their eggs, if their nest happens not be ready or by any accident destroyed.

Or again:

One of the two middle feathers of the tail when it is closed covers the other, enquire whether the right or left feather lies oftener uppermost, or either of them indifferently, as it happens.

and

How many birds have the exterior vanes of their flag feathers [primaries] broader than the interior ones?

These minutiae might baffle a modern ornithologist.

It was no doubt a great load off Ray's mind when he finished the *Ornithology.* He then went to work on the history of fishes and was hopeful that Lady Willughby would sponsor its publication. This, however, she refused to do, but his good friend the Rev. Tancred Robinson (d. 1748) negotiated its publication by the Royal Society in 1686. His next great work was his *Synopsis Methodica Avium,* finished in 1693 or 1694 but published posthumously, in 1713. This work gives synonyms, common names, short descriptions, and information on the distribution and habits of birds and contains many new species not included by Willughby. The plates number one hundred and were drawn and engraved by F. N. Martinet (1731–?). In 1767 this work was translated by F. Salerne (–1760) and published with considerable additional matter.

But it is not only in the *Ornithology* and the *Synopsis Methodica Avium* that Ray's knowledge of birds stands forth. His last publication the *Wisdom of God Manifested in the Works of the Creation* contains many passages which attest his interest in the living bird and point to his having observed and studied and reflected on the meaning of instinct.

This likewise gives impressive evidence of Ray's wide reading and consequent knowledge of all the great works of natural philosophy both descriptive and philosophical and even the ancients were familiar ground to him. His deeply religious character found God in the study of nature.

Ray's last years were marred by failing health but he worked to the last. He died in 1705 [34] and was buried according to his wish with great simplicity in the Churchyard of Black Notley although his family had the privilege of interring the remains in the chancel of the Church. The grave was described in 1908 by Mr. Mullens as "sadly neglected" and in need of care if the inscriptions upon the monument are to remain legible. Dewlawns, the home of Ray's own building, was destroyed by fire in 1900. The name of Ray is commemorated in the Ray Society for the publication of zoological and botanical works, which was founded in England in 1844.

The name of Willughby lived similarly for a few years, in the Willughby Society, for the reprinting of scarce ornithological works. This was founded by a group of English ornithologists, presided over by Professor Alfred Newton, on May 7, 1879. But after the publication of twelve volumes, with reprints of other works, the Society was dissolved in 1884 for lack of funds.

V. EARLY BIRD LORE IN THE WESTERN WORLD

SOME SPANISH AND FRENCH TRAVELLERS

Nothing comparable to the work of Europeans could be done in America prior to its colonization. To the American Indian the study of nature in any orderly or didactic manner for the pure desire of learning was unknown. But the Indian was well versed in the virtues and properties of all that surrounded him, and he was not without affection for animals, as we may judge by the presence of tamed wild birds and mammals of many kinds in his home.

Hence, long before the Red Man of North America was intruded upon by Europeans, he had worked out a system of living in close communion with the natural world. He clothed himself with the hides of wild animals; he fed on their flesh and the fish of the rivers; he adorned himself with the quills, claws and bills of many birds. His kings and chiefs were robed in rich fabrics made of feathers; the medicine men and conjurors chanted the mysterious potencies of owls' eyes and goose gizzards, while docile, bright-plumaged birds lived as pets in his household and served as playmates for his children.

The Indian, however, with all his interest and reverence for nature lacks the scientific curiosity of the European, and never questions himself as to the name or relationship of this or that species. Rather, each group in all its varied forms is *a priori* a part of his world, and he accepts it as food, barter, or companion, according to its qualities.

It is not to the Indian, therefore, that we should look for the beginnings of American ornithology, but to the Europeans who came first on their reconnoitering expeditions, and later with definite intent to colonize.

Few names in our early history are so steeped in glamorous tradition as that of Ponce de Leon (1460–1521), the Spanish explorer, who wished to serve his king and his country by converting the Indian to Christianity. He had heard, too, of the miraculous Fountain of Youth hidden somewhere in the land of Bimini, and longed to visit it. It was first in 1513 that he came over from the West Indies, skirted the Florida coast seeking a suitable bay, and finally cast anchor in a harbor near St. Augustine. He took possession of the land in the name of the King of Spain and from this event Florida derives its name, for it was Easter Sunday when he made his landfall, and he named the country after the Spanish name for Easter, "Pascua Florida."

During the next seven years he was occupied with explorations and in quelling resentful Indians who were hostile to Spanish settlement because of the plundering by unauthorized expeditions.

By 1521 much of his ardor had cooled, but he still wished to serve his king and to settle the country which he felt he had discovered.[1] He obtained a patent from the King to settle Florida, and, carrying clergymen and friars with a goodly supply of livestock, he set about building dwellings for the colonists. The hostility of the Indians made it impossible to remain, however, and, after an encounter in which Ponce de Leon and many others were wounded, they collected their possessions and went to Cuba, where the hero died of his wounds, leaving his life's ambition unfulfilled.

Thus the Spanish project of colonization in Florida rested for some forty or fifty years without any permanent foothold being made, until the Commander of the Spanish Fleet in New Spain, Pedro Menendez, was

---

[34] 1704 is given by W. H. Mullens, *British Birds*, **11**: 299, 1866.

[1] Winsor, 1884–1889: **2**: 231–232.

commissioned to colonize Florida and to introduce all necessary people and a goodly supply of domestic animals.

While these elaborate plans were being carried out, it was learned that the despised French Calvinists or Huguenots had quietly set up a small colony at the mouth of the St. John's River. Although this ill-managed colony of the French was nothing for the Spanish Catholics to fear, a mighty attacking army of 200 cavalry and 400 infantry was forthwith despatched to America. It was planned that, should it be found inadvisable to attack, Menendez (1519–1574), well equipped with 19 vessels and 1,500 people, including farmers and mechanics, was to settle at a neighboring point and bide his opportunity to take the unfortunate Huguenots by surprise. We look in vain among these intrepid Spanish settlers for one who turned to the peaceful study of birds.

But in the adjacent West Indies, which were well organized under Spanish rule, there was some observation of American bird life by Spanish writers. Queen Isabella (1451–1504) of Spain had ordered Columbus (1446?–1506) to bring back birds from his travels and when he made his triumphal parade through Barcelona in April, 1493, he displayed several kinds of live parrots and some bird skins. It was because of the migrating birds, in fact, that Columbus [2] changed his course, and came to the Bahamas much sooner than he would have struck land had he not shifted his direction.

A score of years later in 1514 the Spanish writer, Ganzalo Fernandez de Oviedo y Valdez (1478–1557), went to Hispaniola and he took thirty parrots back to Spain. Accounts differ as to how long he remained on his first trip, but he soon became engaged in a work on the natural history of the West Indies and thus he is called the first historian of the region. His long name is usually shortened to "Oviedo."

He established a home for his family in Santo Domingo City when they first came over, and later they resided on his estate on the Rio Haina, three leagues from the capital. It is interesting to reflect on the numerous ornithological observations made by this early writer on the birds of Hispaniola and we wish his fuller descriptions, such as that of the nesting of the palm-chat, might have been on familiar American species. His observations on the red-tailed hawk, pelican and nighthawk, however, should be mentioned, but his account of the monstrous bird with one webbed foot and one armed with talons, that fed on fish or fowl, must have been a local superstition; this may account for the well-known criticism of Oviedo's work by Las Casas (1474–1566), that staunch friend of oppressed Indians during Spanish colonization, that "Oviedo's writings were nearly as full of lies as of paper."

Oviedo made six voyages to the Indies between 1514, when he came to Santo Domingo as supervisor of gold

smelting, and his death at Valadolid in 1557. He started his career at the age of thirteen as a page in the Court of King Ferdinand (1452–1516) and Queen Isabella of Spain, and became acquainted with Columbus at Granada before he sailed for America, an event which must have influenced him in his plan to visit the New World. He remained in the West Indies for nine years, and upon his return to Spain in 1523 was appointed Royal Historiographer of the Indies. While at home he produced a romance of chivalry, *Claribalte,* but he is much better known for his *Sumario* printed at Toledo in 1526 under the fuller title, *Sumario de la Natural Historia de las Indias.* Only the first part of this large compilation of information on the New World was issued at this time—the remaining portion not coming out until 1851–1855 when J. A. de los Rios edited it for the Spanish Academy of History.

The first part of it became popular in England and France and was widely read as a first hand and fairly reliable account of the Indies. Dr. G. Brown Goode (1851–1896), in an address before the Biological Society of Washington in 1886 informs us that Oviedo was the first to describe several of America's most interesting birds and mammals. Among the birds he lists the pelican, the ivory-billed woodpecker and the hummingbird.

From Richard Eden's (1521?–1576) *The First Three English Books on America,* edited by Edward Arber (1885), but originally translated about 1555, we may read some of Oviedo's description of hummingbirds:

And I haue seene that one of these byrdes with her nest put in a paire of gold weights, altogether hath waid no more than. ii. Tomini, which are in poise. 24. grains, with the fethers with out the which she shulde haue wayed sumwhat lesse. . . . Their beake is verye longe for the proportion of theyr bodies: and as fyne and subtile as a sowyng nedle. They are very hardye: so that when they see a man clyme the tree where they haue theyr nestes, they flye at hys face and stryke him in the eyes, commyng, goynge, and retournynge with such swyftnes that no man wolde lightly beleue it that hath not seene it. And certenly these byrdes are so lyttle, that I durst not haue made mention hereof if it were not that diuers other which haue seene them as wel as I, can beare witnes of my saying.

From this incident of weighing the hummingbirds in the gold scales has been derived one of the popular names for hummingbirds in South America, "tominejo."

Another Spanish writer and one of greater learning was Father Joseph De Acosta (1539–1600). When very young he joined, the Jesuit Society and at about thirty years of age (1571) he emigrated to Peru as a missionary where he became an influential and learned helper of the Viceroy Don Francisco de Toledo. He spent much of his time in the town of Juli on Lake Titicaca where a college was founded, and here he prepared his manuscripts published in 1588 and 1589 at Salamanca. These have been republished in English by the Hakluyt Society, and the reader will find Volume I full of interesting lore touching the winds and their origin,

---

[2] Chapman, 1916: 104–105.

the rains, the tides, the lakes, the mines, the fisheries, and, finally, plants and animals.

De Acosta goes into considerable discussion in his *Natural and Moral History of the Indies,* vol. 1, p. 275, of "Fowles that are proper to the Indies" and argues with himself at some length on distribution, apparently torn between his native adherence to old dogma of the flood and special creation, and his better judgment. Some strange sorts of birds, he grants, were brought there, as the Birds of Paradise, which at that time were popularly believed to have no feet. Others, he argued, must be able to cross the sea and he concludes:

. . . birdes with their wings may goe where they will; and truley many kindes might well passe the gulph, seeing it certaine, as Plinie affirmeth, that there are many that passe the sea and goe into strange regions, although I have not read that any fowle hath passed by flight so great a gulph as is the Indian Ocean, yet I hold it not altogether impossible, seeing the common opinion of mariners, that you shall finde them two hundred leagues and more from the land.

Of American birds he mentions partridges, turtles, pigeons, stock doves, quails, and many sorts of falcons, which were sent from New Spain and Peru to the noblemen of Old Spain, and he apparently was the first to describe the huge "Condores" which "be of an exceeding greatness and of such a force that not only will they open a sheep and eat it, but also a whole calfe." Turkey buzzards were thought by Acosta to be a kind of raven "of a strange fleetness" and "a very quick sight, being very fit to cleanse cities, for that they leave no carrion nor dead thing." He described them as sitting about on buildings awaiting their prey, and was aware that the young were covered with white down and later became black.

GARCILASO DE LA VEGA

Until 1600 there had been no native of the New World who had described, even briefly, the natural history of America. All were Europeans sent by their fatherlands to reconnoitre with the usual appraising eye. But in the writer, Garcilaso de la Vega (1539–1615), we meet the first native American historian of the New World who, when he treats of the natural history, seems to show a real liking for the study.

A Peruvian by birth, he was proud that his mother was an Inca princess, and through his Castilian father, also, he came of a distinguished family. His *Royal Commentaries of the Incas* [3] was written first in the Peruvian language, but was soon translated into Spanish and French, and is available in English as one of the publications (1869–1871) of the Hakluyt Society, having been translated by the English scholar, Sir Clements R. Markham.

The *Commentaries* are very readable, and, despite their being written many years after Garcilaso de la Vega had left Peru and taken up his residence in Cordova, the volumes are full of anecdotes from the author's

---

[3] Vega, 1869 and 1871, publications 12 and 14.

Fig. 14. Garcilaso De La Vega (1537?–1616?), A Peruvian. First New World writer on Natural History. Courtesy of the United States National Museum.

colorful youth. They contain also many accounts secured from friends and schoolfellows by correspondence. For this reason they are not wholly reliable, but, nevertheless, they give many pertinent facts and impressions of things in the New World at a time when England was beginning to contemplate colonization in America.

The *Commentaries* include birds, mammals, fish, reptiles, fruits, trees, and vegetables, all in informal, attractive style. His chapter on the different kinds of parrots with their amusing chatter, of the rats which the Spaniards brought to Peru, and the relay races between the Spaniards' horses and the South American ostrich-like Rheas furnish interesting realism for the modern reader.

Although he had forgotten many things about the bird life of his country, and freely admits the "shortness of his memory," he gives a surprising amount of worthy comment on some species. He tells at length of the condor and of many specimens having been shot and measured to ascertain their wing spread; he describes accurately its apparently double crest and comparatively weak feet "that their ferocity may be tempered," and the loud humming noise it makes when it dashes from on high upon its prey (vol. 2, p. 389). He describes the fishing of pelicans (the Alcatras), and concludes (p. 392):

It is certainly a wonderful sight to behold the multitude of these birds, and it raises one's thoughts to give thanks to the Eternal Majesty for having created such an infinity and for sustaining them with a like multitude of fish.

He speaks also of herons, night herons (a surprising differentiation), cranes, flamingoes, partridges of two kinds, quails, doves, and small grey birds which the Spaniards call sparrows, which breed in the fields. He says "They are like sparrows in colour and size but different in their song, for they sing very sweetly." There are other brown birds which the Spaniards call nightingale from the similarity of color, but they are, de la Vega says, "as different in their song as black is from white. These brown birds sing very badly insomuch that the Indians looked upon their song as an ill omen." It is difficult to identify these birds with certainty from this description, probably a species of blackbird, but it is clear that de la Vega was sensitive to bird song and was a good observer of bird habits. It is remarkable that this account of the bird life of the New World is now nearly four hundred years old, yet it has the attention for detail worthy of a modern observer.

THE FRENCH CONTRIBUTION TO EARLY AMERICAN BIRD LORE

While these Spanish treatises by Oviedo, De Acosta and de la Vega were in progress, the northeastern parts of North America, including sections of the New England coast, were being visited by French and Portuguese fishermen. It was the lowly and prolific codfish, for centuries a principal article of food in northern Europe, that was responsible for the early emigration of these peoples to North America.

The cod was discovered to be abundant in American waters off the Newfoundland Banks as early as the end of the fifteenth century, and by 1504 large numbers of French and Portuguese fisher-folk had established fishing and drying stations which rivalled some of the best in Europe.

These people were not explorers; they merely sought a livelihood; hence very few of their observations are extant, but the Portuguese writer, Antonio Galvano, who collected and published in 1555 an account of the discoveries of the world, makes frequent allusion to the coast of North America, and maps of this region show many Portuguese names. From this the eminent authority on American discovery, J. G. Kohl (1808–1878), adduces that these fishermen must have been driven sometimes by storms to the mainland and undoubtedly made more or less observation on the bird and animal life of the country.

Up until 1523 any expeditions of Portugal were under private auspices, and although King Emanuel (1469–1521) of Portugal encouraged the fisher folk to explore, no plan to colonize by the Portuguese was formulated. France also had fisheries on the Newfoundland Banks, and under Francis I (1494–1547) exploration and discovery were in favor, although the King was much occupied with wars with the neighboring powers. The result was that merchants of the north of France, from Dieppe and other cities of Normandy and Brittany, were the main connections that France had with America.

Following these early contacts with America by French fishermen, the French people under their progressive new King, Francis I, began to feel more interest in discovery. In spite of wars he was interested in furthering art and education, and in 1523 the first official expedition went out from France under the command of Giovanni da Verrazano (1486–1527), a Florentine navigator in the employ of France, who had recently returned from ambitious ventures in the Mediterranean. Four ships "well equipped and victualled" for eight months started out to seek a northwest passage to Cathay. From Verrazano's description it is known that he sighted the United States at Cape Fear on March 10, 1524, and then cruised from Carolina to Maine, making several stops in the Bay of New York. He sighted and named the State of Rhode Island, then passed the triangular-shaped island known as Martha's Vineyard and finally came to the Gulf of Maine. He reported the land high, "full of thick woods; the trees there of firres, cipresses and such life as are wont to grow in cold countrys" and the people clothed with "Beares skinnes and Luzernes [furs of the lynx] and seales and other beastes skinnes" and living by means of hunting and fishing. But the natives were inhospitable, shooting at them with their bows and uttering disagreeable outcries; the land appeared "not apt to bear fruit or seed," and, all things considered, Verrazano was disposed to return to France after an absence of only five and a half months. This expedition covered only 700 leagues, but the leader felt well pleased with such extensive discoveries in so short a period.

Ten years elapsed after Verrazano's inconsequential cruise before another French expedition of more lasting influence was undertaken.

This was the voyage of Jacques Cartier (1491–1557), that keen French navigator, who, from earliest youth, had wanted to follow the sea. He was born in 1491 in the ancient port of France called St. Malo, where talk of ships and their commanders was always to be heard. Naturally, Cartier knew of the explorations of Verrazano and we may suppose, regarded them as rather amateurish efforts. But his were of a different order, resulting in vast additions to the science of navigation and the prestige of France. A twenty-day run brought him to Bonavista, the point of Newfoundland nearest to the old world. Here he first saw the Island of Birds—their white forms literally covered the island, and a huge number of them were loaded into Cartier's boats in the short space of half an hour. Very likely the birds were the once abundant and flightless great auk, which is now extinct, but there has been considerable discussion on the exact location of Cartier's "Bird Rocks" as well as the birds inhabiting them.

Cartier's experience in American waters, covering about ten years in three separate periods, resulted in a vast addition to the general knowledge of Newfoundland, the course and extent of the St. Lawrence River, and the character of the natives. He and his companions mapped the difficult and treacherous coasts, gave names to the principal harbors, gulfs and capes, and, in general, paved the way for the many subsequent military, commercial, and missionary expeditions of the French into Canada.

In Cartier's account of his navigations on the west coast of Newfoundland we encounter another definite mention of the birds of this region. From Cape Anguillo, the southernmost point of the west coast of Newfoundland he sailed west and saw three small islands covered with birds "as innumerable as the flowers on a meadow." These he called "Isles aux Marglaux" and the islands are still the breeding places of immense flocks of sea birds and are still known to all who pass as "Bird Rocks." Whether these are the same as the ones from which he loaded a vast number into his boats is not known. Cartier was very little on the mainland but spent his time cruising for he was primarily a navigator.

SAMUEL DE CHAMPLAIN

Samuel de Champlain (1570–1635), on the other hand, the next Frenchman to undertake work in Newfoundland, Canada, and Norembega, was gifted in other ways—a versatile man who knew how to derive many kinds of information from the general experience of his coming to America.

His first voyage to America was a fur-trading expedition for he came under the patronage of Captain Pierre de Chauvin of Dieppe, who was interested in obtaining a monopoly of the fur trade. Champlain found opportunity to acquaint himself with other conditions, making short trips up the rivers and landing frequently to talk with the natives to learn about the topography of the country and the location of the best fishing and hunting areas. While he was absent on this initial trip in 1599 his friend and patron died, but Champlain, nevertheless, presented his report to the King (Henri IV, 1589–1610) who showed great interest in his findings and continued to favor the plan of a French colony in America.

There chanced to be at that time residing at court a Huguenot nobleman, De Monts by name, who also was interested in the fur trade. He organized a company of merchants of Rouen, Rochelle, and other Normandy cities who were to carry on an active fur trade with the Indians. De Monts obtained from the King a grant extending over Three Rivers, Quebec, and "indeed the whole region of the gulf and river St. Lawrence."

Fig. 15. Samuel de Champlain (1567–1635), Pioneer Bird observer in Canada. Courtesy of the United States National Museum.

De Monts invited Champlain to accompany him, knowing well his value as a recorder, and Champlain promised to write his observations. It is interesting to know that this expedition, after arriving in America, sent out a small vessel to explore our New England coast, and Champlain was put in command. He visited several harbors in Maine, noting the rich forests of evergreen and oak, and observed large numbers of partridge and deer. At Cape Porpoise he made mention of nut trees and grape vines and replenished the larder from the thousands of wild pigeons which had assembled there to feed on the wild currants. These were undoubtedly the now extinct passenger pigeon, *Ectopistes migratorius*.

Again, he tells of hunting with a party of Indians "where there was a large amount of game as Swans, White Cranes, Outarchs,[4] Ducks, Teal, Song Thrush, Larks, Snipe, Geese, and several other kinds of fowl too numerous to mention." Champlain speaks of killing a great number of these which stood them in good stead

---

[4] This is the bustard, a name early applied by travellers to a kind of goose in Canada, probably the Canada goose.

during a shortage of supplies. He describes also a triangular deer trap, 1,500 paces on each side, with a small opening the size of a door through which the deer entered. This huge enclosure was completed in ten days and the hunters secured by it 120 deer in the period of thirty-eight days, exclusive of the days spent in building the trap. Meanwhile, he says, other savages had gone fishing and brought "trout and pike of prodigious size, enough to meet all wants."

This reconnoitering expedition (1605) of which Champlain took command continued down as far as Cape Cod and even landed at Plymouth Harbor. Thus, in this region, Champlain antedated Captain John Smith, who was there in 1614, by nine years, and the first contingent of Puritans by fifteen years.

Champlain's [5] career as an explorer, his record as a soldier, his part in the Battle of Ticonderoga, are all well known to students and readers of American history. It is not so generally recognized, however, that he was an observer of nature of no mean attainments, and took time from his full programme as Commander of the French Colonists to study agriculture, the forests, and the fauna of the country. As a geographer in a strange land it was his principal duty to make maps and drawings of the harbors, to lay out and superintend the construction of living quarters for the Colony, and to act as governor of a small principality. It was his personal wish, rather than his official duty, to go among the natives and hunt and fish with them in the forests, and to observe them at their primitive agriculture and their methods of harvesting and storing their produce.

Intermingled with this accurate picture of the daily life of the Colony, its hardships and its encounters with hostile Indians, are frequent items of natural history. The student of science cannot but be impressed with the careful way in which Champlain differentiates between the forms he knew in Europe and those he was observing in America.

Conspicuous among these findings are his accounts [6] of the horse-foot crab *Similus polyphemus,* the black skimmer and the wild turkey. Of the black skimmer, he says:

We saw also a sea-bird with a black beak, the upper part slightly aquiline, four inches long and in the form of a lancet; namely, the lower part representing the handle and the upper the blade, which is thin, sharp on both sides, and shorter by a third than the other, which circumstance is a matter of astonishment to many persons who cannot comprehend how it is possible for this bird to eat with such a beak. It is of the size of a pigeon, the wings being very long in proportion to the body, the tail short, as also the legs, which are red; the feet being small and flat. The plumage on the upper part is gray-brown, and on the under part pure white. They go always in flocks along the sea-shore, like the pigeons with us.

According to the A. O. U. Check-List, this bird is not now found breeding north of New Jersey and Long Is-

land, but, since Champlain speaks of it in flocks along the seashore, it would seem that the species may have had a wider range.

I quote also his excellent description of the wild turkey which embodies some interesting comments on vultures (Quotation from Vol. 2, p. 88).

The savages, along all these coasts where we have been, say that other birds, which are very large, come along when their corn is ripe. They imitated for us their cry, which resembles that of the turkey. They showed us their feathers in several places, with which they feather their arrows, and which they put on their heads for decoration; and also a kind of hair which they have under the throat like those we have in France, and they say that a red crest falls over upon the beak. According to their description, they are as large as a bustard, which is a kind of goose, having the neck longer and twice as large as those with us. All these indications led us to conclude that they were turkeys. We should have been very very glad to see some of these birds, as well as their feathers, for the sake of greater certainty. Before seeing their feathers, and the little bunch of hair which they have under the throat, and hearing their cry imitated, I should have thought that they were certain birds like turkeys, which are found in some places in Peru, along the sea-shore, eating carrion and other dead things like crows. But these are not so large; nor do they have so long a bill, or a cry like that of real turkeys; or are they good to eat like those which the Indians say come in flocks in summer, and at the beginning of winter go away to warmer countries, their natural dwelling-place.

The turkey likewise has a greatly restricted distribution owing to being nearly exterminated over much of its former range, but other early travellers, notably John Josselyn (1672), also describe it in the fauna of New England. Even then it was less abundant than in the early years of the Puritan settlers.

Champlain is credited with having referred definitely also to the scarlet tanager, and in the memoir of his life by the Rev. Edmund F. Slafter, A.M., published with his Voyages, we find on page 97 the statement that Champlain presented to the King of France on his visit in 1609 two scarlet tanagers "a bird of great brilliancy of plumage and peculiar to this continent." Upon looking up Champlain's own account of his audience with the King, it is found that he presented a belt made of porcupine quills, and "two little birds of the size of blackbirds and of a carnation color." The translator in a foot-note identifies these birds as scarlet tanagers, *Piranga rubra* [erythromelas], of a scarlet color with black wings and tail. "It ranges from Texas to Lake Huron" says the commentator.

But Champlain's failure to mention the black wings opens the possibility that they were perhaps cardinals, although the present more southern range of the cardinal would render this less probable. Purple finches and pine grosbeaks also are possible interpretations.

Following Champlain, a long series of missionaries, soldiers, and travellers could be mentioned as contributing more or less to a record of the birds of the region, and of this intermediate group we should refer to the Franciscan priest, Gabriel Sagard Theodat (fl. 1636),

---

[5] Bishop, 1948.
[6] Champlain, 1880: **2**: 86–88.

Father Louis Hennepin (1640–1706?), and Nicolas Denys (1598–1688), an early governor of Acadia.

Sagard Theodat is known for his long service as a missionary among the natives of Canada—a kind, credulous, and modest man, aware of his shortcomings as a scientist, but willing to offer his honest descriptions of the country, the people, and the bird, plant, and animal life, rendered to the best of his ability. His *Histoire du Canada,* published in 1632, is a good but very simple account, and to the ornithologist is worth while for its frequent references to birds and mammals. He is known also for his dictionary of the Huron Language.

Father Louis Hennepin (17th century), in contrast to Sagard Theodat, was a self-important, though righteous man. His work entitled *A New Discovery of a Vast Country in America extending about 4,000 miles between New France and New Mexico* gathers much interest because of its rarity, but it lacks convincingness because of the author's vanity and bombastic style.

In his first chapter, after referring to his travels in Europe, he says "Not being satisfied with that, I found myself inclined to entertain more distant prospects and was eager upon seeing more distant countries and nations that had not yet been heard of"; and he continues, "In gratifying this natural itch was I led to the discovery of a vast and large country where no European ever was before myself. Thus he goes on, claiming that the undertaking was enough to frighten anyone but himself, but that he gave himself to the resolution "to employ and dedicate himself to the Glory of God and the salvation of souls."

Hennepin came to Canada with La Salle (1643–1687), the explorer, and F. X. de Laval-Montmorency (1623–1708), the Bishop of Quebec about 1640. La Salle and Hennepin disagreed over the practice of bringing girls from France to the French Colony in America; La Salle enjoyed their dances, while Hennepin disapproved and attempted to remonstrate with them according to his principles as spiritual guide. This small enmity stayed by Hennepin all through his travels in America, but the two men travelled together for many years, going west and down the Mississippi to Fort Crevecœur on the Illinois, where La Salle parted from him in February, 1680. Hennepin returned to France in 1682 and obtained permission to publish his *Description de la Louisiane.* Although on his title page he includes the sub-title "with a description of the great lakes, cataracts, rivers, plants and animals," we find upon turning to the chapter on birds and animals that it is a very brief account; the birds taking but a few sentences and the animals little more. His account of the bison, however, is comparatively detailed, with a crude wood-cut of the animals and a small group of pelicans with them.

Of birds he says:

There are also Bustards which have an excellent taste, Swans, Tortoises, Turkey Cocks, Parrots and Partridges.

There are also an incredible quantity of Pelicans whose bills are of prodigious size; and a great many other sorts of Birds and other Beasts.

We read also on page 90, "The Eagles which are to be seen in these vast countries will sometimes drop a Breme, a large Carp, or some other fish as they are carrying them to their nests in their talons to feed their young." Thus Hennepin himself, according to his own narrative, more than once obtained a meal.

NICOLAS DENYS, A FORGOTTEN OBSERVER OF BIRDS

The name Acadia, though familiar to all of us, does not convey a clear conception of the region's early vast extent. Few are aware that in the mid-seventeenth century Acadia included, beside Nova Scotia, all of New Brunswick and Prince Edward Island, a portion of Quebec and a large part of the State of Maine.

It was in this general region that John and Sebastian Cabot were cruising when they discovered the rock-bound coast of Newfoundland and claimed the country for Henry VII of England in 1497. Along the same coast, in 1524, came Giovanni da Verrazano, a Florentine navigator in the service of France, and in 1534 came the famous French explorer, Jacques Cartier, tightening the hold which France had held upon this disputed territory. There followed nearly a hundred years during which England and France were competing for supremacy, and in 1621 the Scot, Sir William Alexander (1567?–1640), statesman, poet and author of "Encouragement to Colonies" (1625) received from the King of England a grant of Acadia with permission to colonize, although at this time it actually belonged to France. He established a colony at Port Royal in 1629, and in 1630 a second expedition with colonists, including the elder La Tour and his English wife, came to Port Royal to take possession of the baronetcy of Nova Scotia under Sir William Alexander who was governor of the whole. This marriage presupposed allegiance to the British crown, and the younger La Tour, holding another baronetcy along the coast, also was expected to give homage and service to the British King. This, however, he refused to do, with the result that Canada and Acadia were restored to France by the Treaty of St. Germain in 1632.

By this time the Company of New France had become a powerful organization in charge of French affairs in America, and a very able commander, Isaac de Razilly (?–1635), was put at the head of the enterprise of exploring, colonizing and exploiting the great country of Acadia.

Alexander's colony at Port Royal surrendered to him, and he fixed his own capital at La Have, a strategic location for the fishing industry and a suitable one also for colonization. Here the first French families of Acadia were planted, and here Nicolas Denys (1598–1688) came in 1632 and eventually made himself a leader in the land. He was born at Tours in 1598 of good and rather noted parentage, but early in life was apprenticed to the fishery business and in his thirties definitely took up his life in America engaging in preparing and shipping lumber and fish to France.

The vicissitudes of his life during the renewed hostilities of the English in Acadia are a long series of hardships and injustices involving the loss of many thousand of francs and unwarrantable imprisonment which was rendered more bitter by the death of his chief and benefactor, Isaac de Razilly, in 1635.

For many years he lived at Miscou with his family, including two children, kept several gardens, and slowly amassed through his other business interests a modest fortune.

In December 1653 he went to France and bought from the Company of New France "a grant [with] the coasts and islands in the Gulf of Saint Lawrence from Cape Causo to Cape Rosiers in the Gaspé Peninsula." This gave him a monopoly of the fur trade, and in 1654, he was made governor of all this territory, including Newfoundland. He controlled also the "sedentary or fixed fisheries as far as Virginia." Thus temporarily securing and having accomplished the surrender of previous commanders in these parts, he was the ranking man of the eastern part of all Acadia and was made governor of it at the age of fifty-six.

After the death of his friend and patron, Razilly, however, and the accession of D'Aulnay, to whom Denys was then subservient, his career was largely frustrated. His gardens at Miscou were seized, and although payment for them was promised, the money was never received. Denys then moved to Nepisiguit, but these properties were likewise seized by La Borgue, and altogether, through the loss of his fortune and his discouragement incident to continual internal strife, Denys was made to appear an incompetent governor in the eyes of authorities in the homeland, and he went back to France, leaving his son Richard in charge of his affairs in Acadia. It was said that he lived in actual want for many years in Paris, but still cherishing an abiding affection for his adopted country in America, he returned to Nepisiguit in 1687 and died at his former home in 1688, an old and disappointed, but loyal, subject of his King at ninety years.

During Nicolas Denys' residence in Acadia, he wrote his experience in a two-volume work, *Description and Natural History of the Coasts of North America,* published in Paris in 1672. This is one of the most thorough early accounts of the region of Acadia, and, although the title in mentioning "Coasts of North America" is far too inclusive, it nevertheless should have been given recognition sooner. It passed unread in America for over a century and received its first mention here in the *North American Review* for 1816; but not until 1908 was it rendered into English and reprinted through the instrumentality of the Champlain Society by a professor of botany at Smith College, Doctor William Francis Ganong. Doctor Ganong's Canadian background and scientific training, received at the University of New Brunswick and elsewhere, has made him appreciative of Denys' knowledge of the plant and animal life of his domain and, since his bird lore has apparently been largely overlooked by ornithologists, I have gone over his account of the birds to try to gain some appreciation of his powers of ornithological observation back in the late seventeenth century.

His long experience in the fishery, fur, and lumber trades gave him above all else a love and understanding of business and his biographer cites the man's chief maxim: "Profit, the chief concern of all men." This does not point to a great aesthetic sense nor does it connote the true scientist. We may, therefore, expect his observations on birds to be a rather dry unembellished record of what he saw as he practiced his various trades—not literary in quality (and of this the author was aware) but practical, with attention to the market value and gustatory merits of the various species.

Nevertheless, his descriptions in most cases embody a great deal of accurate observation of the habits, particularly of the sea birds, and his observations on the land birds contain much of interest to the naturalist as well as many quaint folk beliefs. Because Denys does not appear to have gained recognition among ornithologists it seems desirable to quote rather fully from his chapters on birds (p. 266).

It is also worth while to know that upon the Bank, which is twenty (49) [7] five leagues from the nearest land, there are to be seen so great a quantity of birds as to be almost unbelievable, such as Fulmars (Happefoye), Petrels (Croiseurs), Guillemots (Poules de mer), Great Auks (Pennegoins), and many other sorts.

I shall speak only of these particular ones. The Fulmars (Happefoye) are very gluttonous birds. They are thus called because they live on the liver of the Cod. If they see a ship engaged in fishing they assemble in very great numbers around her to seize the livers which fall into the sea. As soon as one of these is thrown in, more than fifty of these birds pounce upon it, and fight among themselves to secure it. They come close up to the vessel, and sometimes one is able to kill them (50) with a pole. Their gluttony makes them easily taken by means of hooks which are attached at the end of a little line, with which the fishermen are furnished on purpose. This line is supported upon the water by a piece of cork, and a fragment of liver is placed upon the hook. This is thrown as far off as possible. Immediately these birds fight as to which one will capture it. After a smart struggle, finally one seizes it, and is caught by the beak, (and) is drawn on board. It is necessary to take great care that it does not seize the hand. Its upper beak is hooked, and passes much over the under. If it bites it pierces the finger or the hand. When it has been taken from the hook and allowed to go (51) upon the quarter-deck, it does not fly away. It does not know how to rise, at least when it is not on the water. This fishery provides a great amusement.

The Petrels (Croiseurs) are birds which also come to eat the livers, but they do not approach so near. They are called Croiseurs because they are ever crossing on the sea from one side to the other. Their flight is different from

---

[7] The reader may disregard these numbers in parentheses, which refer to the original French.

that of other birds in this, that they fly, so to speak, cross-wise, having one wing up towards the sky and the other to-wards the sea, so that, in order to turn, they bring the upper wing undermost. It is found always from the time one is at sea a hundred leagues from land as far as New France. (52) A day never passes that one does not see them go cross-ing from one side to the other. This is in order to find some little fish to eat, of those which exist between wind and wa-ter, such as the Flying Fish, the Herring, the Sardine, and others on which it lives.

The Guillemot (Poule de mer) is thus called for its re-semblance to this land animal. It lives also on little fish and livers. It is not gluttonous, but tamer than the others. It is always flying around the ship, and if it perceives any en-trails, it throws itself upon them.

Denys' remarks on the great auk are of particular interest since there is no mention of his description of this extinct species in Alfred Newton's abstract of Mr. John Wolley's Researches [8] nor in the review [9] of the paper, "The Gare-fowl and its Historians," by Professor J. J. Steenstrup, nor yet in Hardy's article.[10]

Denys writes of the great auk as follows:

The Great Auk (Pennegoin) is another bird, variegated in white and black. It does not fly. It has only two stumps of wings with which (53) it beats upon the water to aid in fleeing or diving. It is claimed that it dives even to the bot-tom to seek its prey upon the Bank. It is found more than a hundred leagues from land, where, nevertheless, it comes to lay its eggs, like the others. When they have had their young, they plunge into the water; and their young place themselves upon their backs, and are carried like this as far as the Bank. There one sees some no larger than chickens, although they grow as large as geese. All those birds are (considered) good to eat by the fishermen. As for myself I do not find them agreeable. They taste of oil because of the quantity of fish and of livers they eat; and they serve to make fish oil. (54) The fishermen collect them for this purpose. There are vessels which have made as much as ten or twelve puncheons [11] of it. This is nearly everything which is practiced in the fishery for green Cod upon the Grand Bank.

Chapter XIX of the second volume is given over to a further discussion of seabirds, or at least the principal ones, for he says ". . . the number is too great for me to remember them all" (p. 370), an interesting account but, it contains several errors and many omissions, which the editor, Doctor Ganong, has briefly dealt with by means of footnotes. Like most other travellers of this time Denys fell into the common mistake of thinking the American forms like those of Europe, and was primarily concerned with the value of the various kinds of birds as food, although other pertinent facts of interest are included and indicate that he was a good observer. A paragraph on the brant bears out this statement (p. 372).

The Brant (Cravan) is scarcely smaller than the small Goose. Its taste is also very pleasant, (303) roasted and boiled, but not salted. It is browner in plumage, the neck is

shorter, and there is no white under the throat. It is a bird of passage; it only comes' into the country in summer, and it goes away in winter. It is not known whence it comes nor whither it goes. No one has ever seen it producing its young. If it were not for the taste, which is infinitely better than that of the Widgeon (Macreuse) [12] I would say they were the same thing. The plumage is very much alike, but to eat it in Lent would be too delightful. They live also on grass, with some little shell-fish or worms which are found in the sand.

The Ducks are all like those of France, as to plumage and goodness. Those which have the wing blue and the feet red are the (304) best. Those with grey feet, which have also the wing blue, hardly differ in goodness. There is another kind of them which has not the blue wing, but they are not so good. There is seen also another species which has the plumage bright brown; of this species the male is white, with black at the end of the wing. The male and female are never together, and only assemble in spring when they mate. When the females begin to make their nests they separate. The males go in flocks by themselves, and the females the same. If one fires upon the females, unless he kills them en-tirely dead, they are lost; for so soon as they are wounded they dive, and they seize with their beak any, even the small-est, grass they find, (305), and die there, and do not come again to the surface. They are not good in other respects; they taste of oil like the Widgeon.

As for the Teal (Sarcelle), it is familiar in France. One knows its value as well as that of the Great Northern Diver (Plongeon), and the Mud-hen, or Coot (Poule d'eau), and this is why I shall not speak further of them. There are seen also quantities of other birds of the bigness of Ducks, such as the Spoonbill (Palonne), which has the beak about a foot long and round at the end like an oven shovel; the Night Heron (Egret), which has three little feathers straight up on its head; the Sheldrake (Bec de scie), which has the beak formed like a saw; the Long-tailed Duck (Ca-caoüy), because it pronounces this word for its note; the Buffle-head Ducks (Marionet (306) tes), because they run leaping upon the water; the Razor-billed Auk (Gode), a bird which flies as swiftly as an arrow, black and white in its plumage; the Cormorant (Cormorant) which devotes it-self to the catching of fish. Their neck is tied near the stomach, which prevents them from swallowing, and being thus prevented, they carry their fish ashore.

There are Plovers (Allouettes) of three sorts. The larg-est are of the bigness of a large Robin (Merle) of greyish color, and they have long feet. Others, which are scarcely less large, have the beak longer. Others are like Sparrows and little Chaffinches. All that game goes in flocks together, always along the edge of the sea, where there is any beach. The Sandpipers (Chevalliers) are a kind of Snipe (Bec-casse) which have the beak very long. They live (307) on small worms and other things which they find in the sand on the border of the sea. They are of the same size, have legs as long, and the plumage redder than the Small Snipe (Beccassine).

The Terns or Mackerel Gulls (Esterlais) are other birds, large as a Pigeon, which live on Fish. Flying always in the air, if they perceive their prey they fall upon it like a stone, seize it with their beak and swallow it. The Herring Gull (Goislan) is much larger, lives upon fish and livers or en-trails of Cod, but only captures that which is floating upon the sea. There are also a number of others which I do not remember. All those kinds of birds are good to eat, as are also all their eggs, aside from those of the Cormorant. Throughout the country, there (308) are found numbers of Herons (Herons), which are always upon the borders of

---

[8] Newton, 1861: 374–399.

[9] *Natural History Review*, The gare-fowl and its historians, 1865: 467–488.

[10] Hardy, 1888: **4**: 380–384.

[11] Puncheon, A measure of 72 to 120 gallons.

[12] This species was permitted as a Lenten dish because of the supposed resemblance of its oil to fish oil.

the sea or of the ponds, and live on little fish which occur in the holes where the water remains when the tide falls, or [else] on the border of the water in the ponds. They make their nests in the thick woods which occur on islands. They are good to eat and have seven galls and are always thin. As for the young they are better and always fat.

Continuing with the land-birds, Denys writes in Chapter XXI, p. 390:

The Duck-hawk (Faucon), the Goshawk (Autour), and the Pigeon-hawk (Tiercelet) have the plumage like those which are seen in France. The claw and the beak are the same. They prey on (337) the Patridge, the Pigeon, and other birds of that strength. The Pigeon-hawk has not a good claw for seizing the Partridge, though it is good for the Pigeon, and for other little birds. There occurs there another kind of Hawk. This captures only fish. It is always flying over water; if it catches sight of some fish it drops upon it more swiftly than a stone can fall. It takes its prey in its claw and carries it off to a tree to devour it.

There are three kinds of Partridges (Perdix), the red, the grey, and the black. The red is the best, equal to that of France for flesh and taste. The grey has a different taste from that of France; it suggests venison. Some persons find its taste better (338) than that of the red. As for the black it has the head and the eyes of a Pheasant (Faisant); the flesh is brown, and the taste of venison so strong that I find it less good than the others. They taste of Juniper berries, with a flavour of Fir. They eat of these seeds which the others do not. All these kinds of Partridges have long tails. They open them, like a Turkey, into a fan. They are very beautiful. The red has a medley of red, brown, and grey—the grey of two shades, one bright and the other brown, the black of grey and black. They have been brought into France and given to sundry persons, who have had fans made of them, which have been considered beautiful. They all perch, and are so silly that if you meet with (339) a flock of them upon a tree, you may shoot them all one after the other without their flying away. And indeed if they are somewhat low, so that you can touch them with a pole, it is (only) necessary to cut one, and to attach to its end a cord or a little tape with a running knot, then pass it over their necks and pull them down. You may take them all alive one after another, carry them home, place them on the ground in a room, and feed them with grain. They eat it promptly, but they must not be able to get out or they will fly away. I have twice tried to bring some of them to France. They stand well all the length of the voyage, but when approaching France (340) they die, which has made me believe that our air must be contrary to their good.

It is interesting to see that Denys took cognizance of three kinds of grouse in his domain. J. L. Peters, in his *Check-List of Birds of the World,* 1934, lists the spruce grouse, *Canachites canadensis canace,* and the Canada ruffed grouse, *Bonasa umbellus togata,* as characteristic of New Brunswick, and with regard to a third grouse, *Bonasa umbellus thayeri,* he says that it is found in the "Nova Scotian Peninsula, possibly also eastern New Brunswick." Apparently Denys likewise, recognized this variety as occurring in the Gaspé Peninsula where he lived some two hundred and sixty years ago.

It is a regrettable omission that Denys has not made any reference to the Grouse drumming—a feature which usually impressed later travellers. However, so far as I am aware, his account gives the earliest record

of the grouse being transported to Europe, and it would seem that this fine species was no more amenable to artificial environment then than it is today.

There are also Woodcock (Becasses de bois), but they are not common. They are found occasionally at the sources of spring brooks.

All the Crows (Corbeaux) of this country are wholly black. The note is not the same (as ours). They are also as good to eat as chicken.

Also Night-hawks (Orfrayes) are met there, not so large as those of France. In summer they are heard crying in the evening. Their cry is not so disagreeable as in France. They cry mounting in the air very high; then they let themselves fall like a stone to within a good fathom of the ground, when they rise again; and this is a sign of good weather. (341) The Barred Owl (Chat-huant) is of the plumage and size of that of France, and has a little white ruff. Its cry is not similar but there is little difference. All the birds make war upon it, Is better and more delicate eating than the chicken. It is always fat. It feeds upon little Field-mice which are in the woods. It makes provision of them for the winter. It captures some of them, which it places in hollow trees. With its beak it breaks their fore legs in order that they may not escape or crawl out. It collects hay in another tree to nourish them, and brings them every day their provision, whilst it makes its own meals on these little animals in proportion as they grow fat.

(342) There is also a bird which is called the Robin (Merle). It is related to the Starling (Etourneau) being less black than the (our) Merle, and less grey than the (our) Etourneau. It is not bad to eat.

One also meets there the Woodpeckers (Piquebois). They have plumage more beautiful than those of France, and are of the same size. There are others which are called Red-headed Woodpeckers (Gays), which are of a beautiful plumage; the head is all red, and the neck of real flame-colour.

The Humming Bird (Oiseau Mouche) is a little bird no larger than a cockchafer. The female has plumage of a golden green, the male the same, excepting the throat, which is of a red brown. When it is seen in a certain light it emits (343) a fire brighter than the ruby. They live only upon the honey which they collect from flowers. Their beak is long and of the thickness of a little pin. Their tongue passes a little out of the beak, and is very slender. Their flight is swift, and they make a great noise in flying. They make their nests in trees, and these are of the size of a fifteen-sou piece. Their eggs are the size of peas; they lay three of them, or four or five or more. The attempt has been made to rear them, but it has not been possible to bring it about.

As for the Swallow (Hyrondelle) it is the same as in France. It comes in spring, and returns at the end of autumn. They make their nests in houses, or against certain rocks where they do not get wet.

(342) The Bat [13] (Chauve-souris) is also of the same sort as that of this country, but it is much larger. It retires in winter into the hollows of trees, or among the rocks, and only appears in summer.

It is related by the editor of Nicolas Denys' *Natural History* that Denys' name is mirrored in a certain ornithological tradition of the Meliseet Indians of the St. John's River who were under the governorship of Denys. According to Mr. Tappan Adney, the Indians believe that the veery or Wilson's thrush, one of the

---

[13] The bat is not mentioned in Denys's discussion of beasts, hence it would seem that, like many other early writers, he assumed that it was a bird.

most beautiful songsters of this region, says "Ta-ne'-li-ain ni-ko-la Den'-i, Den'-i?" which is to say "Where are you going Nicolas Denys?" Adney thinks this is an echo of Denys' residence there. His name is probably also perpetuated in the River Denys of Cape Breton, but this is not proven, according to Dr. Ganong.

A statue has been suggested to commemorate in 1954 the three hundredth anniversary of his governorship; [14] this to be placed either at Saint Peters or at Nipisiguit (Bathhurst) where his book was written and where his grave is.

Nicholas Denys, according to Tanguay's *Dictionnaire Genealogique,* married Marguerite de la Faye, who bore him one son, Richard, and by a later marriage he had a daughter, Marie.

Tradition says that near the great willow on his old establishment some priests and a French admiral lie buried. The editor of his Journals, Dr. Ganong, says:

This Admiral, I believe, is Nicolas Denys. It is a satisfaction to think that here beside this pleasant basin where the least troubled of his days in Acadia were spent, in the last embrace of the land he loved so well, rests the mortal part of the proprietor and governor of all the gulf coast of Acadia, the first great citizen of that noble domain—a goodly man who fought the good fight and kept the faith—Nicolas Denys.

His biographer has graphically likened this book to a photograph slightly out of focus, and this appears to be true of Denys' bird lore as well as his general descriptions. While in the main his observations on birds are good and bespeak a critical eye, they are damaged by an admixture of inaccuracy, and in some of his descriptions, for example, that of the wolverine and its method of killing moose and the barred owl and its habit of harboring and caring for live mice, we feel that he was not entirely above the weakness of writing to please his public. Likewise the erroneous distribution of some birds, indicated by Denys, is proof that his writing was not entirely of his own observation, but it contained also a considerable amount of hearsay and folk belief. Folk lore is one of the most picturesque elements of a national literature but one that is naturally but slenderly represented in American literature. Let us, therefore, appreciate Denys' bird lore for its first-hand observation of many of our northern birds, and let us enjoy it more because of his colorful blending of fact and fancy.

BARON ARMAND LOUIS DE LAHONTAN

The contribution of the French people to American history is quite generally known, but it is seldom remarked that many French travellers have given us through their writings, a substantial part of our early knowledge of natural history.

Baron de Lahontan [15] (1667–1715) is one of those French writers whose travels abound with intelligent observation of nature. He came to Canada in 1683, a common soldier seeking adventure, but he rapidly rose by his distinctive service to the rank of an officer and became a favorite of that colorful figure, Count Louis de Buade Frontenac [16] (1628–1698).

Much criticism has rained on Lahontan because of certain alleged discoveries by him, which some authorities think are plagiarism, and it is difficult, therefore, to appraise his work. However, it is evident that he knew the woods, the coast line, and the rivers, and brought to his field observation a sympathetic appreciation that is present in but few of the early writers. While in no sense an ornithologist, he had a certain feeling and absorption in observation that is essential to the true naturalist, and while commonly listed as one who included some mention of birds in his voyages, he has not received recognition for his keen interest in all natural history and particularly birds. A résumé of the bird matter contained in his writings may therefore be of interest. There are three small chapters on birds.

1. A list of the Fowls or Birds that frequent the south countries of Canada, p. 350.

2. The birds of the north countries of Canada, p. 351.

3. A description of such birds as are not accounted for in my letters.

There are also accounts and lists of the mammals, the fish, the insects, the trees, and the fruits; and of especial interest in this day of modern fur farming a page on "The Names of the Skins given in Exchange with their Rates." This is an interesting chapter and contains one of the earliest lists of prices in our literature. The best fat winter beavers, for example, being worth four to five livres, or between eighty cents and one dollar per pound; silver-colored foxes, four livres apiece; wild cats, called Enfans de Diable, only one livre and fifteen sous apiece.

Considerable space is given to a discourse on the beaver, with a frontispiece—a beaver twenty-six inches from the head to the tail. Also depicted on the frontispiece are the methods of hunting buffalo, and the means employed by the Indians for drying the meat.

Lahontan was more than an ordinary traveller. The son of a distinguished engineer, the Sieur d'Arce, by his second wife, he was born June 9, 1666. The boy fell heir to all his father's building obligations when a mere child, and naturally also it was expected of him that he be a soldier in keeping with the traditional custom for those of noble birth. To further his advancement, he was pressed into the marine service, then in control of the colonies, because France was looking expectantly to the development of Canada. He was not averse to going, for he had always heard much about Canada, and in the seven years of service there he achieved distinction and honor. Under Frontenac, who had made him an officer, he was active in engagements against the English, and after the French had repulsed the English at-

---

[14] MacLeod, 1903.
[15] Winsor, 1884–1889: 4: 317.

[16] *Ibid.,* 4: 257–263.

tack on Quebec under Sir William Phips (1651–1695) in 1690, Lahontan was sent to bear tidings to the Court of France.

Here began his reverses for his friend and patron, Seignalnay, had died during his absence, and the succeeding ministers, the brothers Pontchartrain, regarded this adventurer with his grandiose plans from America with cold tolerance. Lahontan had some constructive plans for the defense of the colony but the home office felt no inclination for such expense. The result was that when Lahontan returned to Canada he was given the rather dubious distinction of being named Lieutenant Governor of Newfoundland. It happened that his chief there was a man inimical to him and, furthermore, one of capricious disposition, not to be trusted.

Of the two men in power then Lahontan was far preferred by his subjects and the populace, and even the Recollect friars took sides with him against the governor. The result of this breach was the dismissal of Lahontan, who avenged this injustice by caustic and humorous satire upon the French regime in Canada. In fact, the so-called "Dialogue" in his travels, written in imitation of the classic writer Lucian (120?–200), is a vehicle for venting his spleen against the official circle in New France. He had always been inwardly at war with the sham and corruptness of life among the colonists, and in this Dialogue he satirized the pleasure-loving and vicious practices of the French by eulogizing the simple pleasures and benefits of the Indians' mode of life.

The Dialogue teems, therefore, with his love of nature, his enthusiasm for hunting and fishing, and his general knowledge of the birds and beasts and natural conditions of the country. The letters, no less, reflect, in many passages the real lover of nature, and particularly of birds. Take for example his passage on the wood hen (grouse), one of the earliest descriptions of the drumming of this fascinating bird.

But the most Comical thing I saw was the stupidity of the Wood-hens, which sit upon the trees in whole Flocks, and are killed one after another, without ever offering to stir. Commonly the Savages shoot at 'em with arrows, for they say they are not worth a Shoot of Powder, which is able to kill an Elk or an Hart. I have ply'd this sort of fowling in the Neighborhood of our Cantons or Habitations in the Winter time, with the help of a Dog who found out the Trees by scent, and then bark'd; upon which I approach'd to the Tree, and found the Fowls upon the Branches. When the thaw came, I went two or three Leagues further (67) up the Lake, in Company with some Canadese, on purpose to see that Fowl flap with its Wings. Believe me, Sir, this sight is one of the greatest curiosities in the World; for their flapping makes a noise much like that of a drum all about, for the space of a minute or thereabouts; then the noise ceases for half a quarter of an hour, after which it begins again. By this noise we were directed to the place where the unfortunate Moor-hens sat, and found 'em upon rotten mossy trees. By flapping one Wing against the other, they mean to call their Mates; and the humming noise that insues thereupon, may be heard half a quarter of a League off. This they do only in the months of April, May, September, and October; and, which is very remarkable, a Moorhen never flaps in this manner, but upon one Tree. It

begins at break of day, and gives over at nine a Clock in the morning, till about an hour before sunset that it flutters again, and continues to do till Night; I protest to you that I have frequently contented myself with seeing and admiring the flapping of their Wings without offering to shoot at 'em.

Lahontan includes two drawings of the methods of killing the grouse used by the savages. His lists of birds are as follows:

A LIST OF THE FOWL OR BIRDS THAT FREQUENT THE SOUTH COUNTRIES OF CANADA

Vultures.
Huards, A River-fowl as big as a Goose.
Swans.
Black Geese.
Black Ducks.   } such as we have in Europe.
Plungeons. (Loons)
Coots.
Rayles.
Turkeys.
Red Partridges.
Pheasants.
Large Eagles.
Cranes.
Blackbirds.   } such as we have in Europe.
Thrushes.
Wood-Pigeons.
Parrots.
Ravens.   } such as we have in Europe.
Swallows.
Several sorts of Birds of Prey that are not known in Europe.
Nightingales unknown in Europe, as well as several other little birds of different colours, particularly that call'd *Oiseau Mouche,* a very little Bird resembling a Fly; and great quantities of Pelicans.

THE BIRDS OF THE NORTH COUNTRIES OF CANADA

Bustards.   } such as we have in Europe.
White Geese.
Ducks of ten or twelve sorts.
Teals.
Sea-Mews. (Gulls)
Grelans.   } (Terns)
Sterlets.
(238) Sea-Parrots (Puffins).
Moyacks. (Eiders)
Cormorants.
Heath-Cocks.
Snipes.
Plungeons (probably Loons)
Plovers.   } such as we have in Europe.
Lapwings.
Herns.
Courbeious.
The Water-Fowl
  call'd Chevalier
Beateurs de Faux, a Fowl as big as a Quail.
White Partridges.
Large Black Partridges.
Reddish Partridges.
Woodhens.
Turtledoves.
White Ortolans, a Bird no bigger than a Lark.
Sterlings.   } such as we have in Europe.
Ravens.

Vultures.
Spar-Hawks.
Merlins.   } like ours in Europe.
Swallows.
Becs de scie, a sort of a Duck.

In addition to the foregoing lists of birds Lahontan includes brief comments on such birds as are not accounted for in his letters. These are as follows:

Huards. These he says are "fresh-water fowl, as big as a goose and as dull and heavy as an ass." The persecution of these birds by the savages who surrounded them with canoes and caught them when they came up for breath, has led to their complete extermination, and although Lahontan speaks of them as fresh water fowl it seems he must have had the great auk in mind.

Red Partridges, possibly bob-white because he speaks of them as smaller and very different from those of Europe.

Eagles. Bald eagles with the head and tail white.

Fish Hawk, called by Lahontan a sort of vulture with which the eagles had frequent engagements.

Parrots. These were the Carolina Paroquets often referred to by other travellers as present in the Ohio Valley, and now in all probability extinct.

Nightingale, "of a peculiar form, lesser size than those of Europe and bleuish colour, lodging in holes in trees with joynt notes warble o'er their songs." This no doubt was the bluebird.

Flylike Bird, "no bigger than one's thumb and the colour of its feathers is so changeable that 'tis hard to fasten any one colour upon it. They appear sometimes red, sometimes of a Gold colour, at other times they are blew and red; and properly speaking, 'tis only the brightness of the Sun that makes us unsensible of the change of its gold and red colours. Its beak is as sharp as a Needle. It flies from Flower to Flower like a Bee, and by its fluttering sucks the flowery Sap. Sometimes about noon it pearches upon little branches of Plum-trees or Cherry-trees. I have sent some of 'em dead to France it being impossible to keep 'em alive, and they were looked upon as a great Curiosity."

This is a fairly complete and accurate description of the hummingbird for this early period, and Lahontan makes no errors in it except that he infers the sucking of nectar to be accomplished through the fluttering of the wings. The tubular shape of the hummingbird's tongue was apparently unknown to him.

Here the author digresses for a few paragraphs to discuss the ducks and other water birds.

Ducks. "There are ten or twelve sorts of Ducks in this country. Those call'd Branchus are the smallest indeed, but they are much the prettyest. The feathers upon their neck looks so bright, by vertue of the variety and liveliness of their colours, that a fur of that nature would be invaluable in Muscovy or Turky. They owe the name of Branchus to their resting upon the branches of trees. There's another species of Ducks in this Country that are as black as Jackdaws, only their beak and the circle of their eyes are red."

These must connote some species of scoter.

Seamews, Grelans and Sterlets. Probably various terns and gulls.

Sea-Parrots, Puffins.

Moyacks "are a sort of Fowl, as big as a goose, having a short neck, and a broad foot; and which is very strange, their eggs are half as big again as a Swan's, and yet they are all yelk, and that so thick, that they must be diluted with water before they can be us'd in Pancakes."

These are no doubt the gannet.

White Partridges. Probably ptarmigan. Of these the author says: "They are only seen in the winter time and some years they are scarce seen at all, though on the other hand in other years they are so plentiful that you may buy a dozen for Nine pence. This is the most stupid Animal in the World. It sits upon the Snow and suffers itself to be knocked on the head without offering to stir. I am of the opinion that this unaccountable numbness is occasioned by its long flight from Greenland to Canada."

This conjecture is not altogether groundless for it is observed that they never come in flocks to Canada but after the long continuance of a north or northeast wind.

In view of the frequent appearance of "Crazy" grouse nowadays these remarks of Lahontan are entirely rational. Birds in the fall often apparently lose all sense of direction and after long flights are picked up in city streets and other unsuited places. It has been suggested that this may be a provision of nature to extend the distribution of the species.

Black Partridge, Spruce Grouse.

White Ortalans. Probably these are Snow Buntings for the author says they are met with only in winter and refers to their seasonal change from white to brown plumage.

This makes a total of some fifty birds a few of whose names include several kinds as the ducks of ten or twelve sorts. Lahontan's observations on the fish are likewise fairly lengthy and detailed and he includes also shellfish, frogs, adders and insects in which last group he mentions only "Gad-bees" and "Hand-worms." The trees and fruits of the north and south countries are listed and described so that altogether Lahontan's body of natural history is fairly complete and the author in the face of injustice and disillusionment in his public life appears to have cultivated his interest in nature; in fact he turned to it more and more as a recompense.

Lahontan's bitter attitude on life was certainly aggravated by the seizure of his father's estate in France and the fact that his country would in no measure extend to the son the esteem and admiration which his father enjoyed. The young Baron exhorted them to remember his father's engineering genius in deepening the rivers with the resultant wealth for France, but in vain. Thoroughly embittered he befriended a Huron chief by name of "The Rat," then went on a vengeful journey to raid the country of the Iroquois. This chief, he idealized in the character "Adario" of his *Dialogue,* and through the agency of this alliance between the two friends Lahontan spoke his mind on philosophy and conduct.

His quarrel with his superior officer, de Brouillon (d. 1705), Governor of Newfoundland, continued unabated, and finally after accusations against Lahontan had been dispatched to France, the tension became an open attack upon the Baron's quarters and servants. Lahontan, believing his very life to be in danger, determined to desert the hateful situation and secured passage on a small fishing boat for 1,000 livres. At last, after a reckless passage, he reached a tiny harbor in Portugal. Naturally he could not face his country after desertion of his post of duty and so he wandered through Europe securing finally the publication of his Travels in Holland in 1703. After this he visited the Low countries, spent several years in England under the patronage of the Duke of Devonshire and published an English translation of his voyages which enjoyed an immediate popularity. In 1710 he was back on the Continent again but had abandoned all hope of pardon by his King or gaining reinstatement in the service of France. The last chapter in his life sees him attached to the Court of the Elector of Hanover and recognized as the friend and protégé of the philosopher Gottfried von Leibnitz (1646–1716). At this time many of his writings were ready for the press but he died in 1715, the place and exact date not being known. It is said that one of Lahontan's later manuscripts was entitled "Memoir on the fur-trade of Canada," [17] and at one time belonged to the poet Robert Southey (1774–1843).

Without doubt the Baron Lahontan is one of the most colorful and romantic figures, and one with an inherent love of nature. The stigma that has attached to his name through his alleged discovery of the Long River [18] need not concern the ornithologist.

Whether his relation of this tale [19] was a willful lie to help the sale of his book, or whether it was, as his modern editor, Dr. Thwaite, believes, "part and parcel of his satire upon European customs and manners," a play upon their credulity and a forerunner of Jonathan Swift's (1667–1745) *Gulliver's Travels,* may continue to stir historians and geographers. But when his writings are shorn of these moot chapters, there remains in them, for the naturalist and ornithologist, Lahontan's warm feeling for nature and very estimable knowledge of it, unequalled by any of his predecessors.

JEAN BAPTISTE LABAT

There remains to be considered in the group of French contributors to this early period of American bird-lore three other writers—Jean Baptiste Labat (1663–1728), M. de Rabié (d. 1785), and Jaques Le Moyne—the last of whom, though earlier by 150 years, in deference to his pioneer efforts in ornithological art, will be discussed last and in some detail.

Concerning these naturalists little has been written, but Labat's work in six volumes, entitled *Nouveau Voyage dans Isles de l'Amerique* affords insight into his career as a naturalist and missionary to Martinique. It is of special interest in the present study because of the plates of American birds which include the pelican, the flamingo, the frigate bird, and the tropic bird, all well known along our Atlantic Coast. Also pictured

are the West Indian parrot and the black crow-like bird called by the natives "Diablo"—probably the ani.

Although Jean Labat was so warm and likable a character and did much good on the Island of Martinique, details of his life are very few. From the writings of Lafcadio Hearn [20] (1850–1904) we know that among the natives of the Island he lives in legend as the benefactor of the people. He was a soldier, a minister of the church, an agriculturist, a scientist, an organizer of civic affairs—a man of great versatility, possessing a fund of humor that made him beloved of all.

In the midst of his good work in the West Indies he was ordered home to France, and he always hoped and expected to return, yet never was permitted to do so. It appears that a sinister enemy plotted against him, for it came to light some two hundred years afterwards that a letter [21] to Louis XVI mentioned the good Dominican as follows: "No matter what efforts he may make to obtain permission, the Père Labat is never to be allowed to return to the Colonies."

Labat was born in Paris in 1663 and entered the Dominican Order in 1685. In 1687 he was given the chair of mathematics and philosophy in Nancy, and in 1693 he embarked upon his career as a colonial missionary in the West Indies.

Having heard of the plague of yellow fever that was taking its toll of human life there, he determined to drop his professorship and go to the aid of humanity. He remained in the West Indies until 1705, spending most of his time on the Island of Martinique, but he explored also Guadeloupe where he founded the city of Basseterre. He defended Martinique several times against invasion and headed many scientific expeditions, including one against the dreaded fer-de-lance.

In all situations he was a resourceful worker and a good fellow; he could live on roasted parrots when other things failed and, regardless of hardship, was always a priest with the open mind of a scientist. In addition to his work on the Island of Martinique, he visited several towns of Santo Domingo and the islands Tortue, Vache, and Catalina late in the year 1700, making casual mention of pigeons, paroquets, thrushes, and other birds.

After returning to France in 1705, he lived for several years in Spain and Italy and wrote *Voyages en Espagne et Italie* in eight volumes, which was published posthumously in 1730, Labat having died in Paris, January 6, 1728.

M. DE RABIÉ

The name of M. de Rabié did not become associated with ornithology until 1930 when his drawings of birds [22] were brought to light in a London bookshop. Apparently this French engineer who was stationed for many years in the latter eighteenth century on the Island

---

[17] Parkman, 1879: 168.

[18] Thwaite, 1703: 1: 23–24.

[19] Some may be familiar with Pierre F. X. de Charlevoix's (1682–1761) derogatory estimate of Lahontan (*History of New France,* 1: 86–87), but modern research in history and modern appreciation of natural history (which Charlevoix lacked) enable us to see beyond Lahontan's heated maneuvres against his government and to discover the French gentleman and soldier with a sensitive response to nature.

[20] Hearn, Lafcadio, 1890.

[21] Bracey, 1918.

[22] Wetmore, 1930: 481–486.

of Santo Domingo had a great interest in natural history and also considerable ability with the artist's brush for he has given us a four-volume set of good water-color drawings of birds, fish, reptiles, crustacea, and insects, with manuscript descriptions in French. The first volume is devoted to birds with fifty-nine drawings, bearing on the title page the following inscription: *Collection des oiseaux de St. Dominique peints d'après nature par M. de Rabié, maréchal de camp, ingénieur en chef de la partie du nord de St. Dominique, mort à Paris en 1785.*

In some way the drawings came into the hands of the book-sellers, Wheldon and Wesley of London, and from there were sent to Dr. Alexander Wetmore of the United States National Museum for description and identification, and it is from Dr. Wetmore's article that much of this information is extracted.

The drawings were purchased through the interest of Dr. Casey Wood (1856–1942), for the Blacker Library of McGill University which has a large collection of original bird drawings.

De Rabié was a prominent and skillful engineer, as we may judge by certain building commissions he had on the Island of Santo Domingo. Moreau de Saint-Méry in his description of the French part of the island published in 1797 gives an account (p. 330) of Cap-Haïtien where many of the birds were taken and where an elaborate fountain was built in 1769 under the direction of M. de Rabié. There is also a doorway of a church completed in 1774 for which he made the drawings. Another structure was begun in 1752 showing that M. de Rabié was a resident on the Island for many years.

His drawing of the West Indian grebe is interesting for the artist's conception of how the grebes carry their young. He had evidently observed that the old birds hold them under their wings rather than brooding them under their bodies. De Rabié likewise made a drawing of that common American bird, the herring gull, which proved to be the only record of the species for the island.

JAQUES LE MOYNE, THE FIRST ZOOLOGICAL ARTIST IN AMERICA

In conclusion of this résumé of the part played by the French in the development of early American ornithology, it seems fitting that the work of a precolonial traveller, who attempted to make some pictorial record of American birds in addition to the usual journalistic account of his observations, should be treated in some detail. It is unfortunate that this is not more fully possible, since most of the ornithological material is probably lost, but the artist gathers great importance nevertheless from the fact of his priority in America as a painter and sketcher of birds, and also from the fact of his contribution of a very early account [23] including the first map of our southeastern coast.

---

[23] *Brevis narratorio DeBry voyages*, 1591: Pt. 2.

Effort has been made, therefore, to assemble what has been recorded in a number of obscure writings on Jaques Le Moyne (d. 1588) or James De Morgues, as he was also called, the earliest pioneer in zoological art in America.

Some twenty years before Sir Walter Raleigh's (1552–1618) better known attempt to found a colony at Roanoke, the French, having failed in their effort to colonize in Brazil, began to consider a colony in North America which should serve as a haven for the persecuted Huguenots or Protestants of France. Admiral Gaspard Coligny (1517–1572), who was himself a convert to Protestantism, was in charge of the enterprise, and he named Captain Jean Ribault (1520–1565) as the commanding officer of the first of three expeditions by the French to the east coast of Florida, Georgia, and South Carolina. This was in 1562, and although the purpose of the expedition was primarily to reconnoitre, with future colonization in mind, Ribault nevertheless found the country so alluring that he could not forego establishing a small colony of thirty men on the Port Royal River near what is now Beaufort, South Carolina. Of his impression of the fine country to which he had come, he says: "And the sight of the faire meadows is a pleasure not able to be expressed with tongue, full of Hernes, Curlues, Bitters, Mallards, Egrepths, Woodcocks, and all other kinds of small birds."

Having left this group of thirty men he found he was short of help and supplies, and had to return to France without continuing up the coast, as had his predecessor Verrazano, whom he planned to follow.

One of Ribault's officers, René Laudonnière (d. after 1586), accordingly was put in charge of the second expedition in 1564, and one of the officers, Jaques Le Moyne, called a "special painter and mathematician," was chosen by Coligny "to make an accurate description and map of the country and drawings of all curious objects."

So far as is known, this was the first time that an artist had been commissioned to make a study of and to delineate the objects of our natural history. It is disappointing that so little of an ornithological nature appears to have been done, but it is noteworthy that nearly 400 years ago and over 150 years before Mark Catesby set foot on American soil, a French artist lived for nearly a year in the wilderness of South Carolina devoting his time to drawing and observation.

Le Moyne is known, also, for an account of his stay in America. This narrative, the *Brevis Narratorio*, forms the second part of Theodore De Bry's collection of Great Voyages and was published in 1591. It is illustrated by drawings done by Le Moyne, most of which represent the Indians, their customs and ceremonies, and many depict the barbarous treatment of the Huguenots by the neighboring Catholic settlers of New Spain or Florida. One of the large illustrations of the *Brevis Narratorio* includes a group of wild turkeys, one of which is represented in full display with spread tail, dropped wings, and drooping wattle.　Alligators, manatees, stags, and shells also are pictured in the same scene, as well as the native method of stalking wild animals by disguising themselves under deer hides.

According to the noted antiquarian, Henry Stevens of Vermont, the Sloane Manuscript No. 5270, now housed in the Department of Prints and Drawings of the British Museum, contains a mixture of originals by Jaques Le Moyne and John White (d. after 1593), but we do not know which ones precisely are by Le Moyne.

1565) in and around Fort Caroline, and was one of the few, who, with René Laudonnière and Nicholas Challeaux, a carpenter, escaped the Spanish massacre under Pedro Menendez.　We gather also that he accompanied Laudonnière on his exploring trips up the river from Fort Caroline which must have given him impressions of bird and animal life and which he committed to paper.

That he was able to save any of his drawings done at Fort Caroline is questioned by the American historian Jared Sparks, for Le Moyne but narrowly escaped the

FIG. 16.　Life at Fort Caroline as seen by the French artist Jaques Le Moyne in 1564.　Note the wild Turkeys in the right foreground, first illustration of a North American bird.　From the *Brevis Narratorio,* 1591.　Courtesy of the Trustees of the British Museum.

Although Le Moyne's name has been omitted from the usual dictionaries of painting and biography, he does appear very briefly in the German publication *Thieme-Becker Künstler Lexicon,* Vol. 23, p. 31, and from this I learned of the whereabouts of the water colors hereinafter described.

We know from Johann G. Kohl writing in the *Documentary History of the State of Maine* (1869), and from Henry Stevens' work *Thomas Hariot and his associates* (1900), that Le Moyne was a prominent man, well known as an artist; that he spent a year (1564–

massacre and wandered for several days in the swamps and wilderness before being picked up by the French ship *La Perle* on her way to France.　Sparks asserts that such drawings as Le Moyne did must have been done from memory after his return, aided by the accounts written by Laudonnière and the afore-mentioned carpenter of the expedition, Nicholas Le Challeaux. On the other hand, Henry Stevens, one of the greatest authorities on early American history, maintains that Le Moyne not only wrote an account of his experience in America but also brought drawings back to England in November 1565. The *Perle* was driven to Wales by storms and Le Moyne and others bound for France disembarked at Swansea in Wales, remaining there some time until their strength was restored, and then crossed over to Rochelle.

This was during the height of religious wars in France, and Le Moyne, being a Protestant, probably spent more or less time in London. He gathered up his drawings and art materials during the massacre of St. Bartholomew in 1572 and fled to England. No report of his return to France has been found.

It should be mentioned that another member of the Huguenot group who escaped from the Spaniards at Fort Caroline was a young man named De Bry, who probably was a kinsman of the De Bry family of engravers of Frankfurt-am-Main. It was through him that Laudonnière's account of the Florida experience edited by Basanier became known to Theodore De Bry and Richard Hakluyt (1552?–1616). These two enterprising minds were evidently in accord and when Hakluyt heard of the fact through Basanier that Le Moyne had some paintings and drawings of Florida life and conditions, he persuaded De Bry (1528–1598) to approach Le Moyne on the subject of providing illustrations for Laudonnière's Journal.

Accordingly, De Bry came to London in 1587 to see Le Moyne and found him living in Blackfriars, as Stevens says, "in the service of Raleigh acting as painter, engraver on wood, a teacher, art publisher and book seller." De Bry hoped to secure all of Le Moyne's drawings on Florida for publication but Le Moyne was unwilling to part with the entire lot, probably because he had a plan of his own for their publication. But being in the service of Raleigh who at this time had a patent for colonization in America he did not feel free to carry it through.

It is not clear how many of Le Moyne's drawings were secured by De Bry on his first trip to London but he evidently kept the scheme in mind, for the following year, 1588, after Le Moyne's death, De Bry opened negotiations with his widow for more, but apparently not all, of her husband's drawings together with his journal on Florida.

De Bry thus came into possession of materials for the second part of his *Peregrinations* or Great Voyages and was already planning to use John White's account and his drawings as the first part.

Le Moyne by these circumstances had become very closely associated with Sir Richard Hakluyt, Sir Walter Raleigh, Captain John White, Sir Thomas Hariot (1560–1621), and De Bry, and is seen as a key figure in the English enterprise of western planting. By a series of several incidents which turned his findings to the uses of Raleigh, Le Moyne, the French artist and portrayer of the aboriginal American scene, became the one who was responsible more than any other man for the rise of English influence and the wane of French

on our Atlantic seaboard, during the infancy of our history.

Although so little by Le Moyne relating to birds can be definitely identified it is interesting to know that other samples of his art as a painter of natural history subjects have recently come to light. These are a series of fifty-nine water color drawings mostly of flowers and fruits but a few moths and butterflies also appear.

This folio album is now housed in the Victoria and Albert Museum in London. It was exhibited about fifteen years ago as a sample of early book binding. I was hopeful of finding some of his work on birds when I finally learned the whereabouts of this collection, but unfortunately there is not a bird among them. The drawings are beautifully executed with great detail and give the impression of miniatures—the colors are perfectly preserved and the antiquity of the painting makes them of great interest to the modern water colorist and also to the modern naturalist.

In the *Gardener's Chronicle,* an English publication, for January 28, 1922, p. 44, there is an article by S. Savage, now (1949) secretary of the Linnean Society of London, on "The discovery of some of Jaques Le Moyne's Botanical Drawings." According to this commentator the plants are the common garden varieties of England and France and he points out also that the paper on which the drawings were made bears a water mark which identifies the paper as having been made at Paris and Arras in 1568. From this Mr. Savage argues that the drawings were done after his return from America, which was in 1565. The drawings are further authenticated by the presence of the name "domorgures" on one of the folios.

While in London I took opportunity to examine another work by Le Moyne—an exceedingly rare little book of wood cuts of beasts, birds, flowers, and fruits with their names in Latin, French, German, and English, known as *La Clef des Champs* (*The Key of the Fields*), and printed in Blackfriars in 1586. Here I must confess to being struck with the great discrepancy between the crude artistry of these drawings as compared with the beautiful technique evidenced in those recently discovered and preserved in the Victoria and Albert Museum.

The little book is an oblong quarto and contains twenty-four mammals, twenty-four birds, twenty flowers, and twenty-four fruits. No American birds appear in the section on birds except the introduced species, the now ubiquitous house sparrow and the starling. The sparrow is rather well drawn but the work, especially in so far as the bird matter is concerned, is clearly only a picture book of but little scientific value or artistic merit and must represent some youthful work by the artist. However, it is interesting as a very early example of a natural history book and it gathers enhancement by being exceedingly rare, only three copies being known, and by having been done probably by the first artist who worked on American natural history subjects.

Furthermore, the fact that other work by Le Moyne has so recently come to light, leads us to hope that more drawings of birds, which we are assured he did in America, may yet be found.

The dedication of this little book, *La Clef des Champs,* throws some light on the artist's connections in London. Far from being a nonentity, too obscure to merit inclusion in dictionaries of art and biography, he appears to have been well known, if not indeed important, and so closely in touch with leading figures of the romantic years of Elizabeth's reign he naturally became acquainted with some of the most prominent and royally-favored in England.

As testimony of this, *La Clef des Champs* bears the dedication "À ma dame Madame de Sidney," signed "votre trés affectionné Jaques Le Moine dit de morques peintre." On the reverse of the second leaf there is a sonnet "à Elle même" with the initials J. L. M. The lady was none other than Mary Sidney (1555?–1621), Countess of Pembroke, the beautiful and talented sister of Sir Philip Sidney (1534–1586), and collaborator with him in writing poetry as well as a poet and writer in her own name.

This links Le Moyne with one of England's most aristocratic and gifted families. It has been suggested that he may have been in the Sidney home in a tutorial capacity, but be this as it may, the quest for biographical notes on this very early pioneer in zoological art should furnish a task of unusual zest to the ornithologist with an interest in the history of his science.

A few fragmentary notes may be added. Le Moyne was a native of Dieppe, a shipping town on the north coast of France, as were also Jean Ribaut, Laudonnière, and many others of the French Huguenot expeditions. He was born probably about 1530 and was therefore about thirty-five years of age when he visited America. He died in London in 1588, and a search of the registers of the Huguenot Society of London reveals the fact that he was listed in the Return of Aliens living in the Blackfriars district of London in 1582. The entry is as follows: James Le Moyne, alias Morgen, paynter, borne under the obedience of the French Kinge, and his wife came for religion and are of the Frenche Churche. He hath one child borne in England." [24]

VI. EARLY COLONIAL BIRD OBSERVATION IN AMERICA

This brings us to a consideration of some of the earlier attempts by the English to establish a western planting. Those most interested in the project, Sir Walter Raleigh and Sir Richard Hakluyt, had learned a great deal by the failure of the French Huguenot attempts in Florida, and the fact that Jaques Le Moyne, René Laudonnière, and the French carpenter, Nicholas le Challeaux, had all written accounts of their American experience made it

increasingly possible for the English to undertake the enterprise and not make the same mistakes.

Knowledge of conditions in America was spread also by Sir John Hawkins (1520?–1595) who had stopped on the Florida coast in 1565, and the fantastic tale by David Ingram, a sailor of Hawkins' Expedition who went overland from the Gulf of Mexico to Cape Breton provided marvelous adventure to stir the English imagination.

In the beginning of October 1568, David Ingram and about one hundred men were put ashore by Hawkins because he was short of ships and supplies. Ingram was of the town of Barking in the County of Essex and called himself a "saylor." His narrative was reported to Sir Francis Walsingham (1577–1647), and Sir George Peckham (d. 1608) a merchant venturer associated with Sir Richard Grenville (1541?–1591) and Sir Humphrey Gilbert (1539–1583) in American exploration, in the year 1582. Hence it may be that it was written some twenty years after the experience. The journey over Indian trails was a distance of about two thousand miles, but Ingram was able to accomplish this in a year because he never remained in one place more than three or four days. His picture of the red man and his mode of life is very creditable, but the life of the North and South are badly confused, and there are many impossible statements, as for instance, "there are rivers at the heads of which are lumps of gold as big as one's fist, and in the houses are vessels of massive sylver for common use."

While Ingram's natural history remarks on plants are fairly full and accurate for his period, the narrative is but a fanciful tale when it attempts to describe the birds and mammals. For example he speaks of a monstrous beast

twice as bigg as an horse & in every proportion like unto a horse bothe in mane, hoofe, heare, and neighing saving it was small towards the hinde parts like a grey hound theis Beas have two teeth or hornes of a foote long growing straight bothe by ther nostrills they are naturall enymies to the horse.

Likewise "a beast bigger than a beare it had neither hed nor neck his eyes and mouth weare in his breast. This beast is verie ougly to beholde and Cowardly of kind." Concerning birds he says: [1]

Ther are in those countryes aboundannce of Russets parrotts but very few greene.
Ther are also birds of all sorts as we have and many straunge birds to this examinat unknowen.
Ther ys great plenty of Gynney hennes which are tame birds and prog to the inhabitannts as bigg as geese very black of Colour having fethers like downe.
Ther is also a birde called a fflamingo whose feathers are verie red and is bigger then a goose billed like a Shovelle and is very good meate.
Ther is also another kind of fowle in that countrey which haunteth the rivers neare unto the Ilands they are of shape and bignes of a goose but ther wyngs are covered with small

[24] Huguenot Society of London Publications, 1894: **10** (2): 354.

[1] Ingram, 1883: 200–208.

callowe feathers and cannot flie you maie drive them before you like shepe they are exceeding fatt and verie delicate meat they have white heads and therefore the Countrymen call them penguyns (which seemeth to be a welsh name and they have also in use diverse other welsh words a matter worthie the noting.

Ther ys also a verie straunge byrde ther as bigg as an Eagle verie bewtifull to beholde his feathers are more orient than a peacocks feathers, his eyes as glistering as any hawks eyes but as great as a mans eyes his heade and thighe as bigg as a mans heade and thighe. It hathe a crest or tufte of feathers of sondrie Colours on the top of the heade like a lapwing hanging backwards his beake and talents in proportion like an Eagle but verie huge and large.

The mention of russet parrots more numerous than green can be explained only on the basis of the yellow and reddish face of the Louisiana paroquet which was numerous along the coast of the Gulf of Mexico and up the Mississippi Valley. Green hens were probably prairie chickens, grouse, or quail. The flamingo might have connoted the roseate spoonbill which was known to have been abundant in Florida in the sixteenth century. The flightless birds of the rivers were doubtless the great auk, which other travels mention as being driven into boats. But the last paragraph of this quotation dealing with a strange bird "as bright as an Eagle, his eyes as glistering as any hawks eyes, his heade and thighe as bigg as a mans heade and thighe," is beyond identification or even conjecture.

Three other men of the group are mentioned by name as having been put ashore with Ingram in 1568. They are Job Hortop, who published a weird tale of monsters, and two men named Lind and Brown. It is said that Hawkins rewarded these men on their return, but although their inland travels created a stir in England at the time, and still hold some interest for the antiquarian, they are of but slight value to the total narrative of natural history beginnings.

In September 1574 Menendez died on the eve of his becoming the Great Lord of the Spanish Armada, and at once Spanish influence and prestige in North America began to wane. Although Menendez had explored and mapped the coast from Florida to Chesapeake Bay, and had minutely described the coast by written word in such detail that it was considered the best since the work of Oviedo, little recognition has been given him for his exploration. His career of ruthlessness and cruelty overshadows his brilliant ability, and moreover it was the policy of the Spanish government to keep secret as much as possible the findings of the Spaniards in America lest other nations become envious and compete for their share of glory. Accordingly, four years after Menendez's death, Spanish influence was at such low ebb that the way was open for Queen Elizabeth to give a commission to the step-brothers, Gilbert and Raleigh, in 1578, and from this we shall trace the progress of English colonization with special attention to the ornithological matter that may be found in these early writings.

Sir Humphrey Gilbert sailed from Plymouth on June 11, 1583, with five small ships—the *Delight,* the *Raleigh,* the *Golden Hind,* the *Swallow,* and the *Squirrel,* and held the privilege of colonizing the island of Newfoundland. On August 5 he entered the harbor of St. John's and took possession of the country in the name of the Queen. But the country, though promising in its mineral wealth and abundance of bird and animal life, was full of lawless rebels and dissatisfied adventurers—even former convicts had been transported thither with the idea that they might become servants to the colonists. It was a situation Gilbert had no liking for and little ability to cope with. After visiting Cape Sable where the Portuguese fishermen were most kind and generous of their supplies, and urged him not to return to his little ten-ton ship, the *Squirrel,* he resolutely departed aboard his frail craft for the Azores. Here in the southern islands, during a fierce storm, he was lost with his ship, and many are familiar with the words he cast back to the *Golden Hind* as he sat aft with an open book on his knee: "We are as near to heaven by sea as by land."

There could naturally be but slight record of the findings of this expedition, but Hakluyt has preserved Sir Humphrey Gilbert's meagre description of the bird-life as follows:

Foul both of water and land in great plentie and diversitie. All kinds of greene fouls; others as bigge as Bustards, yet not the same. A great white foule called by some a Ganet.
Upon the land divers sorts of hawkes as faulcons and others by report. Partridges most plentiful, larger than ours, grey and white of colour and rough-footed like doves, which our men after one flight did kill with cudgels, they were so fat and unable to flie. Birds, some like black birds, linnets, canary birds, and others very small.

In 1584, Captains Philip Amidas (1550–1618) and Arthur Barlow came to America with a small company of men constituting Raleigh's first reconnaissance expedition. They discovered a part of the coast called "Virginia" where they were received with great kindness by the Indians and engaged in trading with them. A bright tin dish, for example, most pleased the Indian king. He took it and clapped it to his breast, making signs that it would defend him from his enemies. For this tin trifle Amidas received twenty skins worth twenty crowns, while a copper kettle fetched fifty skins.

The English captains were impressed with the fertility of the soil and with the rapidity with which the crops matured, two months, they said, being all the time needed between planting and harvesting. They even planted "pease" themselves, and in the sixteen days they were there the plants grew fourteen inches.

It is recorded in the narrative of this expedition that a party of eight men penetrated twenty miles up the river called "Occam" and the following evening they came to the island called Roanoke. The land is described as "a most pleasant and fertile ground, replenished with goodly cedars and divers other sweet woods, full of currants, of flaxe, and many other commodities which we at that time had no leisure to view."

Many other islands of the vicinity were explored and they were found replenished with "Deere, Conies, Hares and divers beasts, and about them the goodliest and best fish in the world, and in greatest abundance." Of birds the narrative says little but records a flight of cranes as follows: "having discharged our harquebus shot such a flocke of cranes (the most part white) arose under us, with such a cry redoubled by many echoes, as if an army of men had shouted all together."

The second of Sir Walter Raleigh's expeditions to America was made under Sir Richard Grenville as General. It was this voyage which brought to America Sir Thomas Hariot and John White, the former the tutor of Sir Walter Raleigh, appointed by him the geographer of the expedition. Hariot was his devoted friend to the bitter end of his tragic imprisonment. John White was the English painter who made the first known drawings of American birds, some of which are preserved in the British Museum.

Grenville himself did not remain with the colony more than a couple of months, but returned to England with a few men and his cargo of trophies and curiosities from the West Indies and shores of America on the eighteenth of August 1585. Sir Ralph Lane (d. 1603) was left in charge as governor of the colony at Wokokan, consisting of about one hundred persons. Thomas Hariot and John White worked together for upwards of a year at "mapping the country and recording and painting the natural commodities."

Sir Thomas Hariot's narrative, *A briefe and true report of the new found land of Virginia:* (1591), is the first well-planned and orderly account of the country by an Englishman. Hariot was already a scientist famous for his researches in algebra and the use of the telescope, and he proved himself no mean naturalist in the way he went about his description of the country and all it produced.

Hariot's *Report* is in fact the only accurate and fairly detailed account of aboriginal America. Beside several discussions of the merchantable commodities and the habits and manners of the people, it is divided as follows:

The first part of Marchantable commodities. The second part of such commodities as Virginia is knowne to yeelde for victuall and sustenance of mans life, vsually fed vpon by the naturall inhabitants: as also by vs during the time of our aboad. And first of such as are sowed and husbanded. of Rootes. Of Fruites. Of a kinde of fruite or berrie in forme of Acornes. Of Beastes. Of Foule. Of Fishe. The third and last part of such other thinges as is behoofull for those which shall plant and inhabit to know of; with a description of the nature and manners of the people of the countrey.

The section on birds, while brief and inadequate, contains the arresting statement:

Of al sortes of foule I haue the names in the countrie language of fourescore and sixe of which number besides those that be named, we haue taken, eaten, & haue the pictures as they were there drawne with the names of the inhabitaunts of seuerall strange sortes of water foule eight, and seueteene kinds more of land foul, although wee haue seen and eaten of many more, which for want of leasure there for the purpose coulde not bee pictured: and after wee are better furnished and stored vpon further discouery, with their strange beastes, fishe, trees, plants, and hearbes, they shall bee also published.

There are also Parats, Faulcons, & Marlin haukes, which although with vs they bee not vsed for meate, yet for other causes I thought good to mention.

These intriguing little paragraphs started me on a prolonged and ramified search some years ago for more information on this collection of early ornithological drawings. Whether they had ever been found or published I did not know, but my assumption was that they must have been made by John White, and through the writings of the American scholar and bibliophile Henry Stevens of Vermont, I learned of the existence of certain drawings of natural history subjects in the British Museum purporting to have been done in Sir Walter Raleigh's ill-starred Roanoke Colony by one John With.[1a] It was a possibility that this artist was the John White who worked with Sir Thomas Hariot; and finally it was definitely ascertained that the drawings preserved in the British Museum were none other than those fourscore and six mentioned by Hariot in his *A briefe and true report of the new found land of Virginia* has having been drawn in color and named in the country language.

A synopsis of the story of these paintings, done by John White on his first voyage to our southeastern coast,[2] may be read in Henry Stevens' *Bibliotheca Historica*.[3] Here we find (*op. cit.* 224),

In the year 1865 John White's original water colors, made for Sir Walter Raleigh in 1585, fell by purchase into the hands of the writer Henry Stevens, and in March, 1866, fell into the right place in the Grenville Library in the British Museum, at the moderate cost to the Trustees of £ 236, 5s. 0d.[4] They are now a prominent part of the world-renowned Grenville De Bry. A glance at the drawings will show that they are the work of an artist, and *portraits* whether of men, women, animals, fish, fowls, fruits or plants.

During the winter of 1934–1935, while studying at the British Museum, I took opportunity to enquire for these John White originals, and was delighted to find that they were on exhibit as samples of Elizabethan Art.

Through the courtesy of Mr. Eric O. Miller, then Deputy Keeper of Manuscripts, who had informed me of the transfer several years ago of these drawings from the Department of Manuscripts to the Department of Prints and Drawings, I was permitted to study carefully these early samples of bird art, and through the kindness of Mr. A. M. Hind, Keeper of Prints and Drawings, to have several photographic copies made

---

[1a] Hale, 1860.

[2] In 1585 the name "Virginia" was used to designate besides the present Virginia, the territory southward to Florida.

[3] Stevens, 1870.   [4] Winsor, 1884–1889: **3**: 123.

FIG. 17. The Sandhill Crane by John White, artist of the Roanoke Colony in 1585. Courtesy of the Trustees of the British Museum.

from them, two of which are included with this account (figs. 17, 18).

There are three albums of these John White drawings, the first of which bore the following identifying title and number in 1934:

> 1. John White's Original
> Drawings in Water Colours, 1585
> C. 199, No. a.1.

On the first page the following inscription appears:

> From Lord Charlemont's Library, sold at
> Sotheby's August 11, 1885, 769, 228, for £125.

Below is the name "Grenville."

There are also pages cut and pasted in from Stevens' description of Sir Thomas Hariot's *A briefe and true report of the new found land of Virginia,* which establish the authenticity of the manuscript and recount the story of its sale in 1865.

The first volume contains 130 water-color drawings entitled, in the artist's own handwriting,

> The pictures of sundry things collected and counterfeited according to the truth in the voyage made by Sir Walter Raleigh Knight for the discovery of La Virginia. In the

27th year of the most happy reign of our Soveraigne lady Queene Elizabeth and in the year of our Lord God 1585.

These drawings, however, are not all of American subjects. It is said that White had done considerable other exploring, including travels to southern and eastern Europe, and also to Greenland. This explains the presence of esquimos, ancient Britons, and an oriental woman among the drawings which are definitely American; and the American material includes many well executed drawings of Indians, and Indian customs and ceremonies, in addition to the paintings of natural history subjects.

The birds in this album of pictures are numbered as follows; the descriptive notes being offered by the present writer:

58. Alcatras [5]—The head of a brown pelican
59. Timosa—noddy tern
60. A Flaminico—flamingo
61. Hoopoe—not American
62. A large seabird with spread wings—man-o'-war-bird
63. Bobo—booby
64. The Roller—not American
65. Tropic Bird

The present ranges of these American birds would seem to indicate that they were probably drawn en route somewhere in the West Indies rather than in the Roanoke colony.

Of special interest also to ornithologists is White's drawing of an Indian Flyer (No. 16), who, as a badge of his occupation, wears a bird adorning his head. This shows remarkable detail and delicacy of execution in the feathers. The same is true to a lesser extent of the flamingo, No. 60 (Binyon catalogue,[6] No. 62).

It is necessary to state that there is an apparent discrepancy between the numbers on the drawings and the numbers by which the drawings are designated in the descriptive catalogue. For example, No. 60, according to the number on the drawing, is referred to as No. 62 in the catalogue, while the drawing bearing No. 58 is No. 60 in the catalogue. The drawing bearing No. 59 (the Noddy Tern, reproduced *Auk* 1936 (1)) is No. 61 in the catalogue, and the drawing of the Hoopoe bearing No. 61 is No. 63 in the catalogue.

In addition to the birds in this album, there are drawings of other natural history subjects, such as insects, scorpions, turtles, and lizards.

The second of the three volumes of John White's drawings bears the following identifying title and number:

> John White's Drawings in Water Colours
> 1585
> Offsets in 1865

On the inside surface of binding we read:

---

[5] Alcatras is a Spanish name widely adopted by travellers for the pelican.
[6] Binyon, 1898–1907.

Dept. of Prints and Drawings
Books of Prints
C. 199
No. A. 2

These are evidently the offsets which Stevens describes in his *Bibliotheca Historica,* pp. 225–226, as having resulted from a fire at Sotheby's in London in June 1865. The originals remained in a saturated condition under great pressure for three weeks. In spite of this catastrophe the drawings were unharmed, and during that time produced duplicates on the contiguous sheets of paper. Mr. Stevens, the owner, salvaged the treasures and had the "offtracts" as he said, "carefully preserved, reversed in the binding, and sized at no little cost of time and money." These unique by-products of a disastrous fire are surprisingly exact copies of the originals but are somewhat fainter in color, and were sold to the British Museum for 25 guineas.

The third and last volume of John White's drawings bears the following identifying numbers:

Case 199, No. a.3. Sloane 5270 [6a]

Unfortunately for our knowledge of John White and his contribution to American ornithology, the authenticity of some of these water colors has been questioned and, according to the late Dr. Lawrence Binyon, formerly Keeper of Prints and Drawings and author of the Catalogue, some of the drawings in this album may be copies of certain of John White's Originals that have not been found. These paintings are considerably brighter in coloring and show greater detail. No theory as to the identity of the artist who may have copied them is offered, but the assumption is that he was a contemporary, or near contemporary of White. No. 91 of this album, obviously a flicker (*Colaptes*), is reproduced herewith (fig. 17). According to the *Check-List of North American Birds,* the flicker was described by Linnaeus, based on *Picus major alis aureis* of Catesby. This drawing of the flicker indicates that the species was known and pictured nearly 150 years previous to Catesby's description of it.

There are few biographical details of Captain John White. From the researches of Stevens we know that he was a prominent man in London, the friend of Sir Walter Raleigh and Sir Richard Hakluyt, the latter of whom introduced him to Theodore De Bry, the famous engraver of Frankfurt. De Bry was then contemplating the publication of his collection of "Illustrated Voyages," and twenty-three of White's drawings were used to illustrate the first part of these "Peregrinations." Through this association he was also a friend of Jaques Le Moyne, some of whose engravings of Florida Indians,

Fig. 18. The Flicker by John White or a contemporary, 1585. Courtesy of the Trustees of the British Museum.

scenes and natural history subjects were used in Part II of De Bry, published in 1591.

To both of these artists—White, who worked in America, though interruptedly, from 1585 to 1590, and to Le Moyne, who spent a year (1564–1565) with René Laudonnière in and round Fort Caroline, American naturalists and historians might well give a modicum of their interest.

From the writings of Hakluyt, we learn that White made four voyages to America, and on the second one, which left England in 1587, he went as Governor of Raleigh's "Second Colonie," consisting of one hundred fifty persons. Among this number were his daughter and her husband, who were to become the parents of Virginia Dare, the first English child born in English North America. On arriving at Roanoke and finding conditions disappointing, many of the colonists were dissatisfied and persuaded their Governor to return to England. He, therefore, reluctantly went home with some of the colonists, but left many, including his daughter and her family, planning to return to them with all possible haste. While he was at home, however, the fear of Spanish invasion gripped all England, and all suitable vessels were commandeered to the defense of the Motherland. White, therefore, was unable to go to his countrymen in America until 1590, when a fifth expedition was fitted out to carry aid to the deserted colonists. Upon arrival, no trace of them could be found, but Captain White, in going over the ground, found some of his own chests which had been buried, dug up and broken open, their contents of books, maps and drawings torn and stained with the rains and his armor rusted through.

His subsequent career is entirely unknown, except that he retired to Raleigh's estate in Kylmore, Ireland, whence he penned a letter to his friend, Richard Hakluyt, dated the fourth of February, 1593. This is the

[6a] I inspected these drawings again in 1950 and found that they had been cleaned and mounted on cards and are kept in "solanders," a special kind of a box for drawings, designed by the Swedish botanist Daniel Solander (1736–1782). The John White Originals are now kept in Solander 4 of the series of English Drawings. The other two sets continue to have the same identification numbers.

last fragment of his biography, as far as we know, that has been preserved.

EDWARD TOPSELL:
Fowles of Heauen

Before we consider the other publications of early colonists in America it is of interest to note that American birds were beginning to be included in the writings of European authors at this early time. This is true of the work of the English clergyman, Edward Topsell (d. 1638), who wrote an account of birds, including some American species. It came to light when the late Mr. Bayard Christy (1872–1943) was visiting the Huntington Library of San Marino, California. It was known that he was an ornithologist so the Topsell manuscript was offered him to look at, and he has written an account [7] of this interesting old but unfinished work on birds.

Topsell's manuscript cannot take rank with the work of Le Moyne but is of signal interest for its early date and the considerable number of American birds in it.

Little is known of the author except that he had been a student in Christ College, Cambridge and occupied the rectorship of East Hoathly and later became the curate of St. Botolph Aldergate, London. The manuscript has been in the possession of the Huntington Library since 1917 when it came to the Ellesmere Collection of this institution from a descendant of Baron Ellesmere (1540?–1617).

It contains 248 folios, bound in velum and is in fine condition. The size is 8¾ × 12⅞ inches and there are 124 illustrations done in water color and ink and the volume bears the identifying number EL1142.

Topsell, although handicapped by a form of paralysis in the arm, as well as by extreme poverty which he deplores in his dedicatory letter, nevertheless completed two previous works on natural history—the *Historie of Foure-footed Beastes* in 1607, and the *Historie of Serpents* in 1608. Just when he wrote the manuscript on birds is not known, but it is probable it was written about 1614, only seven or eight years after the founding of the colony at Jamestown. The manuscript framed in red lines has nine American birds executed in ink and water-color. The names are given in Indian dialect with the English equivalent, identified by the late Bayard Christy, following:

The Aushouetta	(= the Thrasher—?)
The Aupseo	(= the Bluebird)
The Aiussaco	(= the Flicker)
The Artamokes	(= the Blue Jay)
The Chuguareo	(= the Red-winged Blackbird)
The Chuwheeo	(= the Towhee)
The Chowankus	(= the female Towhee—?)
The Tarawkow Konekautes	(= the Sandhill Crane)

---

[7] Christy, 1933: 275–283.

These are "of Virginia." In addition to these, there is pictured, with the blackbird kind, "a Black-macke of Brasilia which manifestly is a tanager" says Mr. Christy.

The towhee was a gift to Topsell from Sir Richard Hakluyt, and he had likewise received a description of it from Dr. Thomas Bonham (d. 1629), a physician of Cambridge. Although this bird is considered by the describer of the manuscript, Mr. Christy, to be the best of the illustrations, the written matter on the blue jay seems worthy of quotation for its bizarre verbiage. This bird is called the Artamokes, and it was believed to be a woodpecker. His description follows:

woode-spiker hauinge a loftie Combe or Creste arisinge highest at the two Corners behinde and before. . . . It is not good for meate, bycause it liueth like other Woodspikers, upon flyes spiders and oakewormes. For this thinge onelie the poeple of the Countrey admire it, and I doubt whether there be any creature in all the Worlde to paralell it: for it imitateth readilie, all the seuerall voices of other birdes, so as Cleopatra Epiphanius, or Kinge Mithridates. W[ch] had three and twentie languages, are not to be compared to this siely birde, that can singe with the thrushe, croake wth the Rauen, crowe wth the Cocke, mourne with the turtle, hisse wth the peacocke, and soe imitate the residue: for which cause our countrymen in Virginia doe call it a Linguist, as if it had skill in many languages, and the people of the Countrey call it Artamokes.

A copy of the painting of the towhee (Plate X) is included in Mr. Christy's account, and from the context it would seem that Topsell himself did not make the drawing but received, not the bird but the picture, from his friend Sir Richard Hakluyt, and the description of it from Dr. Bonham.

It is probable that most of Topsell's work, both on English and American birds, is a compilation from many sources, and it is interesting primarily because it belongs to the earliest years of English occupancy in America, and because we have held it, until recently, in one of our libraries unmindful of its place in the history of American ornithology.

Topsell belonged to the credulous period and had little learning in natural history on which to draw. He attained fame, however, because of his translation into English of Conrad Gesner's *Historia animalium* in part. This was the popular picture book of the seventeenth century and he rendered, as his dedicatory letter tells us, a faithful transcription of it not omitting any of the fabulous animals.

Says Topsell:

This is my endeavor and Paines in this Booke, that I might profit and delight the reader wherinto he may looke on the Holyest daies (not omitting prayer and the public service of God) and passe away the sabbaoths in heavenly meditations upon earthly creatures. I have followed Gesner as near as I could, . . . He was a Protestant physitian, (a rare thing to find any Religion in a Physitian) although Saint Luke a Physitian were a writer of the Gospell.

Your chaplaine in the Church of
Saint Buttophe Aldergate
Edward Topsell

The date of this work was 1607, the period before Ray and Willughby had produced their first-hand observations, and, like many others, Topsell was content with the limited horizon of his predecessors and what he lacked in originality he balanced with an ostentatious reverence for the works of God.

THE EARLY COLONISTS

At the beginning of the seventeenth century the whole stretch of the Atlantic seaboard was about to enter upon a long era of colonization. There had been many sporadic attempts by various nations to establish colonies here, but at the turn of the seventeenth century the weight of probability was that England would persist while France and Spain, which had been dominant in the past, would be pushed into the background and finally entirely out of the picture.

The American wilderness remained a land of hardship and privation for several generations, and it was the bare necessities of living that engaged the thought of the colonists. Contrary to popular notion the adventurers seeking money and excitement were not numerous; neither were the travellers who had training sufficient to study the physical aspects of the new land. The bulk of the population that settled New England in the early seventeenth century was a rather homogeneous group of good blood and staunch principles, fired with a definite purpose of establishing a new home where they would be free to practice their own convictions in religion and education. One of the first constructive steps of the Massachusetts colonists was the establishment of a printing press; another was the opening of a college, with Harvard University coming into being in 1631.

Literature they had, and a vast quantity of it, but not the kind that is the overflow from beauty-loving minds, nor did it have its beginning in a search for knowledge of the physical world. Rather was it the outpouring of their God-fearing minds so steeped in dogma that every phenomenon and incident was interpreted as a divine message from God, and men in answering, found spiritual satisfaction by the most rigorous and austere inhibition of his human needs and desires.

It is not surprising therefore that in the early days of colonization the settlers showed no interest in birds, beasts, or plants except as they served to provide them with, or deprive them of, the necessities of life. A glance at the earliest publications by the colonists shows a number of simple accounts with mentions of birds, beasts, fish, and plants, usually in separate paragraphs or small sections.

Little can be learned of birds from these meagre lists but it is obvious that the writers viewed them with English eyes and had no understanding that American birds could be entirely different from those of Europe. If a bird appeared larger than some similar bird of Europe it was because of the vastness of this strange country and the difficulties of gaining a living here, whether by man or bird.

In general, water birds and those seen about ponds or marshes attracted much more attention than the land birds. The massed flocks of wild ducks appealed as a ready food supply and were easily seen by incoming vessels in the harbors. Land birds, on the other hand, were shy and silent, and at the approach of man slipped without sound deeper into the forest.

CAPTAIN JOHN SMITH

The first accounts of the colonial period came from Virginia because this section of the Atlantic Coast had been in the public mind as the most promising location for a Western planting ever since Sir Walter Raleigh (1552?–1618) had made such far-seeing plans for extending the rule of Britain.

It is true that these hopes were never realized, and Raleigh ended his life in sorrow and injustice in the London Tower; but even today we are finding scattered fruits of his inspiration, some of which bear upon the beginnings of ornithology in America.

Sir Richard Hakluyt, of whom it has been said "England is more indebted to him for its American possessions than to any other man," was still playing in 1603 a strategic part in the hitherto unsuccessful enterprise of American colonization. When James I, following

FIG. 19. Captain John Smith (1580–1631), Founder of Virginia and an early commentator on New World Natural History. Courtesy of the United States National Museum.

Queen Elizabeth, came to the throne, it was Hakluyt who inspired the petition to King James to grant patents for the settlement of two plantations in the first decade of the seventeenth century. The colony at Jamestown, though pursued by misfortune, represents the first definite transplantation of the English to American soil.

Several brief accounts written between the founding of the Jamestown Colony in 1607 and William Strachey's (fl. 1609–1618) account in 1615 served to fix the public interest in this section and to induce many prominent and wealthy men, lured thither by the reports of gold and incredibly productive land, to come over to reconnoitre. The main restriction as to the personnel was that Roman Catholics were barred.

At the instigation of Hakluyt then, a small group of prominent men in April 1607, under the command of Captain Newport, approached America. The one who was to take charge of the planting of the colony had not been definitely mentioned, King James having sealed his instructions in a box not to be opened until after arrival. But Captain John Smith (1580–1631), who had already distinguished himself in wars on the Continent, was among the group, and through his inherent leadership, the small company deferred to his judgment. Though beset with trouble in the form of high mortality among the men and the destruction of the Jamestown storehouse by fire; beset also with some disloyalty among the colonists, not to mention the romantic but difficult factor of his friendship with the Indian princess, Pocahontas (1595–1617), Captain John Smith nevertheless successfully established the first English colony in America and named it Jamestown in honor of the King.

By 1608 he was already exploring the rivers that empty into Chesapeake Bay, and he prepared a map with descriptions of the country and people which he sent to the Council in England. Here are to be found the first impressions of American birds as gathered by the leader of the earliest English colony in America.

Says the famous Captain in his publication

A Map of Virginia with a Description of the Country, the Commodities, People, Government and Religion, Oxford 1612

Birds:

Of birds, the Eagle is the greatest devourer. Hawkes there be of diverse sorts as our Falconers call them, Sparrowhawkes (15), Lanarets, Goshawkes, Falcons and Osperays; but they all pray most upon fish. Partridges there are little bigger than our Quails, Wild Turkies are as bigge as our tame. There are woosels or blackbirds with red shoulders, thrushes and diverse sorts of small birds, some red, some blew, scarce so bigge as a wrenne, but few in sommer. In winter there are great plenty of Swans, Craynes, grey and white with black wings, Herons, Geese, Brants, Ducks, Wigeon, Dotterell, Oxeies, Parrots and Pigeons. Of all those sorts great abundance and some other strange kinds to us unknowne by name. But in sommer not any or a very few to be seene.

This is a good first list to come from the infant colony, and it is interesting also for the emphasis of the bluff captain on the seasonal movements of certain species. Furthermore, if taken in conjunction with Captain Smith's observations in other departments of natural history, as animals and plants, we must admit him to the better class of early nature observers. His description of the beaver is accurate, calling attention to the difference between the fore and hind feet, the second toe nail being split for combing the fur. He speaks also of the peculiar hairless tail, while the fox causes him to remark on its harmlessness to the hens' eggs and chickens; and of their flyes (fleas?) he says "nor their flyes [8] nor serpents (to be) anie waie pernitious; whereas in the south parts of America, they are always dangerous and often deadly."

This was not his only publication on America, however, for he visited New England in 1614 and subsequently published several pamphlets, the best known of which is *The General Historie of Virginia, New-England and the Summer Isles,* London, 1624.

WILLIAM STRACHEY:
Historie of Traivaile into Virginia-Britannia

Continuing with accounts written in the colonies we find that William Strachey (fl. 1609–1618) was the next to contribute to the story, and meagre though his record is, it is noteworthy because it follows almost immediately upon the first definite settlement. The ensuing years were hard; the colony all but perished, and almost decided to return to England. Lord Delaware then arrived with plentiful supplies and fresh colonists and saved the situation. An account of Lord Delaware's arrival, as well as Strachey's shipwreck on the Bermuda Islands, is recounted by Samuel Purchas (1575?–1626), in *His Pilgrimes.* This early experience of the English in America is believed by many scholars to be the basis for parts of Shakespeare's drama, *The Tempest.*

Strachey, having built a ship and come over to Virginia, became secretary of the colony under Lord Delaware in 1610.

Strachey discourses for two pages on American birds but it is often only a paraphrasing of John Smith's observations. He was impressed by the abundance and variety of hawks and writes as follows:

Likewise, as they have fruicts and beasts, so have they fowle and that great store. Of birdes, the eagle is the greatest devourer, and many of them there; there be divers sortes of hawkes, sparhawkes, laneretts, goshawkes, falcones, and ospreys;

and he lends his remarks credence by occasional personal details as follows:

I brought home from thence (America) a falcon and a tassel (tiersel) the one sent by Sir Thomas Dale to his highness the Prince and the other was presented to the Earl of Salsburye faire ones.

---

[8] Perhaps he refers to bot flies and the "serpents" are the larvae.

Of our now presumably extinct Carolina paroquet he speaks as follows:

Paraketoes I have seen manie in the winter, and known divers killed, yet be they a fowle most swift of wing, their winges and breasts are of a greenish cullour with forked tayles, their heads some crymsen, some yellowe, some orange-tawny, very beautiful.

And of our other lost species the passenger pigeon he says:

A kind of wood pidgeon I have seene in one daie, wondering (I must confesse) at their flight, where like so many thickened clowds, they (having fed to the norward in the daye tyme) retourne againe more sowardly towards night to their roust; but there be manie hundred witnesses who maie convince this my report, yf herin yt testifieth an untruth.

In general Strachey used caution in his observation of nature and attempted to verify his opinions. We may judge this by his attitude toward the prevalent story of lions in America. He would not affirm their presence until he had taken some claws which he found in an Indian house, to England for identification. Of these he says: "They are assured unto me to be Lyon's clawes."

Although mistaken in this and other statements regarding the natural history of America, his account ranks higher than the succeeding one by Raphe Hamor at least as far as the bird matter is concerned.

Strachey evidently returned to England as we may gather from his dedication of his publication the *Laws for Virginia,* Oxford, 1612, which is signed thus: "From my lodging in the Blacke Friars, at your best pleasures, either to returne into the colony or to pray for the success of it here. W. S."

Raphe Hamor was the next observer to produce an account of Virginia. He became secretary of the colony after Strachey and published *A True Discourse of the Present Estate of Virginia* in 1614. The bird matter contained therein is rather less thoughtful than Strachey's and is confined to a single paragraph:

There are fouls of divers sorts, eagles, wild Turkies much bigger than our English, Cranes, (in winter beyond number and imagination myselfe have seene three ore foure houres together flockes in the aire, so thick that even they have shadowed the skie from us.) Turkie Bussards, Partridge, snipes, Owles, Swans, Geese, Brants, Ducks, and Mallard Drakes, Shel Drakes, Cormorants, Teale, widgeon, Curleuves, Puits, besides other small birds as Blacke-birds, hedge Sparrowes, Oxeres, Woodpeckers, and in winter about Christmas, many flockes of Parakertroths.

FRANCIS HIGGINSON

Somewhat better though still casual and superficial is the account given by Francis Higginson (1587–1630) in his publication *New England's Plantation or a Short and True Description of the Commodities and Discommodities of that countrey* (1630). This was written in 1629 when Higginson could not yet have been in America long for in 1627 he was still in Britain, threatened with prosecution for non-conformity to the accepted Church of England. He sought the colonies as a refuge and was made assistant minister at Salem in 1629. To judge from his description of New England he must have been thoroughly satisfied with it, for he speaks with enthusiasm regarding its salutary effect upon the "abundance of melancholicke humors" from which he suffered saying,

Since I came hither on this voyage, I thank God, I have had perfect health and freed from paine and vomiting, having a stomache to digest the hardest and coursest fare who before could not eat finest meat; and whereas my stomache could only digest and did require such drinke as was both strong and stale, now I can and doe oftentimes drink New England water verie well.

In fact, Higginson concludes his eulogy of New England with the sweeping approbation, "A sup of New England's air is better than a whole draught of Old England's ale."

No less sanguine is his feeling for the beasts and birds of the new land. Like some of the other early travellers he yielded to the marvel-seeking cult for he accepted the report of "lyons" in the country, but perhaps he felt a tremor of doubt for he said he had not seen any hides; he believed that the deer had three or four young at birth, and he was one of the first to refer to the flying squirrel which, as he said, "by a certain skill will fly from tree to tree, though they stand farre distant."

His list of birds contains few species but he declared "fowles to be plentiful and of all sorts as we have in England, as farre as I can learn, and a great many of strange fowles which we know not." His account continues: "Whilst I was writing these things one of our men brought home an eagle which he had killed in the wood: they say they are good meate. Also here are many kinds of excellent hawkes, both sea hawkes and land hawkes."

Whether Higginson meant that they were excellent as food or excellent in their fearsome qualities as birds of prey is difficult to say, but perhaps the latter, for he goes on to refer to the "Pidgeons which," as he says, "are of all colours as ours are [in England] but their wings and tayles are far longer and therefore it is likely they fly swifter to escape the terrible hawkes of this country."

The gustatory perfection of the American partridges, turkeys and waterfowl intrigued the early colonists; in fact it was the main basis on which birds elicited their interest. Says Higginson,

And myself walking in the woods with another in company, sprung a partridge so bigge that through the heaviness of his body could fly but a little way: They that have killed them say that they are as bigge as our hens. Here are likewise abundance of turkies often killed in the woods farre greater than our English turkies, and exceedingly fat, sweet and fleshy, for here they have abundance of feeding all the yeere long, as strawberries in summer, all places are full of them, and all manner of berries and fruits.

And of the waterfowl he says—"a great part of the winter the planters have eaten nothing but roast meate of divers fowles which they have killed."

Comments such as these make it clear to us that American bird-life has had a struggle to survive for hundreds of years, and we must realize at last our need and duty to restore its depleted numbers.

Higginson was brought up to be a good member of the Church of England, but having come under the influence of the famous non-conformist, Arthur Hildersam (1563–1632), he was not willing to observe the strict ritual of the Church. Nevertheless he was a popular preacher with his superior officers of the clergy and was repeatedly reinstated after being as frequently asked to withdraw. However, when proceedings were definitely commenced against him, he was glad to offer himself to the Massachusetts Bay Company and accordingly, with his wife and several children, set sail from Gravesend on April 25, 1629.

He had been a leader among the Puritans of Leicester and was active in preparing the youth for the university. Though the climate of New England at first restored him to health, he contracted a fatal fever from overwork and died on August 6, 1630. After his death his eldest son, John (1616–1708), obtained some teaching at Harvard with which he helped to maintain the family.

LOCAL LISTS IN LITERARY DRESS

WILLIAM WOOD

Up to and through these early beginnings of colonization the observation of birds consisted in the merest listing of a few common species, all of which could be seen in the day's work so to speak. The idea of seeking birds out and studying them for their intrinsic interest did not develop for several decades, but we can detect a slightly better attitude, perhaps tinged with some aesthetic appreciation of birds, in the writings of certain men of the 1630's. These are William Wood, Thomas Morton (d. 1646), and William Morrell (fl. 1625).

William Wood in his treatise *New England Prospect,* London (1634), has a very readable chapter, "Of the birds and fowles both of Land and Water." Here we perceive a distinct advance over previous records of American bird life—some thirty-five species being dealt with in pleasing style with good observations on their appearance and habits, not to mention the customary market price of so many shillings for each kind of bird. This was always important to the commercial-minded settler.

Wood prefixes his chapter on birds with an account in verse. This is probably the earliest poem about American bird life although a published statement gives Jakob Steendam this distinction.[9]

Nearly three decades separate these poetic lists, but it is probable that even if they had been written at the same time, they would have been equally dissimilar for each reflects its author's general attitude toward the world of nature.

---

[9] Martin, 1914: 191.

Wood's lines are marked by superior observation and poetic diction:

The Princely Eagle, and the soaring Hawks,
Whom in their unknowne wayes there's none can chawke:
The Humberd [10] for some Queenes rich Cage more fit,
Than in the vacant Wildernesse to sit.
The swift wing'd Swallow sweeping to and fro,
As swift as arrow from Tartarian Bow.
When as Aurora's infant day new springs,
There th' morning mounting Larke her sweete lays sings.
The harmonious Thrush, Swift Pigeon, Turtle-dove,
Who to her mate doth ever constant prove:
The Turky-Pheasant, Heathcocke, Partridge rare,
The carrion-tearing Crow, and hurtfull Stare,[11]
The long liv'd Raven, th' ominous Screech-Owle,
Who tells as old wives say, disasters foule.
The drowsie Madge [12] that leaves her day-lov'd nest,
And loves to roave when day-birds be at rest:
Th' Eele-murthering Hearne,[13] and greedy Cormorant,
That neare the Creekes in morish Marshes haunt.
The bellowing Bitterne, with the long-leg'd Crane,
Presaging Winters hard, and dearth of graine.
The Silver Swan that tunes her mournefull breath,
To sing the dirge of her approaching death.
The tatling Oldwines,[14] and the cackling Geese,
The fearefull Gull that shunnes the murthering Peece.
The strong wing'd Mallard, with the nimble Teale,
And ill shape't Loone who his harsh notes doth squeale.
There Widgins, Sheldrackes and Humilitees,[15]
Snites,[16] Doppers,[17] Sea-Larkes,[18] in whole millions flees.

Here are thirty-three groups of birds, not counting the several "sorts" which are found in some of the groups—a very fair showing of ornithological observation for 1630.

As in all the early Chronicles, the eagle, the turkey, and the hummingbird received a large share of attention, but with Wood, we note a careful effort truthfully and feelingly to appraise the other sorts. His choice of epithets is good: "princely Eagle," "bellowing Bitterne," "swift-winged Swallow," "harmonious Thrush," "drowsie Madge," and throughout the text are good observations on their natural history. A glance at Jakob

---

[10] Humberd—hummingbird.

[11] Stare—intended for starling, but blackbirds were of course the birds he had seen. Starlings were not introduced into the United States until 1890.

[12] Madge—an old name for the barn owl, which sits in a hole of a tree trunk or in some old and tumbling building during the day, coming out at night to feed on small animals.

[13] Hearne—this probably connotes "heron" of various species.

[14] Old wines—sometimes written "old wives" and appears to means either gulls as with some writers or a species of diving duck, *Clangula hyemalis,* called now "old squaw." Their habit of "talking" among themselves in large flocks seems to indicate that Wood in the present instance means "old-squaw."

[15] Humilitees—as may be inferred from the text, are sandpipers and plovers of several species, although the writer did not recognize more than two as different. Even today, after three centuries of persecution, these birds are rather tame and easily approached. Fortunately most of them have been removed from the game list.

[16] Snites—sandpipers.

[17] Doppers—grebes.

[18] Sea-larkes—used for the smaller members of the Scolopacidae and the Charadriidae, families of shore birds.

FIG. 20. Jakob Steendam (1616–ca. 1672), Clergyman and first colonist to write a poem on American birds. Courtesy of the United States National Museum.

Steendam's ornithological effort will convince us of its author's disinterest and therefore the inferior quality of his observation.

AN EARLY POETIC LIST OF AMERICAN BIRDS BY JAKOB STEENDAM

Of Birds, there is a knavish robbing crew,
Which constantly the smaller tribes pursue;
The hawk and eagle swoop the azure blue,
    With sharp eyes prying.
The chicken saker-hawk, with talons fell;
The sparrow-hawk; the vigilant castrel
Watching his enemy, till he may reel
    And faint in flying.
The duck, the goose, the turkey, the proud swan,
The diver and the heron and the crane,
The snipe, the curlew, merlin and moorhen,
    The foremost vieing:
The dove and pheasant, thievish blackbird, quail;
The widgeon, which an epicure may hail;
The teal and bob-o'-lincoln, all avail
    For man's enjoyment.
But names are wanting wholly to explain
The numerous species of the feathered train;
And surely the recital were a vain
    Misspent employment.

THOMAS MORTON OF MERRY-MOUNT

Of a different order is the treatise *New English Canaan,* and the author likewise seems a far cry from the God-fearing pious writers of his day. He was frankly regarded by the Plymouth colonists as a reprobate and outlaw and was sent back to England because of his licentious parties at Mount Wollaston. His book is regarded as a pernicious satire upon Puritanism.

Little is known of Morton in England except that he was an attorney of Cliffords Inn. From his account of New England we gather that he had considerable interest in the classic writers and derived much enjoyment from hunting and other field activities. This background makes for much greater accuracy and breadth of subject matter in his account of the birds of New England, and little significance need attach to the unsavory reputation of the man as a trader with the Indians or as a renegade from the straight and narrow teachings of the Puritan Fathers.

The following list of birds is compiled from his chapter "Of Birds and Feathered Fowles" which occupies ten pages of *New English Canaan.* A running commentary shows his first-hand observation of some of them, though naturally there are many mistakes and omissions.

Swanne
Geese { Brant / White / Gray
Ducks { Pied Ducks / Gray Ducks / Black Ducks
Teales { Green winged / Blew winged
Widgens
Snipes
Sanderlings
Cranes
Turkies
Pheasants
Partridges
Quailes
Larkes
Crowes
Kights
Rooks
Hawkes { Lannaret / Fawcous / Tassel / Gentles / Goshawks / Marlins / Sparhawkes
Humming-bird

His information on hawks, waterfowl, and upland game species is much more complete than for the other groups. This may be explained by the fact that he was a veteran hunter of game birds and also was a devotee of falconry. He tells us he had been brought up in "so generous a way," having had the use of them in England, that he developed keen interest in this ancient and patrician sport.

Morton is the first of the colonists to give any attention to the hawks except as fearsome birds of prey, and his descriptions denote the connoisseur of falconry with an aesthetic appreciation of nature.

On his first arrival here he speaks of taking a Lannaret (probably a duck hawk) which, as he said "I reclaimed, trained, and made flying in a fortnight, the same being a passenger at Michaelmas." Of this magnificent species he makes true estimate in the words:

I found that these are most excellent mettell, rank winged, well conditioned and not tickleish footed; and having whoods, bels, luers, and all things fitting, was desirous to make experiment of that kind of Hawke before any other.

In speaking of the upland game birds he differentiates among turkeys, pheasant, partridge, and quail; the pheasant being the ruffed grouse, the partridge the heath hen,[19] and the quail the bob-white. Of the name pheasant for the ruffed grouse he says:

but whether they be Pheysants or no, I will not take upon me to determine they are in form like our Pheisant henne of England. Both the male and the female are alike; but they are "rough footed and have stareing feathers about the head and neck. The body is as bigg as the pheysant henne of England, and are excellent meate, yet we seldome bestowe a shoote at them."

"Rough footed" and "stareing" refer, of course, to the pectinations on the sides of the toes commonly called "snow shoes" and the ruff of feathers about the neck.

Morton's observations on the large group of small, dooryard birds is, however, far from equal to his account of ducks, upland game species, and hawks. He mentions only larks, crows, and hummingbirds, and is incorrect in saying that the larks of America do not sing. They do not, it is true, sing on the wing for such lengthy periods as do the English skylarks, but our horned lark has a simple little song given as it mounts into the air; then closing its wings it descends plummet-like almost to earth, and opening its wings again gracefully alights.

It is suggested by William Brewster cooperating with the editor of *New English Canaan*, Charles Francis Adams, Jr., that possibly Morton had in mind the titlark (*Anthus praetensis*).

Morton's description of the hummingbird is similar to many other accounts of it during the early colonization of America. This group of birds being confined to the New World naturally attracted attention, and by some it was considered a hybrid between a fly and a bird.

It has been questioned whether Morton published his book before or after William Wood brought out his *New England Prospect*. According to Justin Winsor, publication date of 1637 at Amsterdam, is correct.[20] It is true, however, that several years elapsed between the writing and the publication, owing, no doubt, to the vicissitudes of the man's life which more than once banished him from the Massachusetts Bay Colony. Morton is said to have made much money in fur-trading with the Indians but he died in poverty at his American retreat in 1646.

---

[19] Extinct since 1934.
[20] Winsor, 1884–1889: **3**: 348, notes 1 and 2.

WILLIAM MORRELL

This brings us to the last of the three writers of the seventeenth century who attempted to write in verse about the birds of New England. William Morrell (fl. 1625), another clergyman, was sent over to the Plymouth Colony in 1623 to act as a superintendent over the churches, but he gave little time to these ecclesiastical duties, preferring to study the country and to write Latin verse. His *Poem on New England* consists of some fourteen pages of tedious, heroic couplets which, even when rendered into English, are rather dull and antiquated but nevertheless show some first-hand knowledge of nature and not a little sense of beauty.

His list of birds is small, however, mentioning, as usual, principally water species, but it brings in the new thought not previously found in other writers, of birds' feathers as articles of adornment for women. Twelve lines are all Morrell gives to birds, as follows:

The fowles that in those bays and harbours feede,
Though in their seasons they do elsewhere breede,
Are swans and geese, herne, phesants, duck and crane,
Culvers and divers all along the maine:
The turtle, eagle, partridge, and the quaile,
Knot, plover, pigeons, which doe never faile,
Till summer's heat commands them to retire,
And winter's cold begets their old desire.
With these sweete dainties man is sweetly fed,
With these rich feathers ladies plume their head;
Here's flesh and feathers both for use and ease
To feede, adorne, and rest thee, if thou please.

This poem was reprinted in the *Collections of the Massachusetts Historical Society* for the year 1792, Vol. i, Boston, 1806. It is interesting primarily as a relic of our earliest literary history and for the fact that it departs from the usual subject of religion in the early years when religion was practically the only basis for literary expression, and takes up several phases of natural history.

If we should attempt to put any literary evaluation upon any of the poetic descriptions of the three men, William Wood, Jakob Steendam, and William Morrell, the laurels must go to Wood who exceeds the others both in point of species mentioned and in the quality of his poetic descriptions; Steendam's being but labored and inept humorous rhyming, which the author regards with all seriousness, and Morrell's being very brief and superficial.

VII. THE MID-SEVENTEENTH AND EARLY EIGHTEENTH CENTURIES

In the mid-seventeenth century, between 1637 and 1672, there was no appreciable publication including matter on American birds by any of the English colonists, Thomas Morton's *New English Canaan* being the last until the work of John Josselyn (fl. 1675) in 1672. However, the work of a prolific Spanish writer, Francisco Hernandez (1514–1578), which did not become well known until 1651, helps to bridge this period although it was concerned with the natural history of Mexico and only touched at a few points the ornithology of the present United States.

Hernandez was the personal physician to King Philip II of Spain (1527–1598) but Philip sent him to America to study the rich resources and natural history of the New World in 1570. He remained here until 1577 but died in 1578, before he had opportunity to publish his notes. A large part of his manuscripts was burned in 1671, but some of his writings were assembled in 1615 by Francisco Ximenez (*ca.* 1615) under the title *Cuatro libros de la naturaleza y virtudes de las plantas, y animales que estan recevidos en el uso de medicina en Nueva España* (Morella, 1615). An Italian physician, Dr. Nardus Antonius Reccho, of Naples, made a compendium of Hernandez's writings and published them in Mexico in 1628. These writings were much read as a source of information about the New World by later authors, and a larger version, illustrated with woodcuts, was published in Rome in 1649 under the title *Rerum medicarum novae Hispaniae thesaurus etc.* The edition of 1651 is the work of several authors, but the section entitled *Historiae animalium et mineralium novae Hispaniae* bears Hernandez' name. This section contains more than two hundred birds briefly described and a few are illustrated, notably the white pelican and the American merganser. A number [1] of North American birds are represented, among which may be mentioned:

Ardea herodias (great blue heron)
Agelaius gubernator (bicolor redwing)
Nycticorax (black-crowned night heron)
Steganopus wilsoni (Wilson's phalarope)
Regulus calendula (ruby-crowned kinglet)
Strix flammea (short-eared owl)
Mimus polyglottus (mockingbird)
Quicalus macrurus (great-tailed grackle)
Trogon mexicanus (probably the coppery-tailed trogon)
Podylimbus podiceps (pied-billed grebe)
Spatula clypeata (shoveller)
Anser albifrons (white-fronted goose)
Dafila acuta (pintail)
Bubo virginianus (great horned owl)
Larus delawarensis (ring-billed gull)
Grus canadensis (little brown crane)
Pyranga hepatica (hepatic tanager)
Sialia (bluebird)
Bombycilla cedrorum (cedar waxwing)

To this period belong also two other diligent workers from foreign lands; men who, though natives of Europe, laid the foundation of South American zoology at the time of the Dutch occupation of northern Brazil. These are George Marcgrave (1610–1644),[2] a brilliant young

---

[1] List compiled from a pamphlet on Hernandez by the late Alfredo Dugés in the American Museum of Natural History, written in Guanojuato, Oct., 1889.

[2] Swainson, 1840: 252–259.

naturalist of Saxony, and Johann Moritz (1604–1679), the Prince of Nassau-Siegen to whom was entrusted the entire command of the Dutch conquests in the New World.

Marcgrave was born in Liebstadt September 10, 1610, of well educated parents who wanted him to travel and acquire knowledge of many places. To this end he attended nine German universities and became learned in theology, Latin, Greek, and natural philosophy. A man named Jan De Laet (1593–1649), then managing director of the Dutch Indies Company, invited Marcgrave to be astronomer to the Company and, accordingly, he left Holland January 1, 1638. An expedition to Brazil under the leadership of Johann Moritz had gone out the previous year. Marcgrave soon met with the Prince in Brazil and through his knowledge of military architecture, gained favor with him. The Prince built for Marcgrave an observatory of stone from which to study the stars. Johann Moritz provided him also with a cohort of soldiers for his explorations, for the Prince was a lover of science as well as statesmanship and wanted to foster natural knowledge during his rule in Brazil. His collecting expeditions were equipped in every way for the safety and health of the men who were ordered to bring back live specimens of birds, mammals, and fish. For these wild creatures the Prince had large cages, gardens, and ponds built in the city of Mauritia.

Marcgrave made at least three collecting trips into northern Brazil, the states of Pernambuco, Parahyba, and Rio Grande do Norte, but, although he kept full notes on his findings, very few of his journals have been found.

Another important member of this expedition was Willem Piso (1611–1678), physician to Johann Moritz and the soldiers. He served also as the head of the scientific work, since he was an older and more experienced man than Marcgrave. But he understood only medical research, while Marcgrave worked in general natural science, geography, and astronomy, thus rendering himself indispensible to the Prince.

Relations between Piso and Marcgrave thus became strained and it is said that Marcgrave wrote much of his material in cipher to protect himself from any possible infringement upon his findings in case he should not live to publish them himself. Jan De Laet, who first had invited Marcgrave into this work, became his literary executor but, although he was a man of much learning, he was handicapped by his lack of knowledge in natural science. Furthermore, Marcgrave's notes were not in order, although he intended to put them in condition for publication on his return to Europe. This, unfortunately, he did not live to do, for he died, a victim of the climate while exploring the coast of New Guinea in 1644.

The work done in Brazil is the most important early contribution to the zoology of South America, and, if the author could have edited his own manuscripts, it is probable that many North American forms, as well as those of South America, would have been known to science sooner. There are many birds we know as breeding species in the spring in the United States that migrate to various parts of South America to spend the winter; some of these must have fallen under the gaze of Marcgrave or the Prince of Nassau-Siegen when they were collecting and observing in Brazil in the mid-seventeenth century.

It came to my notice, while studying the writings of the eminent scientist George Brown Goode, that some unpublished American bird drawings from this expedition were still housed in the Royal Library of Berlin, now known as the Preussische Staatsbibliotek, and in 1936 I stopped in Berlin to see whether, from the incomplete description of them which I had, they could be found. I had written previously and was told that such a manuscript was there, but to a stranger it seemed that many mishaps might befall the quest. However, when I showed my letter from the Keeper of Manuscripts, the attendants showed me a catalogue in which I was able to find the manuscript described. Four ponderous tomes were soon wheeled in to one of the manuscript tables and I began to pick my way through a maze of Latin phraseology, from which I could piece together the assurance that I was on the right track.

The first volume was devoted to fish; the second to birds, with a title page resplendent with macaws, a roseate spoonbill, a nesting eagle, a barn owl and other small birds all in circular arrangement.

There were 110 bird-drawings in this heavy tome of coarse folios, all painted on dark paper cut and pasted into this giant picture book. The title of these water colors was "Brazilianische Naturøgegenstände," bearing press numbers A36 and A37.

There were many birds that I recognized as our North American species and, as always in the search for these early drawings, it gave me keen pleasure to notice that the pioneering artist had seen his bird aright. It would make too long an account to describe all of these birds from my notes but a selected two of the drawings may serve as samples of the work of these two artists. As I turned the heavy rattling leaves of this manuscript it seemed to me that folio No. 11 was the most interesting one. This represents the anhinga, that sinuous sinister looking snake-bird of our southern swamps. One of these grotesque birds had but recently caused me a wasted day when, camped on the scorching shore of a Florida stream I was in charge of two young captive swallow-tailed kites, while my husband spent interminable hours in a tree-top trying to get a pair of these birds to go through their amazing feeding operation before his motion picture camera. Perhaps, with this rueful reminiscence, it gave me particular satisfaction to track one of these creatures back to 1640. Anyway, there it was before me, as Marcgrave had drawn it—black, lithe, and totipalmate, with a yellowish gular pouch and a bill like

Fig. 21. The Black Skimmer, by George Marcgravius, scientist and artist on the Dutch expedition to Brazil, 1660. From MS. Libr A 33. no. 40. Brazilianische Naturgegenstände. Courtesy of the Preussische Staatsbibliotek, Berlin.

a javelin, while its head, neck, and foreback were clothed in feathers of a strange whitish and stringy appearance. It was an excellent likeness made perfect by the glint of its yellow eye.

The other one was the black skimmer, a bird that has always fascinated me because of its graceful flight, striking black, white, and red color-pattern and strange feeding adaptation in having the lower mandible protruding beyond the upper to serve as a blade with which to slash the water as it skims over the surface. Its tiny red webbed feet were another mark of beauty and interest, and George Marcgrave, three hundred years ago, had caught and pictured all these points. The likeness is a bit over balanced by the disproportionately large head and small feet and the plumage lacks the sheen of life but, nevertheless, a creditable addition to our growing list of early American bird drawings.

Some of the notations on the drawings are said to be by the Prince himself and one commentator, Henry Lichtenstein [3] (1780–1857) who made a careful study of them, asserts that some of them were drawn by Johann Moritz himself.

The authorship of these drawings, however, is not of so much interest as their antiquity and the fact that they represent a contribution from two other nationalities, the Netherlands and Germany, to the ornithological incunabula of America.

Here is another friendship between pioneer workers in science that suggests the cooperation between John Ray and Francis Willughby. Marcgrave, the disciple and devoted friend of the Prince of Nassau-Siegen, was, like Willughby, cut off in his career at thirty-four. But could he have published his voluminous work, or could he have had such an able editor as Ray, many mistakes in identification which have puzzled scientists for centuries would have been avoided and Marcgrave would thus have become the undisputed authority for many American forms.

[3] *Abhandlungen der Königlichen Akademie der Wissenschaften,* Berlin, 1817: 155 et seqq.

JOHN JOSSELYN (fl. 1675)

When these explorations of Marcgrave were going on in Brazil, England's American colonies were still very young and inexperienced, and the only description of the country coming from them was in the form of travels, with short accounts of the natural history. The amount devoted to birds varied from a few sentences to a few pages, the birds themselves being for many years badly confused with European species. The first writer to attempt a book on the natural history of America was John Josselyn. He was somewhat similar to Thomas Morton in that he was wholly out of sympathy with the Puritan régime and took no part in their busy pious pursuits but devoted himself to reading and to natural history—in his own words "to discover the natural physical and chirurgical rareties of this new found world." He is believed to have come from Kent, the second son of Thomas Josselyn who had a plan of coming to America in 1639 under Sir Fernando Gorge's scheme of colonization. This plan never materialized but John, the son, at the invitation of his brother Henry, then resident at Black Point or Scarborough Manor, came to America on a visit, arriving in Boston July 2, 1638. He remained only about a year returning to England in October 1639.

Twenty-five years later with some financial aid from his kinsman, Samuel Fortrey, Esq. (1622–1681), he came again and this time tarried for eight and a half years on his brother's plantation. His two books, *New England Rarities Discovered* (1672) and *An Account of Two Voyages to New England* (1674) are the first of their kind, being an attempt to make scientific lists of birds, beasts, plants, fish, mollusks, and even the insects of the new continent. We gather that Josselyn wandered about more or less a recluse disinterested in the strong religious atmosphere of the colony, and earnestly trying to add a serious contribution to the world's knowledge of natural history.

From the point of view of plants, the contribution that he made is rather worthy, giving their medicinal values accompanied by ten simple drawings. Indeed, a modern doctor [4] finds in Josselyn's writings the *Genesis of the American Materia Medica* which is the title of a paper he has prepared, together with a short biography of this early writer. From the point of view of birds, however, Josselyn composed such incomplete lists and wove into his account such impossible folk beliefs, that it is in effect little more than amusing. The following are some of the remedies, furnished by birds, to which Josselyn gave credence:

Hawks grease is very good for sore eyes.
Gripes—(Eagles) the bones of their head hung about the neck helpeth the headache.
The egg of an owl put into the liquor that a tospot useth to be drunk with will make him loathe drunkenness ever after.
The Wobble (the great auk) very soveraign for aches.

[4] Felter, 1927: Bull. 26.

The preparation of this remedy involved making a mummy of the bird, then salting well, or burying it underground for a day or two, then stewing it in a tin stewpan with very little water.

As usual with early chroniclers, Josselyn lists the hummingbird, "turkie," and the eagle among the most interesting birds of America—the last described as a "monstrous great Bird, a kind of Hawk, some say an Eagle four times as big as a Goshawk." Troculus, the chimney swift, also received a prominent place in his short list of about a score of birds. The chimney swift, he says, is known to make a "glewy" nest but does not fasten it to the chimney like the swallow, but hangs it by a clew-like string a yard long," and when they depart always throw down one of their young birds into the room by way of "gratitude."

In speaking of turkeys, he needs must include something of their gustatory merits. Says he "Of turkie cocks, several credible persons affirmed that they weighed forty, yea sixty pound." But Josselyn from his own "personal experimental knowledge" had eaten his share "of a turkie cock that when he was pulled and garbidged weighed thirty pound." Even at this early date in the history of American wildlife, he says the English and Indians had killed off vast quantities of wild turkey so that it was very rare to meet with a wild turkey in the woods.

The goose, he maintains, lives to a great age—a belief which still persists—and as proof of this he tells of finding a white goose which was so old she had three hearts, adding she was "so tuff that we gladly gave her over although exceedingly well roasted."

The gripe (bald eagle) and vulture he designates as cowardly kites "feeding upon fish cast upon the shores," and he speaks of a great influx of gripes in 1668 at Casco Bay when there was a great mortality of eels. The gripe's quill feathers, he says, make excellent text pens while their tails are "highly esteemed by the Indians for their arrows as they will not sing in flying," and "The skin of a gripe drest with the down on is good to wear upon the stomach for the pain and coldness of it." The osprey, he says, is white mailed, and their beaks excell for the toothache—"picking the gums therewith until they bleed."

A puzzling bird mentioned by Josselyn is the "wobble" which the author described as "an ill-shaped fowl having no feathers in its pinions which is the reason they cannot fly—not much unlike the penguin." This must connote the great auk, a flightless bird which was found as far south along the coast as Long Island and which became extinct in 1834, owing to the slaughter of the birds and the stealing of their eggs.

Finally, having discussed the owls as numbering three kinds, "the grey, the quite grey, and the white—and the Turkie Buzzard as a kind of kite but as big as a turkie and very good meat," he dispatches the balance of our avifauna thus:

Now by what the country hath not, you may guess at what it hath; it hath no nightingales nor larks nor Bullfinches, no sparrows nor Blackbirds nor magpies nor Jackdaws nor Popinjays nor Rooks nor Pheasants nor Woodcocks nor quails nor Robins nor cuckoos, etc.

Of course, most of these birds are found here, at least many species of sparrows, also blackbirds, and woodcocks, robins, and cuckoos. Equally inept is his statement that porcupines lay eggs, and the dunneck, or hedge-sparrow, is "stark naket" in its winter nest. What this means, when we have no hedge sparrow nor yet any bird which sheds its feathers entirely, is difficult to ferret out, but possibly it has reference to the snow bunting which turns white in the breeding season as a protective measure to make it inconspicuous on its snow-covered nesting ground in the far north.

We find in *Two Voyages* less emphasis upon medicinal values and more emphasis upon the enumeration of the many forms. Many names are unintelligible to the modern reader, but the search for their equivalents in old dictionaries, as used from two to three hundred years ago, gives zest to this antiquarian phase of ornithology.

There are several descriptions of the cruel slaughter of birds by the Indians and early travellers, as for instance the killing of shorebirds (called by Josselyn sanderlins) in the fall, to be cut up and used in place of suet in the Englishers' pudding, and the murderous annihilation of cormorants in their colonies whilst they slept at night.

It may well be said that Josselyn's accounts, naïve, superstitious, and ridiculous as they are, are a useful commentary on the latter half of the seventeenth century and represent the earliest attempt at a scientific treatment of the natural history of New England.

As an indication of the changing estimate put upon these early writings, as our knowledge grew and matured, it is interesting to read what was said of Josselyn by his countrymen a hundred years later. In a letter of Peter Collinson (1694–1768) to John Bartram concerning Josselyn (February 1757) we read:

He must have a fine palate and a good digestion to say a Turkey Buzzard is good meat. The porcupine shooting his quills is a vulgar error. As thou lovest curiosities and novelties, I herewith send thee a book will let thee see the notions of a virtuoso about one hundred years agone.

Out of Josselyn's conglomerate assortment of bird notes, it is possible to garner two interesting observations which may have been original with him; one, that the Troculus (climbing swift) has feathers whose points [5] are sharp, and two, that the females of the birds of prey are larger than the males. He appears to be the first traveller to have made these discerning observa-

tions.[6] Throughout his works, however, we see that he was not an accurate observer, and he was not trained as a naturalist, for such observations as he did make were offered with the unmistakable taint of pedantry. The many absurdities and superstitions that he obviously believed, point vividly to the nascent science of a new country.

When Josselyn made his second trip to America, he was already past middle age and after eight years seemed to be fatigued with his experience and glad to return home as evidenced by these words from his second book:

Now by the merciful Providence of the Almighty, having performed two voyages to the northeast parts of the western world, I am safely arrived in my native country; having in part made good the French proverb "Travel where thou canst but dye where thou oughtest," that is in thine own country.

SOME EARLY ANATOMICAL STUDIES OF BIRDS

The long struggle that Europe had to condition public opinion to human dissection was one of the greatest steps forward in the advancement of science in the sixteenth century. Vesalius (1514–1564) published his epoch-making *De Humani Corporis Fabrica,* in 1543. It was natural, following this milestone in anatomical study, that the schools of anatomy should emphasize the study of mammals.

However, there had been scattered studies of bird anatomy going on already for a hundred years before Vesalius. Leonardo da Vinci (1452–1519), though a sculptor and artist, was intrigued by the flight of birds and studied the mechanics of flying and the anatomy of the bird's wing. Likewise the hyoid bones and the tongue of the woodpecker, and dissections of the muscles of the nictatating membrane in the owl are credited to Leonardo.

We have already considered the comparative studies of the various bird skeletons by Coiter and his embryological studies in the developing chick. Belon's study of the skeletons of man and bird achieved his lasting fame as the founder of comparative anatomy. Dr. F. J. Cole in his recent book on the *History of Comparative Anatomy* (1944) points out some of Belon's errors, but nevertheless Belon seldom erred in his identification of the principal bones of the two skeletons.

To these progressive studies should be added Coiter's recognition of the air sacs in birds; he failed, however, to be the one who recognized their connection with the hollow bones of birds. This actually was seen by Fred-

---

[5] Points. Josselyn has reference to the rachii (central shafts) of the chimney swift's tail feathers, which protrude beyond the barbs (the separate parts of the web of the feather), thus making an efficient tool to assist the bird in clinging to the chimney or other rough surface.

[6] Cotton Mather was much interested in natural history, and published in his *Christian philosopher, a collection of the best discoveries in nature with religious improvements,* 1721, Essay 30, some paragraphs on the "feathered kind"—an outline of the external and internal parts of birds, all with appropriate religious interpretations. He seems to have examined the feather structure for he refers to the "textrine art of the plumage." Feather structure is figured by William Derham in his *Physico-Theology* 1798 (pl. H, fig. 12). The drawing shows not only the rachis and barbs but also the hamuli, or hooklets.

erick II nearly three hundred years earlier and even Aristotle commented on them.

Other studies of bird anatomy were those of Casserius (1552 or 1561–1616). Though he started life as a servant he rose to a professorship at Padua where he advocated comparative studies of the lesser animals in order to increase intelligent understanding of human anatomy.

His main work is his study of the sense organs and voice and in his investigations of the larynx he included dissections of four kinds of birds, the turkey, goose, heron, and cormorant. In spite of his good descriptions he appears not to have recognized the syrinx as the seat of voice in birds. This was first understood and described by Blasius of Amsterdam (*ca.* 1625–1692) in his dissection of the heron in 1674.

To Perrault (1613–1688) we owe further study of the nictatating membrane in birds and also a complete monographic study of the anatomy of the cassowary. This, however, was published posthumously in 1778, Perault having died in 1688.

Another complete dissection of a bird with anatomical text and plates is Dr. Edward Browne's account of the young male ostrich presented to the Royal Society in 1682.

At this date, in England, Nehemiah Grew (1641–1712), the Secretary of the Royal Society, was at work on a study of the stomach and guts, not only of birds, though he dissected forty different kinds, but of animals in general.

Prior to the opening of the British Museum in 1758 all specimens of scientific interest were sent to the Royal Society and when Grew became Secretary of the Royal Society it devolved upon him to prepare a catalogue of these specimens. The combined titles are as follows:

Musaeum Regalis Societates
or a
Catalogue and Description of the
Natural and Artificial Rarities
Belonging to the
Royal Society and preserved at
Gresham Colledge
whereunto is subjoined the comparative anatomy
of
Stomach and Guts
London 1681

After a flowery dedication to the founder of the Museum, he concludes with the hope that others may use the "redundant" part of their estates either to a charitable end or the promotion of "masculine studies," as in the present case.

In his study of the alimentary tract Grew is more interested in mammals than in birds but he dissected out the guts of forty species of birds among which are the following: starling, yellowhammer, bullfinch, wryneck, reed bunting, jackdaw, cuckoo. The difference in length and shape of caeca in birds is figured in some but not explained. Indeed even today it is not clearly un-

derstood except that large caeca go with vegetable feeders while they tend to be small in meat eaters. It is believed also that the gut together with these paired blind sacs at the lower end of it has some taxonomic significance. It is therefore interesting to see that Grew, two hundred and fifty years ago, with his dissections and observations was working toward some such understanding of this part of a bird's anatomy.

All these scattered studies of bird anatomy together with the microscopic dissections of Malpighi mark the seventeenth century as one of good progress, ornithologically speaking. Malpighi did a great deal of work on insects but was in the habit of making vivisections on birds and other animals which, though we may deplore such practices, we must acknowledge as helpful to the understanding of anatomy.

But while all this activity was going on in the schools of Europe it found no echo in America. Only occasionally was someone in the Colonies moved and qualified to conduct some anatomical investigation.

John Clayton (fl. 1671–1694) was one such who was interested in the internal structure of birds. His account is in the form of a letter to the Royal Society and he calls himself, Rector of Crofton.

This Clayton is not to be confused with a younger John Clayton, born in Fulham in 1689 and believed to be his nephew. He also went to Virginia in 1705 and sent his herbarium to Gronovius (1730–1777).

John Clayton, the Rector of Crofton, is known to have come to Virginia prior to 1671, because a manuscript [7] by him on Virginia, in the possession of the Royal Society, is dated 1671. It is not known, however, exactly when he first came, but, from the fact that he left certain drawings of parts of birds in the custody of the Royal Society, we know he had some interest in birds before he left England.

Of these drawings, Clayton says:

Dr. Moulin and myself when we made our anatomies together when I was at London, we shewed to the Royal Society that all flat-billed Birds that groped for their meat has three pair of nerves that came down into their Bills; whereby as we conceived they had that accuracy to distinguish what was proper for Food and what to be rejected by their Taste when they did not see it; and as this was the most evident in a Duck's Bill and Head, I drawed a cut thereof and left it in your custody.

He discovered by anatomical study, also, that Rooks had only "two nerves come down betwixt the eyes and the upper bill, smaller than the three pairs in Duck's bills but larger than the nerves of any of the round-billed birds."

Another anatomical study in which Clayton was interested was the hearing and singing apparatus in birds, for he observed that the song seemed to be modified by the size of the space existing between the two plates of a bird's skull. These were rather difficult studies for

---

[7] Britten, 1909: 297. Apparently the *Dictionary of National Biography* has mixed the two names.

Clayton, a busy clergyman, to be engaged in, and, while they do not bear out the facts as known today, they are interesting for their earnest and scientific point of view.

Clayton intended making a collection of birds in America but, as he says "falling sick of a gripping of the Guts some of them for want of care corrupted; for I was past taking care of them myself there remaining but small hope of my life."

His list of birds, however, though informal and interrupted in many places, is good, showing that he observed critically with close attention to detail. This may be judged by his reference to the long "heel" of the lark; and in referring to the meadowlark he says:

They have another bird which they call a lark which is much larger, as big as a starling; It has a soft note, feeds on the Ground and, as I remember, has the specifical character of a long Heel; it is more inclined to yellow, and has a large half moon on its Breast of yellow; if it have not a long Heel, Querey, whether a species of the yellow hammer?

Clayton apparently had forgotten which one of the larks had the elongated hind-toe nail. This is characteristic of the true larks (Alaudidae) but not of the meadowlarks' family, which is the Troupials (Icteridae).

This was the outstanding list of birds for the decade 1680–1690, but because it was published only in the *Philosophical Transactions* of the Royal Society it never reached the general public.

His casual enumeration of birds, interrupted with personal comments, queries and bits of folk-belief, runs as follows:

Eagles } 3 sorts { Grey Eagle / Bald Eagle / Black Eagle
Fish Hawk
Kingfisher
No Cuckoos
Jay
White and Brown Owl
Scritch Owl (Screech Owl)
Barn Owl
Raven
Carion Crow
No Rooks
Turkey Bustard (Buzzard)
Night Raven (Perhaps the Whip-poor-will?)
No Jackdaws or Magpies

He says the people in America prize the Magpie as much as we do their Redbird.

Great variety of Woodpeckers

He mentions the large blackish-brown one with large crest, and four or five others—the black and white most lovely to behold.

There's a Tradition amongst them that the Tongue of one of these woodpeckers dryed will make the teeth drop out if picked therewith, and cure the toothache (tho' I believe little of it and look on it ridiculous) yet I thought fit to hint as much that others may try; for some such old Stories refer to some peculiar Virtues tho not to all that is said of them.

Perhaps Clayton was not past the credulous stage himself but deftly tried to maintain a safe median attitude.

To continue the list:

Wild Turkies to the weight of 50 to 60 lbs. [Largest one he had seen 38 lbs.] Their feathers are of a blackish shining colour that in the sun shine like a Dove's neck very specious.

The following passage is quite unfathomable but holds such humorous reasoning as to merit quotation.

Hens and Cocks are for the mostpart without Tails and Rumps, and as some have assured me our English Hens after some time being kept there have their Rumps rot off, which I am the apter to believe, being all their Hens are certainly of English breed. I'm sorry I made no anatomical observations thereof; and Remarks about the use of the Rumps in Birds which at present I take to be a couple of Glands containing a sort of juice for the varnishing of the feathers; having observed all Birds have recourse with their Bills to the Rumps when they dress their Plumes whereby they sail through the air more nimbly in their Flight.

Continuing the list:

Partridges
Turtle Doves
Thrush and Feldfare
Mocking Bird

In speaking of the mockingbirds Clayton refers to the grey and red varieties, having in mind probably the true mocker and the brown thrasher. In the redbirds likewise he distinguishes between the crested and smooth-feathered, meaning probably the cardinal (grosbeak) and the summer tanager. In the early days of science it was natural to think that birds of similar external characteristics, such as plumage, were closely related, but as a matter of fact these two birds, though both red, belong to different families.

Other interesting observations on the turkey vulture follow:

There's a great sort of ravenous Bird that feeds upon Carrion, as big very nigh as an Eagle, which they call a Turkey Bustard, its Feathers are of a Duskish black, it has red Gills, resembling those of a Turky, whence it has its name; it is nothing of the same sort of Bird with our English Turky Bustard, but is rather a species of the Kites, for it will hover on the wing something like them, and is carniverous; the Fat thereof dissolved into an Oil, is recommended mightily against old Aches and Sciatica Pains.

The balance of his list he passes over with brief comment, but his remarks, nevertheless, show first-hand information. He tells of a Doctor Bacon making the Martins his favorites and constructing pigeon-holes at the end of his house for them. The swallows and sparrows he groups as "not much different from those in England"; the snowbird he says is like the English hedge-sparrow, but the hummingbirds, the smallest of all birds, he says are sometimes kept alive and fed on water and sugar.

The concluding birds of the list are water species, as follows:

Herons three of four several sorts.
Another [8] that comes only in summer,
Milk white with red legs, very lovely
to behold.
Bittern Curlews, sandpiper snipe and Tewits.[9]
The wild-geese—Brent geese winter in mighty
flocks, Wild-ducks innumerable with Teale
Wigeon, Sheldrakes, Virginia-Didapers,[10] the
Black-diver,[11] etc.

Clayton's chapter on birds closes with an account of skirting along an ice-floe off Newfoundland where numerous small black divers were seen "diving the constantliest and longest of any bird that ever I saw." These were probably dovekies and cormorants; many bannets (gannets) conclude the list.

To sum up Clayton's birds, we find that his list mentions forty-five birds, not including the several sorts which some of the groups include. This is a considerable advance over William Wood's thirty-five kinds, and, with the descriptive matter of a very superior quality, we can see that Clayton, in 1688, was the best bird observer in the colonies.

It would be interesting to know more of Clayton's life. He was evidently a man trained in science as well as in theology, for in his letter accompanying his *Account of Several Observables in Virginia* he speaks of losing all his "Books, Clynical Instruments, Glasses and Microscopes" in a storm at sea. He was discouraged therefore from making "so diligent a scrutiny" as he otherwise would, and, in fact the letter he sent to the Royal Society with profuse apologies for the weakness of his memory was written two years after his sojourn in America.

Clayton came to America in the ship *Judith,* Captain Trim commanding, in the spring of 1686 [12] and he was one to whom the Captain turned for aid when the ship sprang a leak that threatened to sink them. By an ingenious use of a speaking trumpet, the leak was located and successfully stopped. The natural history of the voyage is limited to discussion of wind and currents and descriptions of jelly-fish, which Clayton took to be seaplants, or, according to the ship's crew, carvels. On returning to England they captured a sea turtle called the hawk's bill turtle, and Clayton undertook the dissection of it, for, he said, he found many of these carvels in its guts.

No doubt John Clayton was a man of native ability in scientific investigation, and if he had been able to study

in America with the aid of his books and instruments, a treatise of considerable worth and completeness would have resulted. But even without this fuller account his work is outstanding for its period.

JOHN LAWSON (d. 1712)

With Lawson we enter upon a distinctly superior account of American natural history of which some twenty-four pages are devoted to birds. These are divided into Birds of Carolina, and Waterfowl. Sometimes the description seems better than that of Clayton, his immediate predecessor, but again Lawson succumbs to hearsay and sets down the idle tales of the natives. In fact, Lawson's account is a strange mixture of superstition and yet very accurate personally-acquired information. His writing shows none of Josselyn's pedantry but is modest and simple throughout, showing that the author recognizes his limitations and leaves for future observers the many problems that he cannot explain.

It was more by accident than plan that John Lawson, Gentleman, Surveyor-General of North Carolina, came to be a writer on American natural history. In 1700 he decided to travel and he tells us in the introduction of his book *The History of Carolina* [13] that he chanced to meet a gentleman who assured him from his own experience that Carolina was the best country he could go to. At the very time of this conversation a ship was waiting in the Thames bound for America and Lawson immediately made ready to take it.

This *History* is the account of a thousand miles of travel among the Indians from South to North Carolina. It is mostly a journal about the Indians and their customs, together with the topography of the land, but there are also chapters on the vegetation, the birds, the beasts, and the fish.

The list of birds exceeds anything published by earlier travellers, containing fifty-six land birds beside extra "sorts" under each of several groups and fifty-three water fowl. Both lists are full of quaint names so that the modern student is puzzled to ferret out modern equivalents. This, however, can be done approximately, from the descriptions of the birds given at length in the accompanying text. Thus the herring-tailed hawk is our swallow-tailed kite; the merlin, our pigeon hawk, the green plover our killdeer. It should be remembered, in considering Lawson's lists, that it was made over a century and a half before the concept of geographical distribution had dawned on science—before, indeed, any investigator of animal life had tried to enquire why or how the world's fauna came to be placed as it is. This was the first scientifically worked out by Mr. P. L. Sclater (1829–1913)[14] and the account of his studies is set forth in *The Ibis,* 1891 (pp. 514–557). So it becomes plain why early travellers, being in total ignorance of geographical distribution consistently correlated American forms with European and assumed that the

[8] This is probably the large white ibis.

[9] Tewit is an inclusive term for several kinds of shore-birds. In England it connotes the lapwing, which has a long crest or "Toppin." Clayton notes the American tewits have no "toppins" but are like the young beginning to fly. Hence tewit probably here includes many sandpipers.

[10] Grebes, probably the pied-billed grebes.

[11] May be one of the scoters, or the loon.

[12] The context of Clayton's account indicates that he came to America in 1686 and communicated his letter to the Royal Society in 1688. However his drawings left with the Royal Society indicate that he came before 1671. Possibly he made two trips to America.

[13] Lawson, 1714.

[14] Sclater, 1891: 514–557.

birds and animals of this continent were the same species that they knew in the Old World. Thus Lawson lists the bullfinch, the nightingale, the hedge sparrow, meaning without question the purple finch, the mockingbird and some one of our sparrows, probably the field or chipping sparrow.

The list prefixed with the remark "Birds in America more beautiful than in Europe," contains so many puzzling and bizarre names not traceable to England that some of these should be mentioned, with their connotations, as nearly as these can be ascertained.

Diveling—Swift
Yellow wings—Perhaps the yellow or other warbler
Will Willet—The willet, a large shorebird
Oldwives—A kind of gull or the old squaw
Blue Peters—Probably gallinules or coots
Sandbirds—Small shorebirds, as least and semipalmated sandpipers
Runners—Sandpipers
Black Flusterers—Gulls
Tutcock—Snipe
Swaddle-bills—Possibly scaups (greater and lesser) both of which are ducks with very broad bills
Bullnecks—Probably snow geese

With the exception of some of the gulls, the "Blue Peters" (gallinules) and the pelican, practically the entire list is "good meat," so here we have some explanation of the sore depletion of American bird life in our early history. Even the pelican, which was not eaten, was killed that people might "make tobacco pouches of his maw."

The amount of description given to each bird is very uneven—to some a page or more, depending on the reports he had heard and his own observation; to others just a line or two. Sometimes he showed but mediocre powers of observation and did not notice the difference between our chickadees and the English great tit and blue tit. And he was singularly obtuse about bird song. Says Lawson, "The Throstle, the same size and feather as in Europe but I never could hear any of them sing."

Of wood ducks he says "Ducks pied build on trees. She has a great topping, is pied and very beautiful. She builds her nest in a woodpecker's hole, very often sixty or seventy feet high."

Of turkeys he has a page or more with this interesting bit of Indian lore: "I have been informed that if you take these wild eggs [of the turkeys] when just on the point of hatching and dip them (for some small time) in a bowl of milk-warm water, it will take off their wild nature and make them as tame and domestic as the others."

Of mergansers (called by Lawson Fishermen) he says: "Fishermen are like a duck but have a narrow bill with sets of teeth.[15] To cure these Fishermen they should have the oil box (oil gland) pulled from the rump and they should be buried five or six hours under ground. Then they become tolerable."

---

[15] Tooth-like projections on the edges of the mandibles, but not true teeth.

On a few of the birds, however, Lawson makes careful descriptive observation. Of the lark, for instance, he says:

The Lark with us resorts to the savannas or natural meads, and green marshes. He is colored and heeled as the lark is, but the breast is of a glittering fair lemon color and he is as big as a field fare,—

Unfortunately he adds the usual mundane appraisement, "and very fine food."

Lawson's observations in the main may be said to set a new standard for he made specific differentiation regarding nearly every species he mentioned, and the fact that his book passed through three English and two German editions between 1709 and 1722 gave both popularity and publicity to his list of birds. Though he erred frequently in the matter of comparative size and showed consistently but a poor appreciation of bird song, even failing to notice the vociferous wrens' songs and scolding notes, he succeeded in choosing characteristic markings to record. Furthermore, it is not unlikely that his frequent introduction of Indian lore, indicating a mild belief in it himself, may have added to the interest of his book when it was published. The most conspicuous error of his book is in regard to the bat which Lawson assumed to be part bird and part mouse, and he states the efficacy of the bat as follows:

The Indian children are much addicted to eat dirt and so are some of the Christians but roast a bat on a skewer then pull the skin off and make the child that eats dirt eat the roasted rearmouse and he will never eat dirt again. This is held as an infallible remedie. I have put this amongst the beasts as partaking of two natures of the bird and mouse kind.

Lawson's list of mammals is small—only twenty-seven in number—but like Francis Higginson he repudiated the presence of lions in America, in spite of persistent rumors about them, and said he never saw any, nor could he imagine how they would come there.

John Lawson was a native of Scotland and, according to his own account, spent eight years in Carolina, coming over as a young man, to Charleston in September 1700. After several months in Charleston, of which he gives an attractive and appreciative criticism in his book, he left on his explorations accompanied by five Englishmen, four Indians and one Indian woman, the wife of a guide. They went first by canoe to the Santee River and then started inland on foot. His account seems to show that he enjoyed the writer's craft for he faithfully set down his impressions wherever he happened to be and thus accumulated a lively and rather literary account of his travels. After he was made Surveyor General of North Carolina, he became well-known but not liked by the Indians who resented his visits which it seemed to them always resulted in greater and greater encroachments upon Indian rights and land by the English.

Whether Lawson returned for a time to England or not, is not known, but it is recorded that in 1712, four years after his eight years were up, while on a trip with

Baron die Graffenried, a Swiss, the two men were seized by a group of Tuscarora Indians. The Swiss, for some reason, was released upon ransom but Lawson was murdered, either by burning—probably by the grewsome method described in his own book of having the victim's body stuck with resinous pine sticks and set alight, or else his throat was cut. This occurred on the banks of the river Neuse in western North Carolina, the last fragment of the meager facts that are known concerning this real pioneer in ornithology.[16]

JOHN BRICKELL

Nearly thirty years passed by, with one volume of Catesby's work intervening in 1731 before John Brickell brought out in Dublin his *Natural History of North Carolina* (1737). For some reason he is supposed to have based his descriptions, even to the point of plagiarism, upon John Lawson's work of 1709. But on examining the two books, it is obvious that Lawson's work, being written more from the naturalist's point of view is better, although he, as well as Brickell, includes a considerable admixture of Indian lore.

Brickell apparently used Lawson as a suggestive guide but endeavored to improve and enlarge what Lawson had to say with the result that his work in many parts becomes unreliable, and contains less careful observation and much more emphasis on the Indian beliefs in the medicinal properties of birds. Professor Stephen B. Weeks in the introduction staunchly defends Brickell's work calling attention to the greater bulk of his writing and its significant scientific value as evidenced by the author's frequent reference to birds as the physician's stock in trade. This, however, must be largely discounted for even in Brickell's day the intelligent were becoming less credulous. Brickell was a physician and his chief interest in birds seems to have been their strange potency (as he thought) for man's physical ills. From the ornithologist's point of view, however, we must throw into the discard the efficacy of distilled buzzard's feet for sciatica, the crane's gall for palsy, consumptions, blindness, and deafness, the bittern's bill ground to a powder for sleep, and, most amazing of all . . . "the dung of the 'goss hawk' which being drank while fasting in wine, will cause conception."

Brickell's statement that the Eagle breeds constantly, using its downy young as incubators for additional settings of eggs must also be taken as pure imagination. His impression of the cuckoo, that it sucks small birds' eggs, that it hides in hollow trees in winter, loses its feathers and becomes scabby is equally credulous, while his assertion that its ashes will cure epilepsy and its dung given in canary will cure the bite of a mad dog,

---

[16] A monument to John Lawson has been erected in Goldsboro, North Carolina, near the scene of his execution on the Neuse River in Craven County. This was accomplished through the efforts of the Society of Colonial Dames. See Sprunt, 1916: 584 and note 2.

exceeds even Josselyn of fifty years earlier for chirurgical hallucination.

As an offset to these hyperbolic and pseudoscientific remedies, Brickell writes very creditably of many species; of the sparrow hawk and its insect diet, of the beneficial owls, of the parakeetoes (Carolina paroquets), the turkey and several others. In his account of the turkey Brickell quotes Lawson verbatim, without crediting him for his view, on hatching turkey eggs. Likewise his account of the lark is very reminiscent of Lawson. His remarks on the hummingbird are among his best bird observations and this is one of the few species whose medicinal virtues he does not claim to know.

John Brickell lived for many years at Edenton, North Carolina, practicing as a physician. He had come over with George Burrington, who became governor, and like Lawson twenty years before in the eastern section, Brickell was helpful to the governor in conciliating the Indians on the western border. Thus Brickell, as well as Lawson, gathered a fund of knowledge about the Indians, their customs, their husbandry, and an elementary knowledge of the plant and animal life of the region.

Brickell came from Ireland, and compared American plants and animals with those of his home country. His book, as published in 1737, contains some crude plates of the beasts, birds, and fish of North Carolina, but the source of these and their artist are not mentioned. The following birds are pictured: wild turkey, red bird, East India bat (intended for nighthawk but a poor likeness), pelican, turtle dove, woodpecker, mockingbird, a jay, killdeer, hummingbird, cormorant, shag.

V·III. MARK CATESBY, FOUNDER OF AMERICAN ORNITHOLOGY

Now embarked upon the full tide of the new century, we find that many changes and events which tended to augment and disseminate the general body of natural history lore had taken place.

Emigration to New England had somewhat abated, but many thousands of Dutch and Germans were coming over to settle in parts of New York and Pennsylvania, while a Swedish element was attempting to establish a new home in Delaware. Naturally, we cannot expect anything comparable to the scientific work of Europe in those busy and unsettled years. The most that came out of such transplantings, that had any bearing on natural history, was an occasional chronicle of the new region describing the Indians, the condition of the soil, the commodities that might be raised and a brief listing of birds, animals, and plants. We have already seen several such accounts.

Nevertheless a hundred years had passed since the first English settlements, and the century had brought many improvements. Instead of a few hazardous ventures across the sea, several regular crossings were made between England and America each month, and new colonists, visitors, travellers, and exploiters were contin-

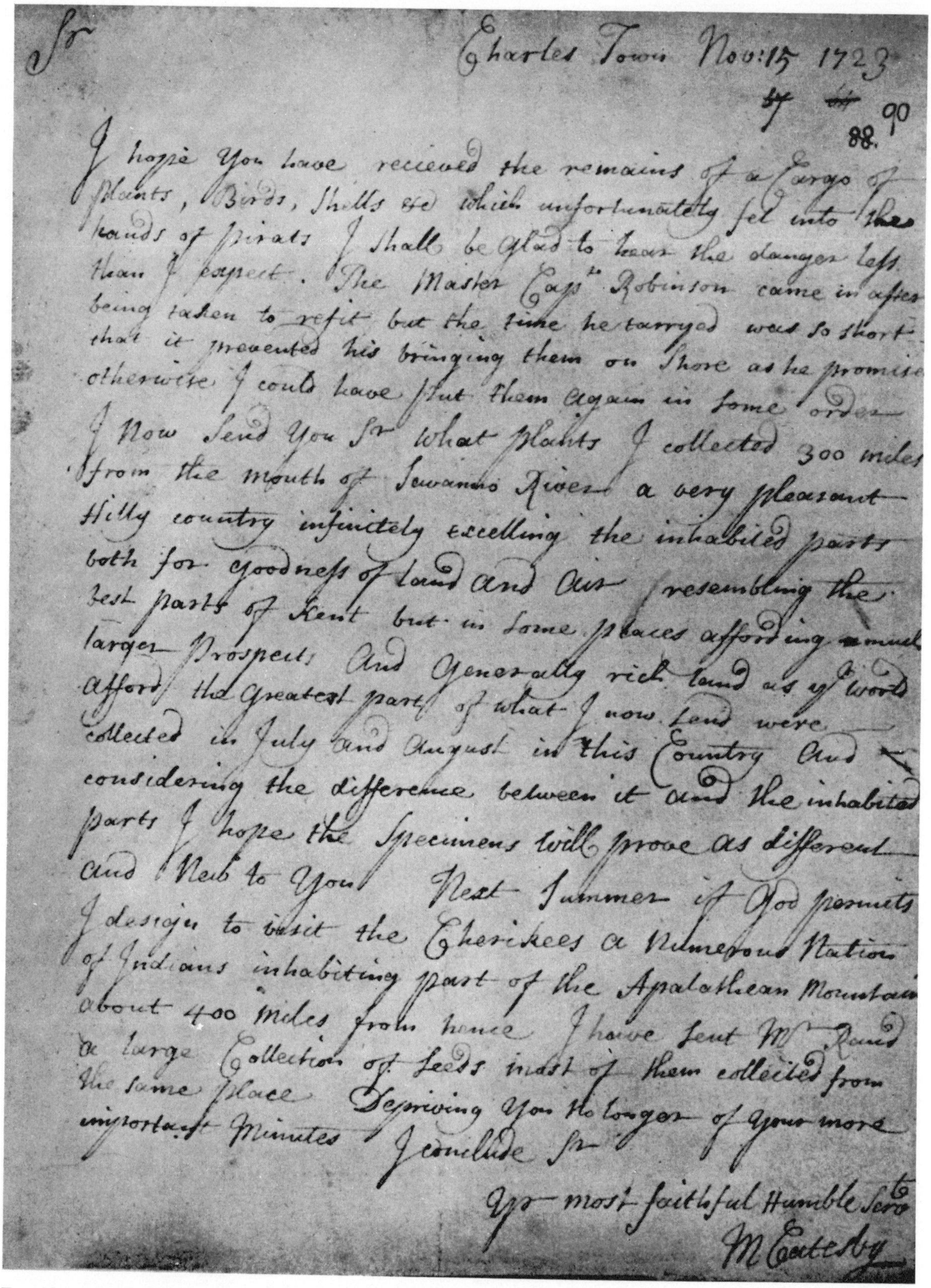

Sr

Charles Town Nov:15 1723

~~87~~ ~~88~~ 88. 90

I hope You have recieved the remains of a Cargo of
plants, Birds, Shells &c which unfortunately fel into the
hands of pirats I shall be glad to hear the danger less
than I expect. The Master Captn Robinson came in after
being taken to refit but the time he tarryed was so short
that it prevented his bringing them on Shore as he promised
otherwise I could have put them again in some order
I Now Send You Sr What plants I collected 300 miles
from the mouth of Savanna River a very pleasant
Hilly country infinitely excelling the inhabited parts
both for goodness of land and Air resembling the
best parts of Kent but in some places affording much
larger prospects and generally rich land as ye woods
afford the greatest part of what I now send were
collected in July and August in this Country and
considering the difference between it and the inhabited
parts I hope the Specimens will prove as different
and New to You Next Summer if God permits
I design to visit the Cherikees a Numerous Nation
of Indians inhabiting part of the Apalathean Mountains
about 400 miles from hence I have sent Mr Rand
a large Collection of seeds most of them collected from
the same place Depriving You no longer of Your more
important Minutes I conclude Sr

Yr most faithful Humble Servt

M Catesby

FIG. 22. A letter from Mark Catesby in America to Sir Hans Sloane in London in 1723. Courtesy of the Trustees of the British Museum.

ually coming and going. The marvel-seeking and credulous tales about the New World were fast being superseded by accurate accounts, many of which were followed up and corroborated by actual specimens sent abroad.

This was true mostly of plants and trees for natural science in England and Europe was still under the influence of that great botanist John Ray. Botany, in fact, enjoyed a long period of ascendancy over the other sciences during the eighteenth century a factor which brought great progress in the two sister sciences of surgery and materia medica. The study of animals, on the other hand, was largely undeveloped and was engaged in only secondarily by a few of the botanical collectors.

Such was the naturalist Mark Catesby (1682–1749?), who came to America first probably as a gentleman of leisure, but who remained nearly seven years and became so engrossed in the study of American natural history that he returned to the Colonies a second time, and eventually produced a sumptuous two-volume work, the *Natural History of Carolina, Florida and the Bahama Islands* (1731–1743). This was published in sections between 1731 and 1743, and the quality of the work was so superior to foregoing accounts that Mark Catesby ranks as the first real naturalist in America.

Catesby was sent here as a botanical collector but through the most intense concentration and despite frequent illness, he successfully completed over one hundred plates of American birds.

Each species is associated with the characteristic vegetation of its environment or some plant or fruit on which it feeds, a plan inaugurated by him and further emulated by Wilson and Audubon.

It is difficult in this day of attractive and accurate zoological illustration to appreciate the almost epochal importance of Catesby's zoological and botanical work in his own time. To the modern reader, most of the engravings appear quaint but we should remember that in his time American science was quite undeveloped.

In the original printing of Catesby's *Natural History* the birds are confined to the first volume, which contains 109 plates, and the text concerning each species is on the opposite page in parallel columns of English and French. The translator, Catesby does not reveal, for he was "too modest" to have his identity made known.

Catesby's list of birds is as follows: (The 71 starred plates were used by Linnaeus as the basis of his descriptions. Spellings and capitals on Catesby's plates differ in many cases from those in the descriptions of the same birds in his text. Hence it seems advisable to use Catesby's names as published by the American Ornithologists' Union in the Check-List of North American Birds, 4th ed., 1931, Lancaster, Pa. Parenthetical identifications are the modern correct common names.)

Catesby, *The Natural History of Carolina, Florida and the Bahama Islands*

MDCCXXXI

Vol. 1

*T1. The Bald Eagle, Aquila capite albo (southern bald eagle)

*T2. The Fishing Hawk, Accipiter piscatorius (osprey)

*T3. The Pigeon Hawk, Accipiter palumbarius (eastern pigeon hawk)

*T4. The Swallow Tail Hawk, Accipiter cauda furcata (swallow-tailed kite)

*T5. The Little Hawk, Accipiter minor (eastern sparrow hawk)

T6. The Turkey Buzzard, Buteo, specie Gallo-Pavonis

*T7. The Little Owl, Noctua aurita minor (southern screech owl)

*T8. The Whip-poor Will (eastern night-hawk imm.)

*T9. The Cuckoo of Carolina, Cuculus carolinensis (yellow-billed cuckoo)

T10. The Parrot of Paradise of Cuba, Psitticus Paradisis

*T11. The Parrot of Carolina, Psitticus carolinensis (Carolina paroquet)

*T12. The Purple Jack-Daw, Monedula purpurea (purple grackle)

*T13. The Red-wing'd Starling, Sturnus niger, alis superne rubentibus (eastern red-wing)

*T14. The Rice-bird, Hortulanus carolinensis (bobolink)

*T15. The Blew Jay, Pica glandaria caerulea cristata (northern blue jay)

*T16. Largest White-bill Woodpecker, Picus maximus rostro albo (ivory-billed woodpecker)

*T17. Larger red-crested Woodpecker, Picus niger maximus capite rubro (southern pileated woodpecker)

*T18. The Golden-winged Woodpecker, Picus major, alis aureis (southern flicker)

*T19. The red-bellied Woodpecker, Picus ventre rubro

*T19. The hairy Woodpecker, Picus medius quasi villosus (eastern hairy woodpecker)

*T20. The Red-headed Woodpecker, Picus capite toto rubro

*T21. The Yellow belly'd Woodpecker, Picus varius minor, ventro luteo (yellow-bellied sapsucker)

*T21. The smallest Spotted Woodpecker, Picus varius minimus (southern downy woodpecker)

FIG. 23. "The Pigeon of Passage, Palumbus migratorius." Plate number 23 of Catesby's great work, The *Natural History of Carolina, Florida and the Bahama Islands* (1731–1743). Courtesy of the Cornell University Library.

T22. The Nuthatch, Sitta capite nigro (white-breasted nuthatch)

T22. The Small Nuthatch, Sitta capite fusco (brown-headed nuthatch)

*T23. The Pigeon of Passage, Palumbus migratorius (passenger pigeon)

*T24. The Turtle of Carolina, Turtur carolinensis (eastern mourning dove)

*T25. The White-crown'd Pigeon, Columba capito albo (white-crowned pigeon)

*T26. The Ground Dove, Turtur minimus guttatus (eastern ground dove)

*T27. The Mock-Bird, Turdus minor cinereo-albus non-maculatus (eastern mockingbird)

*T28. The Fox-coloured thrush, Turdus ruffus (brown thrasher)

*T29. The Fieldfare of Carolina, Turdus pilaris, migratorius (eastern robin figured dead; lying on back on stump)

T30. The red-legged Thrush, Turdus viscivorous plumbeus (from Andros and Ilathera)

T31. The Little Thrush, Turdus minimus (perhaps hermit thrush, but "abides all the year in Carolina")

*T32. The Lark, Alauda gutture flavo (northern horned lark)

*T33. The large Lark, Alauda magna (eastern meadowlark)

*T34. The Towhe-bird, Passer niger oculis rubris (red-eyed towhee)

T34. The Cow-pen bird, Passer fusca (female cowbird)

T35. The Little Sparrow, species uncertain.

*T36. The Snow-bird, Passer nivalis (slate-colored junco)

*T37. The Bahama Sparrow, Passer bicolor bahamensis (Bahama grassquit)

*T38. The Red-Bird, Coccothraustes ruber (eastern cardinal)

*T39. The blew Gross-beak, Coccothraustes caerulea (eastern blue grosbeak)

T40. The Purple Gros-beak, Coccothraustes purpurea (Bahaman grosbeak)

*T41. The Purple Finch, Fringilla purpurea (eastern purple finch)

T42. The Bahama Finch, Fringilla bahamiensis

*T43. The American Goldfinch, Carduelis americanus (eastern goldfinch)

*T44. The Painted Finch, Fringilla tricolor (painted bunting)

*T45. The Blew Linnet, Linaria caerulea (indigo bunting)

T46. The Chatterer, Garrulus Carolinensis (cedar waxwing)

*T47. The Blew Bird, Rubicula americana caerulea (eastern bluebird)

*T48. The Baltimore-Bird, Icterus exaureo nigroque varius (Baltimore oriole)

*T49. The Bastard Baltimore, Icterus minor (male and female orchard oriole)

*T50. The yellow brested Chat, Oenanthe americana, pectore luteo (yellow-breasted chat)

T51. The Purple Martin, Hirundo purpurea

*T52. The Crested Fly-catcher, Muscicapa cristata, ventre luteo (southern crested flycatcher)

T53. The Blackcap Flycatcher, Muscicapa nigricans (phoebe)

T54. The Little brown Flycatcher, Muscicapa fusca (perhaps least flycatcher)

*T54. The Red ey'd Fly-catcher, Muscicapa oculis rubris (red-eyed vireo)

*T55. The Tyrant, Muscicapa corona rubra (eastern kingbird)

*T56. The Summer Red-Bird, Muscicapa rubra (summer tanager)

*T57. The Crested Titmouse, Parus cristatus (tufted titmouse)

T58. The Yellow-rump, Parus uropygeo luteo—figured dead hung by spider web (probably myrtle warbler)

T59. The Bahama Titmous, Parus bahamensis (Bahama honey creeper)

T60. The Hooded Titmous, Parus cucullo nigro (hooded warbler)

T61. The Pine-creeper, Parus etc. (probably pine warbler)

T62. The Yellow-throated Creeper, Parus etc. (yellow-throated warbler)

T63. The Yellow Titmous, Parus luteus (yellow warbler)

*T64. The Finch-Creeper, Parus fringillaris (This is probably the parula warbler)

*T65. The Hummingbird, Mellivora avis carolinensis (ruby-throated hummingbird)

*T66. The Cat Bird, Muscicapa vertice nigro (catbird)

*T67. The Red-start, Ruticilla americana (American redstart)

T68. The little black Bulfinch, Rubricilla minor nigra (Mexico)

*T69. The Kingfisher, Ispida (eastern belted kingfisher)

T70. The Soree, Gallinula americana (sora)

*T71. The Chattering Plover, Pluvialis vociferus (killdeer)

*T72. The Turn-Stone, Morinellus marinus (winter plumage, ruddy turnstone)

*T73. The Flamingo, Phoenicopterus bahamensis (flamingo)

T74. Caput Phoenicopteri (head of flamingo)

*T75. The Hooping Crane, Grus americana alba (head only, whooping crane)

*T76. The Blew Heron, Ardea caerulea (little blue heron)

T77. The little white Heron, Ardea alba (probably immature little blue heron)

T78. The brown Bittern, Ardea Stellaris (resembles more an immature night heron)

*T79. The Crested Bittern, Ardea stellaris cristata americana (yellow-crowned night heron, labelled "Ardea" on plate)

*T80. The small Bittern, Ardea stellaris minima (eastern green heron)

T81. The Wood Pelican, Pelicanus sylvaticus (wood ibis)

*T82. The White Curlew, Numenius albus (white ibis)

T83. The Brown Curlew, Numenius etc. (immature white ibis)

*T84. The Red Curlew, Numenius ruber (scarlet ibis)

T85. The Oyster Catcher, Haematopus (American oyster-catcher)

T86. The Great Booby, Anseri Bassano etc. (immature gannet, head only)

T87. The Booby, Anseri Bassano affinis fusca avis (white-bellied booby)

*T88. (The Noddy), Hirundo marina minor capite albo (noddy tern)

*T89. The Laughing Gull, Larus major (laughing gull)

*T90. The Cut Water, Larus major Rostro inequali (black skimmer)

*T91. The Pie-Bill Dapchick, Podiceps minor, rostro vario (pied-billed grebe)

*T92. The Canadá Goose, Anser canadensis (head, common Canada goose)

*T93. The Ilathera Duck, Anas bahamensis rostro plumbeo, macula Aurantii coloris (Bahama pintail)

*T94. The Round-crested Duck, *Anas cristatus* (hooded merganser)
T95. The Buffel's Head Duck, *Anas* etc. (buffle-head)
T96. The Blue-wing Shoveler, *Anas* (shoveller, male in eclipse plumage)
*T97. The Summer Duck, *Anas americana* (wood duck)
T98. The Little brown Duck, *Anas minor* (female buffle-head)
T99. The Blue-wing Teal, *Querquedula americana variegata* (female or eclipse, blue-winged teal)
*T100. The White face Teal, *Querquedula americana variegata* (male blue-winged teal)

Nine other birds are illustrated in the Appendix of Volume II; three of these, the heath hen, *Urogallus minor, fuscus cervice, plumis Alas imitantibus donata*; the bob-white, *Perdix sylvestris americana*; and the chimney swift, *Hirundo cauda aculeata americana*, were used as bases of Linnean species.

Although today the birds of the eastern United States number some four hundred species and Catesby figured only one hundred nine, which he deemed were practically all, it is remarkable that in the time he could spare from his collecting assignment he could study even this number and make such faithful recordings of their plumages and habits. Certain groups, such as the birds of prey and the woodpeckers, he treats rather fully, but others, such as the warblers, thrushes and sparrows, are very incomplete and confused with other groups. It is obvious that he could not go in search of birds but took them mostly as they crossed his path while he was collecting plants for his patrons in England.

The list is notable much more for its quality than its length: measurements, weights, coloration, habitat, and feeding habits to some extent, all figure in Catesby's accounts. He had a zeal for direct and absolute knowledge and a keen desire to convey it accurately to his readers. Of the goatsucker of Carolina, our nighthawk, he said their call was a "screek," and he believed that the "booming" of the nighthawks was produced by their flying with their mouths open, "precipitating and swiftly mounting again to recover themselves." Thus he thought they made "a hollow and surprising noise." Although, as in this case, Catesby was often not correct (for the booming is made by the currents of air passing between the nighthawk's stiffened primaries [1]), he was far ahead in scientific attitude. He even investigated the contents of the nighthawk's stomach and found it to be quantities of "scarabei and other insects."

The plates themselves display varying merit. One is impressed with the excellent and life-like postures of the woodpeckers, but one is disappointed with the stilted characterization of the mocker, the thrasher, the catbird, the cardinal and the meadowlark. However, practically all are recognizable. One can detect in some instances the artist's lack of familiarity with certain birds. To Catesby, nevertheless, belongs praise for actual field ob-

servation of the birds and the careful notations on feet, bills, and plumage made after the birds were collected. His fragments of Indian lore, also, are interesting. Catesby has been criticized for depicting the dead robin, called by him the "fieldfare" of Carolina, but in reality, this is one of his best plates, showing good draughtsmanship and accurate coloring of the plumage. In some cases the postures are inaccurate and, again, in the feather detail he does not understand the tricks of the good artist. For example, in his drawing of the pileated woodpecker, the crest of this species is shown in the form of long, curly feathers.

There are no birds in Volume II of the set in the Cornell University Library, but, according to Coues' Bibliography, Volume II, published in 1743, contained 200 plates, although Coues does not state how many are birds. According to Casey Wood, copies of the various printings of this work are fairly common, but complete sets containing all the plates are rare. I may say that in London I examined the British Museum copy and found in Volume II a few bird plates, but such as were there seemed to be an after-thought, being included at the end of the volume in an appendix. The birds of Volume II in the British Museum set are as follows:

1. Prairie chicken. Catesby made this drawing from specimens of this bird held by the Earl of Wilmington, in Chiswick.
2. Razor-billed blackbird of Jamaica (ani) pictured with a good drawing of our pink lady-slipper or moccasin flower (*Cipripedium acaule*). This bird is not found in the southern United States, except as an accidental visitor.
3. The American swallow—our chimney swift—pictured sitting on its nest in a chimney.
4. Head of the largeste crested heron—probably the great blue heron.
5. The American partridge—our bob-white.
6. The golden-crowned kinglet called by Catesby *Regulus cristatus*. Catesby describes accurately its association with creepers, titmice and nuthatches, but the drawing is awkward.
7. Whip-poor-will. This is one of Catesby's poorest plates showing a long-tailed large-footed bird of yellowish brown color with peculiar hair-like bristles around the bill. The bird, probably dead, was sent to him by a Mr. Clayton, of Virginia, and this may account for the poor likeness.

One hundred and nine is the total of Catesby's bird plates in the two volumes of his *Natural History*. He pronounced them "all the birds I have ever seen or could discover between the 30th and 45th degrees of latitude."

We know from Catesby's Introduction that he had long been interested in natural history and went to London young in life in order to be near men of similar interests. When he came to America he was already familiar with the birds of England; and, in naming American birds, he used the generic name of some similar European group and added a distinguishing epithet or phrase to fit the American specimen.

It should be remembered that this was before scien-

---

[1] Primaries—the outermost wing feathers.

tific nomenclature had been systematized, before the Swedish botanist, Linnaeus (1707–1778), had completed his revolutionizing system of binomials for all botanical and zoological forms. In fact, Catesby's work was coming out over the exact period of years when Linnaeus was engrossed in his *Systema Naturae*. Linnaeus had no first-hand knowledge of American birds; consequently in applying his system of binomial nomenclature to American species, he used the new work of Mark Catesby as a basis, often selecting one of Catesby's polynomials. Thus it has come about that, although Catesby was the real pioneer in American ornithology, there is little to remind us of his earnest labor in the books.

In spite of this obvious indebtedness of Linnaeus to Catesby there are very few mentions of Linnaeus in Catesby's letters and there are so far as I know only two letters [2] extant from Catesby to Linnaeus. This further strengthens the impression of diffidence and self-effacement which the study of his work creates. In fact it is probable that Catesby's friends and patrons took care of most of his dealings with the world-renowned botanist.

In a letter of Peter Collinson (1694–1768), an intimate friend of Catesby, to Linnaeus, we gather that Linnaeus was adding Catesby's *Natural History* to his own library. The letter is dated May 8, 1749 and runs in part as follows:

> I am glad to hear by yours of Oct. 30 that Mr. Catesby's nobile and elegant work is like to grace your Library. Our ingenius friend, Mr. Catesby died the 23 December last aged 70, much lamented. His widow to encourage the sale of his work abates half a guinea on every book, so eleven books at a guinea and a half come to £ 17. 6s. 6d.

Practically all references to Catesby and his work contain high terms of praise for the man and his contribution to science. It was therefore a shock to encounter the following caustic criticism by Alexander Garden (1730–1791) of Charleston who collected fish for Linnaeus. The letter is dated April 12, 1761 twelve years after Catesby's reported death but Catesby's work was still considered in good standing as we may judge by the fact that two editions of it came out subsequently to this date. Garden in collecting fish apparently consulted the *Ichthyology* of Artedi (1705–1735), as well as the tenth edition of Linnaeus' *Systema Naturae* (1758), and finally Catesby of whom he writes in the following scathing words:

> I have also consulted Catesby as it seemed proper to do so but never without disgust and indignation. I cannot endure to see the perfect works of the most High so miserably tortured and mutilated and so vilely represented. His whole work but especially his second volume is so imperfect and so grossly faulty that to correct its errors and supply its deficiencies would be no less laborious than it is necessary.

This brutal criticism need not concern us for this is the only derogatory remark on Catesby and his work

[2] Library of Congress, Department of Manuscripts and Linnean Society of London.

that has been found—all others attesting his conscientious effort, and his pioneering ability both in botany and zoology.

It is interesting to read in his letters of the difficulties encountered in preserving his specimens; of plants he writes in a letter from Charles city [*sic*] dated May 10, 1723:

> Its hardly credible the long time plants take in cureing in this moyst country I have frequently had them moldy and spoiled by omitting Shifting the next day after gathering, one with another. Less than a fortnight does not cure them and for the first week they require shifting every day.[3]

We may surmise that the troubles incident to curing bird-skins were equally great, for at that time the removal of the bodies was unknown, the viscera only being taken out, and the bird was then stretched out, salted, and sometimes wired in a poor attempt to reconstruct the life-like form.

For shipping Catesby advised: "Birds are best preserved (if not too large) by drying them gradually in an oven; and when sent, cover them in tobacco dust."

As for the large snakes and fish which he collected, he was often in dire straits, for he said: "There is no other way in preserving fish, and reptiles, than in spirits or rum, which method will also due for birds." But he often lacked the large bottles and spirits in which to ship them.

Catesby, however, was not a demanding nor a complaining field man. One must search to find any reference in his letters to the practical difficulties of collecting in those times, although these must often have been almost insurmountable.

FAMILY, PARENTAGE, AND BIRTH

According to C. W. Bardsley's *Dictionary of English and Welsh Surnames* (1901), the Catesby family is from the fertile inland county of Northampton, and all the Catesbys in the *Dictionary of National Biography* may ultimately be traced to this interior section of England and probably had their name originally from the Parish of Catesby four miles from Daventry.

On his mother's side Mark Catesby was a direct descendant of Thomas Jekyll (1570–1653), an antiquary and historian of the Counties of Essex, Norfolk, and Suffolk. There were two rather distinguished sons of this Thomas Jekyll: Thomas Jekyll (1648–1698), a divine, and Sir Joseph Jekyll (1663–1738), Master of the Rolls, knighted in 1700 and a member of the Privy Council, who left part of his private fortune to relieve the national debt. A third son of Thomas Jekyll was Nicholas Jekyll, apparently not known in public life. Nicholas Jekyll was the grandfather of Mark Catesby, and the father of Catesby's mother, Elizabeth Jekyll. On his father's side also Catesby was of the blood of lawyers; for his father, John Catesby, was a magistrate of the town of Sudbury in Suffolk and several times its mayor—and a very spirited gentleman and politician he

[3] Darlington, 1849: 323.

FIG. 24. Sheepcotes, Castle Hedingham, England. The probable birthplace of Mark Catesby. Courtesy of Mrs. C. F. D. Sperling.

was. He owned considerable property in London in the neighborhood of Fleet Street, as well as several farms, dwellings, and other holdings in Suffolk, some of which he left to his son Mark.

The marriage of Mark Catesby's parents took place May 16, 1670, and is recorded in Foster's *London Marriage Licenses, 1524–1869:* "John Catesby, gentleman, about 28, bachelor, and Elizabeth Jekyll of Castle Hedingham, spinster, 18, her father consents, at St. Andrews, Holborn, or Gray's Inn, or Charter House Chapel, London." There were numerous offspring of this marriage: twin sons recorded in the *Registers of St. Gregory's Church,* Sudbury, 12th September, 1675; Elizabeth Catesby who, against her father's wishes, married Dr. William Cocke of Virginia; Jekyll Catesby; John Catesby; and Ann and Mark Catesby. The exact order in which these children were born I have not yet worked out, but Mark and Ann were both of the decade 1680–1690.

The date and place of Mark Catesby's birth are entered variously and with question marks, as probably Sudbury or London in 1679 or 1680. A search of the parish registers of Sudbury failed to reveal Mark's birth, but yielded that of his sister, Ann, in 1688. However, knowing that his mother was from the village of Castle Hedingham, about eight miles from Sudbury in Essex, just over the little bordering river Stour, I took occasion to examine the registers of the old Norman church of Saint Nicholas, and was glad to find Mark Catesby's birth and baptism [4] there entered in fairly legible form, as follows: "Mark Catesby, son of John Catesby, gent and Elizabeth, his wife, Baptize—March 30, 1683,

Nates March 24th, 1682." He was thus a year old at baptism.

In all probability Mark was born in the village of Castle Hedingham in the house which, it is likely, was built and occupied by his grandfather, Nicholas Jekyll. This house is still standing—a picturesque seventeenth century type—at the south end of the village. It has been said that the Jekyll family owned and operated the old castle [5] now in ruins which stands on a hill overlooking this village and known as Hedingham Castle. But this erroneous statement has doubtless grown out of the confusion existing in the use of the names Castle Hedingham and Hedingham Castle indiscriminately for both the castle and the village. I am indebted further to the late Mr. Sperling for an explanation of this matter. He pointed out to me also the epitaph which formerly stood over the grave of Mark Catesby's maternal grandmother in the church of Castle Hedingham, and also the old Jekyll home known as "Sheepcotes," in the village.

We know from the entry in the *Parish Register of Saint Nicholas* that Catesby was three years younger than his reported age at death, the date of which has been published as December 23, 1749. In Lewis H. Jones's *Captain Roger Jones of London and Virginia,* Albany, 1891, there is a notice purporting to be an excerpt from a London newspaper, as follows:

On Saturday, December 23, 1749, died at his home behind St. Luke's church in Old Street, the truly honest and ingenious and modest Mr. Mark Catesby. . . . He lived to the age of 70 [his proved date of birth makes him only 67 at death], well known to and esteemed by the curious of this and other nations, and died much lamented by his Friends, leaving behind him two children and a widow who has a few copies of his noble work undisposed of.

Also, in the *Gentleman's Magazine* (vol. 19, p. 573) there is a list of deaths for the year 1749, and we read: "Mr. Mark Catesby, F.R.S., aged 70, author of the Natural History of Carolina, a large and curious work which is the chief support of his widow and two children."

Regarding Catesby's education it is difficult to learn anything, but it is probable that he attended the old Grammar School of Sudbury founded in 1491 by William Wood. However, upon going there to consult the files, I was informed that all the records previous to 1837 had been burned.

Catesby is said to have gone early in life to London, because of his interest in natural history, and in the preface to his *Natural History* he regretfully refers to his distant residence from London, the natural Mecca of the learned.

MARK CATESBY'S PLACES OF RESIDENCE IN LONDON

Catesby lived in three different parts of London proper: Fulham, Hoxton, and Old Street in St. Luke's

---

[4] I wish to express my appreciation to Mrs. C. F. D. Sperling for making this possible. Mr. Sperling, recently deceased having legal business in Castle Hedingham, invited me to accompany him and Mrs. Sperling by car. With the assistance of Mr. Heifer, the vicar then of St. Nicholas Church, Mark Catesby's birth and baptism entries were first found in 1935. These were verified in 1948 and a copy of the records obtained from the present vicar, the Rev. W. R. H. Cozens.

[5] Jones, 1891.

Parish in Middlesex.   No letters that have yet come to light were written in Fulham, but in "Britten & Boulger, *British, and Irish Botanists* (1931)," he is said to be "of Hoxton and Fulham."   We know from a letter of Mark Catesby to his niece, Mrs. Jones, that in 1730 he was living in Hoxton, a part of London where several botanists and nurserymen resided, notably Thomas Fairchild, the author of *The City Gardener* (1722), and an experimenter in the hybridization of plants. Catesby's latter years, at least, were spent in the Parish of St. Luke—Old Street—a poor section of London at that time and also today, although the buildings of the mid-eighteenth century have been largely replaced.

It is probable that he was buried in the old churchyard of St. Luke, but the only entry in the church register possibly referring to him is in the name of Skeatesby being death entry No. 26 for that month, and with the cause of death given as "age."   Errors in names such as this were very common in those times for they were often set down by uneducated assistants of the undertaker, and unless death occurred from a few definite diseases they were said to be due to "age."   It is evident, however, that Catesby was suffering from a dropsical condition shortly before his death, as we may gather from a letter [6] of Mr. Knowlton to Mr. Richard Richardson, dated July 18, 1749.   Speaking of a trip to London he says:

I saw likewise Messrs. Catesby and Edwards who has materials for a third volume of Birds, Flies and Animals, etc., but poor Mr. Catesby's legs swell and he looks badly.   Drs. Mead and Stack said there was little hope of him long this side of the grave.

In talking with the vicar of this church in 1936, I learned that although many tombstones still remain, the graves have in most cases been used and reused, and most of the tombstones, except the large sarcophagi, have been arranged around the periphery of the churchyard as a sort of wall.[7]   The name "Catesby" is not to be found among them and it is probable that Catesby's widow was too poor to afford any memorial.

CATESBY'S MARRIAGE

Catesby's wife was named Elizabeth, but I have not been able as yet to learn where the marriage is recorded. However, the widow's will presents a few facts of interest to us especially that she left two children, Mark Catesby and Ann Catesby.   A daughter, Elizabeth Rowland, is likewise mentioned in her will and it appears that this person must have been her daughter by a former marriage and therefore a step-daughter to Mark.   This gathers new interest for us and might cause confusion in biographical research, in the light of a recorded marriage of Mark Catesby to Mrs. Elizabeth Rowland, both of the Parish of St. Lukes, Middlesex, on October 8, 1747, in St. George's Chapel in Mayfair.   This was one of the

famous churches where marriages were performed without license or publication of banns, and although they were considered clandestine, were nevertheless valid and binding.   Be this as it may, the will of Mark Catesby's wife, Elizabeth, presumably his first, who was buried in London, February 18, 1753, establishes the fact that she and Mark Catesby were the parents of two children, Mark and Ann, of whom the mother's will speaks as follows:

I, Elizabeth Catesby of the Parish of St. Lukes, Old Street, widow, being weak in body but of sound mind and memory, do make this my last will and testament in manner and form following, that is to say, imprimmis, I will that all my debts and funeral charges be paid.   Next, I give to my loving daughter, Elizabeth Rowland, ten pounds.   I give to my loving cousin, Jekyll Catesby,[8] a second volume of Mr. Catesby's Natural History, to make his set complete.

I give to Martha Arther a guinea as a token of my love—all rest, residue and remainder of my estate, whatever money, goods, plates, and all that I may be possessed of or entitled unto, I give and devise to my two loving children, Mark Catesby and Ann Catesby, to be equally divided between them, share and share alike, and I appoint my loving cousin, Jekyll Catesby, my sole executor to this my last will and testament.

IN WITNESS WHEREOF I have hereunto set my hand this 4th day of January, 1753.

Elizabeth Catesby.[8]

Witness: Peter Collinson
          Mary Arther

This will was proved at London on the 29th day of August, 1753, after Mrs. Catesby had died of consumption in February 1753.   Her burial took place February 18, as entered in St. Luke's register.

MARK CATESBY'S FIRST TRIP TO AMERICA

The earliest period of Mark Catesby's life to which there is any published reference concerns his first trip to America in 1712, probably prompted by the fact that his sister Elizabeth, having married Dr. William Cocke, the Secretary of State under Governor Alexander Spotwood (1676–1740), was living in Virginia.   On the first expedition he was neither painter nor collector, although he did a little desultory painting and collecting, especially of plants, and sent some tubs of growing American plants to the Chelsea Gardens, the oldest botanic garden in England, founded in 1673 by the Apothecaries' Society.   In 1715, he made a trip to Jamaica, but there are apparently no zoological nor botanical results that are known.

Catesby was well connected in America through his association with the Governor of Virginia and his aforementioned brother-in-law, Dr. William Cocke, the Secretary of State.   He spent some time also at Windsor, the seat of Major Woodford, who had married Catesby's niece, Ann Cocke.

---

[6] Richardson, 1835: 400.

[7] The wall had been removed when I visited the Church in 1949.

[8] It is necessary to state that the term "in-law" was not in use in England at this time but the term "cousin" was used a great deal for lateral and marriage relatives; and unquestionably Jekyll Catesby was Mark Catesby's brother, i.e., Mrs. Catesby's brother-in-law.

In 1719 he returned to England but regretted that he had not devoted more time to natural history, for as soon as he was home he at once began to plan to return to the Colonies. He soon became acquainted with Sir Hans Sloane (1660–1753), a learned physician, President of the College of Physicians, and himself also a traveller to Jamaica in 1707 where he went as physician to the Duke and Duchess of Albemarle. The Duke, however, died there the first year, and the Duchess's wish to return home obligated Sir Hans to return to England with her long before he had planned to do so. We may imagine, therefore, that Catesby's trip to Jamaica, the scene of Sloane's unfinished work, made a bond of interest between them.

From a letter written by his good friend, Samuel Dale (1659–1739), to the famous botanist, William Sherard (1659–1728), we may gather a note or two concerning Catesby's first trip to America, which is practically a lost chapter in his life. The letter is dated Braintree, October 15, 1719 and reads:

Mr. Catesby is come from Virginia he hath brought me about 70 specimens of which about half are new; these I shall likewise send up in a box for your view and where there are Duplicates, they are at yours and Mr. Dubois service. He [Catesby] intends again to return and will take an opportunity to waite upon you with some paintings of Birds etc. which he hath drawn. Its pitty some encouragement cant be found for him, he maybe very useful for the perfecting of natural history.

By identifying the persons concerned with this letter, we may quickly arrive at some understanding of the interests and identity of this little-known naturalist. The writer of the letter, Samuel Dale, a physician practicing in Braintree, Essex and the author of an important work on pharmaecology, was, like many other physicians of his time, deeply interested in botany and particularly in the mosses.

The recipient of the letter, William Sherard, was a well known botanist, who founded the Chair of Botany at Oxford. It was largely through his interest and patronage that Catesby returned to America for the purpose of collecting plants. Charles DuBois (d. 1740), Treasurer of the East India Company, who is mentioned in the letter was also a botanist of lesser note and cultivated exotic plants at his home in Mitcham in Surrey. He had considerable dealings with Catesby although Catesby was never able to make him a subscriber to his *Natural History.*

From this we see that Catesby's connections in London were primarily with the scientific groups and although it is possible to detect in his letters a particular interest in birds, his best chance and means of returning to America lay in his being selected as a botanical collector.

On returning to England in 1719, Catesby seems to have had a sense of lost opportunity, and looking back on those years of his young manhood, he set down these

words in the preface of his great work on the *Natural History of Carolina, Florida and the Bahama Islands:*

I thought then so little of the Design and Nature of this Work that in the Seven Years I resided in that Country (I am ashamed to own it) I chiefly gratified my inclination in observing and admiring the various Productions of those Countries.

We see him then after coming home eager to acquaint himself with every opportunity that might lead to his return to America.

At this time, 1719, an expedition to Africa was being discussed amongst the savants of London, and both Catesby and a man named Eleazar Albin (fl. 1713–1759), author of a book on insects, and later of a three-volume work on birds, as well as one on spiders, were discussed as possible candidates for the task of collecting in this distant land. It seems that upon Albin's declining the offer, negotiations were opened with Catesby to go. From Dr. Richard Richardson's (1663–1741) *Scientific Correspondence of the Eighteenth Century* (1835), it is possible to glean the fact that Catesby, although his first wish was to go to Carolina, changed his plan when opportunity offered, and was seriously contemplating the trip to Africa. In a letter from Dr. William Sherard, who later became one of his patrons, to Dr. Richardson, dated March 28, 1721, we read:

Mr. Catesby is not yet fixed with the African Company, but will be I believe this week. What he sends from thence you may depend to receive a share of. 'Tis a sickly place; and I could wish he had held his resolution of going to Carolina; but he's now so far engaged with the Duke of Chandos to think of that.

Be that as it may, this plan, though all but settled, was abandoned by Catesby and furthermore the Duke of Chandos, who at first wished to sponsor the African trip, finally stood at the head of the list of patrons for the trip to America. William Sherard, Sir Hans Sloane, and Mr. Dubois were other supporters of this plan, and Sherard in a letter to Richardson dated December 7, 1721, wrote: "I believe Mr. Catesby will be going to Carolina in a month. I have procured him subscriptions for near the sum he proposed." As a matter of fact, however, it was April 1722, before Catesby got off on his second trip to America.

CATESBY'S PATRONS

It is well known that in the early days of the study of natural science, collectors who went to foreign lands were almost always wholly dependent upon the personal patronage of wealthy noblemen. It was no reflection upon their ability that they had to seek such assistance and to foster and cultivate the interest of their benefactors. Catesby was no exception and, although it appears that he was at one time the owner of considerable property, he was at the time of his second trip to America no longer a man of means. Sherard, in recommending him for his post, refers to him as a gentleman of "small fortune" and may have had in mind the

Fig. 25. Sir Hans Sloane (1660–1753), Catesby's friend and patron. Courtesy of the United States National Museum.

various properties left him by his father in the Parish of St. Brides, London, and his extensive holdings in Sudbury. What became of these parcels of land is not known, but it is easy to conjecture that much of his inheritance was used in his young manhood, for his father died in 1705 when Mark was only twenty-three years of age. It is interesting therefore to see the list of distinguished men who were willing to subscribe to Catesby's enterprise of collecting in America.

At the head of the list stands the august personage, his Grace, the Duke of Chandos (1673–1744), owner of palatial homes in Edgeware and Cavendish Square, member of the Privy Council, friend of the composer Handel, who lived with him for two years and composed his oratorios in his drawing-room. Next, the Right Honourable Thomas Earl of Oxford; the Right Honourable Thomas Earl of Maccelesfield; the Right Honourable John Lord Percival, member of the Irish peerage and one who aided in the colonization of Georgia; Sir George Markham, Bart, F.R.S.; Sir Hans Sloane, Bart, President of the Royal Society and of the College of Physicians; the Honourable Colonel Francis Nicholson (1660–1628), F.R.S., Governor of South Carolina; Richard Mead, M.D., F.R.S., a famous physician; Charles Dubois, Esq., a botanist; William Sherard, LL.D., and F.R.S., founder of the Chair of Botany at Oxford. Sir Hans Sloane, Colonel Francis Nicholson,

Dr. Richard Mead (1673–1754), William Sherard, and George Markham were all members of the Royal Society. Charles Dubois was the only one apparently who had not achieved notable distinction and even he was an authority on cultivating exotic plants. Catesby was further aided by a pension to which reference is made in the Council Minutes of the Royal Society of London (vol. 2, p. 324, 1632, 1643–1727).

At a meeting of the Council held October 20, 1720, we read:

Colonel Francis Nicholson (F.R.S. 1706), going Governor to South Carolina, was pleased to declare that he would allow Mr. Catesby, recommended to him as a very proper person to observe the rarities of that country for the uses and purposes of the society, the pension of twenty pounds per annum during his government there, and at the same time to give ten pounds by way of advance for the first half year's payment and so for the future half a year's pay beforehand.

THE MEN FOR WHOM CATESBY COLLECTED

These persons also are interesting in that they serve to clarify the nature of Catesby's mission to America and to give some understanding of his connections in London. Chief among them were William Sherard (1659–1728) and Sir Hans Sloane (1660–1753). Sherard was primarily a botanist. He had studied at Paris and Leyden and had made trips to Geneva, Rome, Naples, and Asia Minor in the interest of botany and archaeological antiquities. Most of Catesby's letters that have been preserved are to Sherard, but there are a few to Sir Hans Sloane in the Manuscript Department of the British Museum and a very significant one to Dr. Dillenius (1687–1747) at Oxford. Sherard's entire collection of plants, many of them collected by Catesby, was a nucleus of the Oxford Herbarium.

Sir Hans Sloane was considerably more of a zoologist than Sherard and Catesby's letters to him contain more or less ornithological observation. Sloane was likewise a very distinguished and beloved man in London, a President of the Royal Society, also of the College of Physicians and the founder of the British Museum. Here was to be housed his vast collection, including some of the plants and, for a time at least, many birds, shells, snakes, and other specimens collected and preserved by Catesby. The birds and other zoological specimens have long since perished but there are two large portfolios of plants which are interesting to go over. Many of the sheets have long legends on them in Catesby's own handwriting; some have sketches of fruits and seeds. It is said that Catesby introduced the catalpa into England in 1728, but at this time we know by a letter of his kinsman, George Rutherford, that he was living in London. Undoubtedly, however, he did bring or send it over as well as the acacia, horse chestnut, and other species. There are in Volume 212 of the Sloane Herbarium ninety-five sheets of plants collected and mounted by him but the great majority of his specimens is at Oxford.

Charles Dubois contributed to the third edition of John Ray's *Synopsis of Plants* published in 1724. There are but few references to this gentleman in Catesby's letters but he was evidently a close associate of Sir Hans Sloane and of Sherard as Catesby sent specimens to them jointly. There were times, however, when Catesby was hard pressed to keep all his friends satisfied, as may be seen by this excerpt from a letter to William Sherard dated December 9, 1722:

I hope it is not expected that what I send should be to everyone separately but in the manner I have now sent, for indeed it is almost impracticable without half my time lost besides the difficulty of having them put in a dry place, for it's no small favour from a master [i.e., of a ship] to secure [the safety of] a single box or parcel, and much more, many distinct parcels and boxes.

John James Dillenius was another to whom Catesby sent specimens. He was a Dutch botanist, highly regarded by Linnaeus, whom William Sherard brought to England to become the first Professor of Botany at Oxford.

Isaac Rand (d. 1743), the son of James Rand who with thirteen other apothecaries decided to build a wall around the Chelsea Botanical Gardens, was another of Catesby's botanist friends. He was located in the section known as the Haymarket, adjacent to Piccadilly, and was interested in inconspicuous plants, especially in and near London. He was appointed Praefaectus Horti of the Chelsea Garden in 1724 and gave bi-weekly demonstrations there for the public in summer.

Catesby likewise sent plants and specimens to William Sherard's older brother James (1666–1738), also a Fellow of the Royal Society, and to Samuel Dale of Braintree, Essex. The latter seems to have been a personal friend of his, for Catesby was often at Dale's home and carried letters and specimens from Dale to Sherard in London, and there are many references to Dale's admiration for Catesby in the Dale letters to Sherard which are among the manuscripts of the Royal Society.

Still another associate of Catesby, especially during his residence in Hoxton, after his second trip to America, was John Cowell, a gardener of that section (then called Hogsden), and author of a book, *The Curious and Profitable Gardener* (1730).

Thus it is seen that all the men for whom Catesby collected, except perhaps Sir Hans Sloane, were primarily botanists. Botany was the great science of the day and zoology in all its branches had to take second place. But the fact remains that Catesby somehow managed to do a great work on birds, covering about one hundred species, first depicted in the field with each one's particular plant or tree associate, and later etched and colored by himself or under his direction in England. In fact, his letters left me amazed at his capacity for work and his devotion to his task in the face of all odds.

A few excerpts from these letters may serve to throw some light on the man's character and will show some of the difficulties under which he worked, for he was often short of materials and frequently distressed by the lack of letters from home to tell him the fate of what he had previously sent with the utmost care.

Charles Town, Aprile 6, 1724

f. 176

Honrd Sir:

I was sensably troubled with your last Lr. of complaints. It was without any date. My uneasiness is somewhat mitigated when I reflect that by this time and by what I shall now say, if I may be credited, your resentment is abated. I shall not vindicate my remissness in writing or anything else I am knowingly tardy of. But I profess before God I never *can* be more industrious in collecting whatever I could possibly meet with, either those few days I was at Savanna Garrison or since. . . .

It may seem as an excuse to say that the floods or late frosts have impeded it [i.e., his collecting] but the falsity of such a pretense would be very foolish when you may so easily be informed, particularly by Con. H. Johnson who assisted me in getting many and particularly endeavored to get the cones of pines and acorns. . . .

You say Sr. several of my subscribers complain, which surprises me. I could not learn by enquiry and asking those I saw that collections would be acceptable to any but Sir Hans, yourself and Mr. Dubois. I wish I could know what was required and by whome. I hope it can't be expected I should send collections to every of my subscribers which is impracticable for me to doe. However, I'le doe to ye best of my abilities nor can I say or doe more. I should have thought abundance of my time lost if at my return to England I could have shown no more than the collections I send. Not that anything obstructed my collecting plants and seeds which all gives place to when opportunity offers.

These words seem rather significant and lead us to wonder when he found time to do his extensive bird collecting and painting. There is only infrequent mention of this work in his letters, yet the volumes on birds speak earnestly if not eloquently on the great amount of labor required to bring it into being. For Catesby was not an artist either by training or talent—he accomplished his work in a manner similar to that of his successor, Alexander Wilson, nearly a hundred years later—that is, by stern application to work.

It is clear too that only by careful planning and crowding of his time could he afford to work on birds. Perhaps it is possible to read a note of justification for his bird work into the following excerpt from his preface.

There being a greater variety of the feathered Kind than of any other animals (at least to be come at) and excelling in the Beauty of their colours besides having oftenest relation to the plants on which they feed, and frequent, I was induced chiefly (so far as I could) to compleat an account of them, rather than to describe promiscuously Insects and other Animals by which I must have omitted many of the Birds for I had not time to do all by which method I believe very few Birds have escaped my knowledge except some water fowl and some of those that frequent the sea.

Therefore, we may suppose that Catesby like the zealous field man of today found many opportunities when he could, as it were, "Kill two birds with one stone," and thus accomplish a prodigious amount of work. Yet he remained true to his first duty, the collection of plants which in his own words: ". . . all gives place to when opportunity offers."

CATESBY'S PLAN TO GO TO MEXICO

From his letters we gather also that Catesby planned to make a trip to Mexico with a friend, a Dr. Couper, a learned and successful physician in the Colonies. He wrote to Sir Hans Sloane asking his advice on the matter, expressing his determination to go whether his subscriptions continued or not, and spoke of securing a letter of passport from the Spanish government to protect him from "so treacherous and jealous a people as the Spaniards." He expressed satisfaction that the Indian tribes through whose country he would pass were at war and therefore so occupied that they would probably not molest him. This trip probably never materialized for in his last letters he was still waiting to hear from Sherard and Sloane regarding it.

He did go, however, to several of the Bahama Islands. The first three years of his second period in America he spent in Carolina, Georgia, and Florida. He then visited Providence Island to which he was invited by the Governor of the Island, Charles Plinny, who showed him much kindness and hospitality. After this, he went to Ilatera, Andros, and Albacco where he studied marine forms mostly. His collections from these places he gave to Sir Hans Sloane to whom he felt under most obligation.

UNPUBLISHED DRAWINGS BY CATESBY IN THE BRITISH MUSEUM

In addition to a few manuscript letters by Catesby in the British Museum, there are several unpublished drawings by him. These are to be found in the *Index to Additions to the Department of Manuscripts of the British Museum, 1783–1835,* and in 1936 were available in the Prints and Drawings Department. Under Mark Catesby there are the following entries: drawings of insects, chiefly from Surinam and Guinea bearing number 5271; drawings of fish and also several birds, bearing number 5269; drawings of plants and trees bearing number 5283. In the description of this manuscript Catesby is referred to as "Doctor."

Number 5269 is a volume of water colors entitled *"Bibliotheca Sloaniana"* and I merely list the various drawings by Catesby found therein: The green woodpecker, blue-winged teal, small water rail, yellow-hammer, siskin, lapwing, redpoll, cock sparrow, swallow, marsh titmouse, greater sparrow, green plover. There are also many fish and shells and a few molluscs.

Following these are the eel, crayfish, ray, seahorse, and crab, a pencil sketch of a frog, fifteen different species of fish and three plates of shells.

CATESBY'S PUBLICATIONS

These are few in number, being only three in addition to his sumptuous two-volume work, *The Natural His-*
tory of Carolina, Florida and the Bahama Islands, published in 1731.

In view of the fact that up to the time of this work, birds had been but very superficially described, Catesby ranks as the first ornithologist in America even though he must divide his laurels with the botanists. His contribution may be said to have laid the foundation of popular ornithology inaugurating the combination of attractive lifelike portraits with appropriate environment, and short accurate accounts—the beginning, on a small scale, of Wilson's and Audubon's system of illustrated ornithological life histories.

It may seem that the books were unduly ornate. Indeed Catesby's friend and contemporary George Edwards (1694–1773), who wrote much on birds, definitely disapproved of Catesby's showy and expensive plates. But we must remember that the ambitious young naturalist was doing something that had never been done before and he should therefore be pardoned for his apparent vanity. Furthermore, it was customary to have large and beautifully illustrated volumes displayed on tables in the drawing rooms of the colorful reign of Queen Anne. We should remember also (and this is greatly in his favor) that Catesby finding the cost of reproducing the plates very expensive decided to learn the arts of etching and engraving himself.

He had planned on his return from the Colonies the second time, when he brought his collection of paintings home, to go to Amsterdam or Paris to have them done, but on the advice of Mr. Joseph Gouky, a painter, he decided in his own words, ". . . to be initiated into the way of Etching which though I may not have done in Graver-like manner, choosing rather to omit their method of cross-hatching and to follow the Humour of the Feathers which is more laborious and I hope has proved more to the Purpose." This method of workmanship caused his birds to appear flat, and comparatively unlife-like. However, Catesby realized his shortcomings in this regard as we see by the following words from his Preface:

As I was not bred a Painter I hope some faults in Perspective and other niceties may be more readily excused, for I humbly conceive Plants and other Things done in a Flat tho' exact Manner may serve the Purpose of Natural History, better in some measure than in a more bold and Painter-like Way.

Though not an artist, he was by feeling a true naturalist, fully appreciating the value of studying the living object of his art, for again, to quote his own words he says:

In designing the Plants I always did them while fresh and just gathered: And the animals particularly the Birds, I painted them while alive (except a very few) and gave them their gestures peculiar to every kind of Bird, and when it would admit of, I have adapted the Birds to those Plants on which they fed or had any Relation to.

These principles of workmanship were a new departure in the portrayal of natural history subjects and, although crude in execution, proved their worth to the public of Catesby's time, and, furthermore, were emulated by subsequent artists. It is, therefore, not surprising that two later editions of Catesby's *Natural History* were published and edited by George Edwards and put out in four smaller volumes in 1748, only a year or so before Catesby's death, and a German edition published in Nuremberg in 1771.

It is probable, because of the great popularity of the study of botany in London, that Catesby was much more in the public eye for his botanical work and many successful efforts to naturalize American plants and trees in England, than for his zoological work. His experiments in this field are incorporated in a book, the *Hortus Britanno-Americanus,* or a *Curious Collection of Trees and Shrubs, The Produce of the British Colonies in North America; Adapted to the Soil and Climate of England with Observations on their Constitution, Growth and Culture, and Directions how they are to be Collected, Packed up and Secured during their Passage. Embellished with Copper Plates neatly engraved by Mark Catesby, F.R.S.* (1737). The Chelsea Gardens still contain several trees introduced by Catesby.

In addition to these books, the *Natural History* and the *Hortus Brittanno-Americanus,* Catesby has two other publications to his credit, a lecture on "Birds of Passage" delivered before the Royal Society, March 5, 1746, which was published in the *Philosophical Transactions,* and one on the same subject in the *Gentleman's Magazine and Historical Chronicle.* 1748, Vol. 18, 445. These are of particular interest for they offer Catesby's theories of the causes and method of migration. He believed that the main cause inducing birds to migrate was the search for food. His explanation of the method, as set forth in the *Gentleman's Magazine and Historical Chronicle,* is more fantastic, as follows: when the birds are fully fed and vigorous they undertake their most difficult flight, which is perpendicular, until they reach such a high altitude that they can see the view of the land to which they are going and descend thereto on an inclined plane. Says Catesby in this article:

> The conjecture which I offer seems to be more probable and to be attended with less difficulty which is that when these three sorts of birds of passage are strong and vigorous and full-fed, their first attempt is to perform the hardest part of their journey and what requires most pains. Thus they gain such an assent as gives them a distant prospect of those countries which are to be their next abode, to which they direct their course on a declining plane. This is performed with more ease and despatch than any other direction.

This view, while perhaps less naïve than the one which asserts that swallows dash themselves into the mud and lie torpid for the winter, is nevertheless absurd. His ideas on migration as expressed in his lecture before the Royal Society, and which can be read in the *Philosophical Transactions,* show far greater scientific insight into the subject although they appeared a year earlier.

It should be mentioned that Catesby, according to Allibones's *Dictionary of Biography,* is credited, according to Richard Weston (1733–1806) with the authorship of a book called, *The Practical Farmer.* Upon referring to Weston's book, *Tracts on Practical Agriculture and Gardening,* to which is added a complete chronological catalogue by English authors on agriculture, gardening, and the like, I found no mention of Catesby as the author of *The Practical Farmer,* but his *Eighty-five Curious American Plants adapted for Britain and Europe* is listed at £2/2/–.

The foregoing publications do not conclude Catesby's writings, however, for after he returned to England, his letters to John Bartram and William Bartram point to other books in progress. These men were father and son and were very active in the early history of American zoology and botany. Although the Bartrams came of old Quaker stock and were therefore not given to much affectionate expression, they seem to have held Catesby in high esteem and warm regard in their hearts as we may judge by John Bartram's letter to him dated London May 20, 1740:

> The reading of thy acceptable letter incited in me the different passions of Joy in receiving a letter of friendship and respect from one so much esteemed, and sorrow in considering what time we have lost, when we might have obliged each other.

In fact the elder Bartram expressed regret that they had not been corresponding for ten years. In this correspondence it appears that Catesby was at work not only on birds, but on plants, vegetables, shell animals, fish, and mammals. Of it he says:

> the whole book when finished will be in two folio volumes, each consisting of an hundred plates of animals and vegetables. This laborious work has been some years in agitation and as the whole when finished amount to twenty guineas, a sum too great probably to dispose of many, I chose to publish it in parts. [*Memorials, J. Bartram and H. Marshall,* Phila., 1849.]

In this letter he refers to the chuck-wills-widow as follows:

> There is a bird in Virginia and Carolina and I suppose in Pennsylvania that at night calls whipper will and sometimes whip will's widow, by which names it is called (as the bird chinketh the fool thinketh.) I have omitted to describe it and there fore I shall be glad of it. I believe it is a kind of cuckoo.

Here he refers also to our house-swallow showing that he realized the difference between the swallows' and swifts' tails, in these words:

> your house swallow is different from ours and different in its tail and nest which is artfully made of small sticks and cemented together with a kind of glue. The bird with the nest would be acceptable.

In a letter to John Bartram dated April 15, 1746, Catesby laments the loss of things he had sent to America, and his failure to receive two cargos of specimens intended for his study from Bartram. His forebearance in time of misfortune and annoyance and his sincerity toward his work emanate from these words of his reply to Bartram:

> . . . yet nevertheless your kind intentions equally oblidge me as if attended with success and require a retaliation which I shall endeavor, the first opportunity to acquit myself of. In the meantime, accept this book [9] of birds.

CATESBY'S AFFILIATIONS IN LONDON

It remains to discuss, in so far as information can be found, Catesby as a man of achievement, for which he was invited to become a member of two very distinguished organizations: The Royal Society of London and the Gentleman's Society at Spalding.

CATESBY AS A MEMBER OF THE ROYAL SOCIETY

The Royal Society was organized for the advancement of learning in the late seventeenth century, and the Charter of Incorporation was granted by Charles II. It was a distinct honor to be elected, as it still is, and the aspirants had to indicate their own desire to be members and then to await invitations to attend the meetings for the purpose of being appraised, so to speak, at the desire of persons already within the fold. Before the organization of the British Museum in 1758, the Royal Society was the obvious repository of all natural rarities. It follows, then, that much of Catesby's material probably went to the Royal Society of London.

The Society met weekly and from Volume 15 of the "Journal Book" we learn that at the meeting held November 23, 1732, "Mr. Catesby presented to the Society the fifth part of his *Natural History of Carolina* which was referred to Dr. Mortimer for an account of it. He was not yet a member at this time but in the minutes for December 21, 1732, it is stated that Mr. Catesby was present at the desire of Dr. Amman; [10] also at the meeting of February 1, 1732, Mr. Catesby was present at the request of Mr. Collinson. At this meeting, it is entered in the minutes that Mr. Catesby was put up as a candidate for election in pursuance of the following certificate:

> Mark Catesby, a gentleman well skilled
> In Botany and Natural History, who
> travelled for several years in various parts
> of America, where he collected the materials
> for a Natural History of Carolina
> and the Bahama Islands; which curious
> and magnificent work he has presented
> to the Royal Society; is desirous of being
> a member thereof, and is proposed by us
>   Hans Sloane
>   Roger Gale
>   Robert Paul
>   John Martyn
>   Peter Collinson
> Feb. 1:1732/3

Catesby again had leave to be present on March 8, 1732 at the desire of Dr. Amman, and at the meeting of April 26, 1733, there is an entry as follows (p. 263):

"Mr. Mark Catesby was put to the ballot and elected Fellow." It was a rule of the Society that every name had to be read ten times prior to balloting and the dates of such readings appear at the left of the certificates. Catesby's certificate somehow bears an error for at the bottom he is said to have been elected February 26, 1733, but in fact it was not until April 26.

CATESBY'S SPONSORS

Some of the members had as many as ten sponsors but in Catesby's case there were only five, headed by his long-time friend and benefactor, Sir Hans Sloane. Another name familiar to students of early American science is Peter Collinson, friend of the Bartrams and, we learn also, of Catesby, the publication of whose book he helped to finance. Collinson, referring to his copy of Catesby's work says:

> This edition of this noble work is very valuable as it was highly finished by the ingenious author who in gratitude made me this present for the considerable sums of money I lent him without interest to enable him to publish it for the benefit of himself and family else through necessity it must have fallen a prey to the book sellers.[11]

Roger Gale (1672–1744) was best known as an antiquary; he was a vice-president of the Society of Antiquaries, and for some time treasurer of the Royal Society. Robert Paul was a writer on miscellaneous subjects and John Martyn (1699–1768) was a botanist of the first rank, holder of the chair of Botany at Cambridge, 1732–1768, and the author of many botanical works and translations. It is obvious that Catesby was held in high esteem by the membership of the Royal Society, but it does not seem that he was a very outstanding or active member of the group. Being by this time a man of very modest means and apparently retiring by nature, he was not apt to put himself in the foreground of the Royal Society's activities. He was, however, a regular attendant at the meetings and took some part at least in their discussions as well as in the Society's acquisition of new members. He appears to have had a broad appreciation of ability in others, for he sponsored several members from widely varying walks of life. Among these may be mentioned Dr. Thomas Stack, physician, well known for skill in chemistry, anatomy, and natural history, elected in 1737; Mr. John Maud, chemist, and a gentleman well versed in several parts of polite literature, elected 1737; John Mitchell (d. 1768), long resident of Virginia, and, like Catesby, describer of many American plants, elected 1748. Lastly, Catesby sponsored General James Oglethorpe (1696–1785), famous and progressive colonist of Georgia, skilled in natural history, mathematics, and all branches of polite literature, elected 1749.

Thus we see that Catesby took a real share in the work of the Royal Society and by the fact that he recommended General Oglethorpe whom no doubt he knew

---

9 Darlington, 1849: 323.
10 Dr. John Amman. This is a pseudonym of Wilhelm Sulpy.

11 Brett-James, Norman G., 1925: 120–121.

while he was living and working in Georgia, and who was not elected until November 9, 1749, we can assume that nearly up to the time of his reported death he was a faithful and interested attendant at the meetings.

It should be mentioned, however, that one person whom he recommended, Iodo Mendez Laquet, apparently an army physician of Portugal, failed to achieve election, although he was balloted upon February 5, 1746/7. It is likewise on record that George Edwards, who reissued Catesby's *Natural History* in 1748, was sponsored by Mark Catesby, his contemporary and peer in ornithological study. Edwards, for some unaccountable reason, withdrew his name for election at this time (1744) but was finally admitted in 1756, some years after Catesby's death.

THE GENTLEMAN'S SOCIETY AT SPALDING

This organization was founded by the distinguished antiquary and barrister, Maurice Johnson (1688–1755), a grim and learned gentleman who banned within the Society all discussion of politics, "in which," as he said, "every man thinks himself wise"; he likewise frowned upon any sort of gaming "which most young men esteem as their beloved evening's recreation." To keep the ideals of the Society thus pure and intellectual, the good man was forced to depend chiefly on the strength of his own children (of whom he had twenty-six, sixteen of whom sat down at his table), and his near relations whom, as he said, "he took care to train up to a liking of it from their infancy," and who, he trusted, would keep it up when he should leave them.[12]

Despite these austere regulations, the Gentleman's Society was an aggregation of the leading literary and scientific men of the day, some of the most striking of whom were Sir Isaac Newton (1642–1727), Sir Hans Sloane, Sir John Evelyn (1620–1706), several bishops, John Ray, George Edwards, Pope (1688–1744), Addison (1672–1719), Steele (1672–1729), John Gay (1699–1745), and many others. Into this august assemblage was inducted with due ceremony the modest naturalist, Mark Catesby, and although I have searched the minutes of the Society for some contribution made by him to the entertainments thereof, I can learn only that he was a member. The subjects usually discussed were antiquities, but there were also lively scientific discussions, for instance, on bird migration, and we may reasonably imagine that Catesby contributed to these.

MARK CATESBY'S DEATH

There remains one other point which I hesitate to bring up since I cannot yet offer conclusive evidence, but for the sake of clarifying this investigation and removing a possible pitfall in future biographical research, it seems wise to record the fact that there is a will in the Principal Probate Registry, London, by a Mark

---

[12] From a letter of Mr. Johnson to Mr. Gale, 1743, in the *Reliquiae Gallaenae*, 390.

Catesby, which gives much evidence of being by the Mark Catesby of this study. The signature appears to be identical with the signature of Mark Catesby's letters, and the sole executor of the will is the brother of its author, Jekyll Catesby, often referred to in Catesby's letters and whom, we recall, Catesby's wife had as the sole executor of her will. From this newly discovered document (formerly it was thought Catesby left no will) which I found in 1936 I learned that Mark Catesby was "going to the Seas" in the ship *Portfield* of the East India Company and made his will the thirtieth day of October, 1749, just before going on his intended voyage. Upon looking up the log of the ship, I found it duly recorded, that Mark Catesby departed this life at 3 A.M., April 20, 1750, having died of a fever, and at 8 A.M. "amid faint airs and a calm sea, his body was committed to the deep." Not ready to discredit his reported death on December 23, 1749, and knowing that Mark Catesby, the naturalist, had a son Mark, my first thought was that this man was his son. This, however, is not possible since three years later, in 1753, Catesby's wife in her will refers to her son Mark then still living.

In conclusion regarding Catesby, I cannot refrain from expressing regret at the lack of information concerning his ornithological itinerary and the stops he made for the collection of his specimens. We know that on his second trip to America he remained a year on the coast and probably spent many enjoyable days with Governor Francis Nicholson, who sponsored his coming and showed him much kindness and hospitality. After his year on the coast, he then went to the upper and more sparsely settled parts of South Carolina and continued in and about Fort Moore on the banks of the Savannah River, three hundred miles from the sea. He covered great distances on foot each day, carrying a box for specimens and one for painting and drawing materials, so that he could set things down from life. Some of the time he employed an Indian to carry equipment for him. Later he planned to buy a negro boy, to whom he refers in a postscript to a letter dated January 4, 1722/3, to the Honourable Consul Sherard as follows:

In my last I beg'd the favour (which I now repeat) that you would be pleased to pay a 20£ Bill for I conceive you have so much in your hands. The making large collections of seed & C is so fatiguing that I cannot effect it with [*sic*]; [doubtless "without" intended] help for which reason the next negro ship that arrives here, I design to buy a negro Boy which I cannot be without.

He also spent a good deal of time at Newington Plantation in Dorchester County, South Carolina, not far from Charleston. From his letters I learned that he stayed occasionally at the home of Colonel Blake where he had a memorable snake experience which furnishes one of the rare bits of personal history in his hidden biography. This incident is in the form of a postscript to his letter to Consul Sherard written from Charleston Jan. 16, 1723/4:

I fear Sr I have tired you already yet Ile venture to relate (in as short a manner as I can) an odd accident that hapened about the beginning of last February I being at the house of Coll Blake a negro woman making my Bed a few minutes after I was out of it cryed out a Rattle Snake we being drinking Tea in ye next room which was a ground flore and being surprised with ye vehemense of the wenches bauling went to see the cause and found as the wench had said a Rattle snake actually between the sheets in ye very place I lay, vigorous and full of ire biting at everything that approacht him. Probably it crept in for warmth in the night, but how long I had the company of charming Bed-fellow I am not able to say.

It is evident from his letters that he took the utmost pains about his work but I gather that his expedition was really too strenuous for his physical condition. He speaks as if the Indians through whose country he trav-elled were always very kind, providing him with game which they shot, and building a shelter of bark for him and his cargo when he arrived. Despite this, overwork often confined him to a crude camp with poor care, and then his efforts to make up the loss of time amounted almost to heroism.

From a letter [13] to Sherard written December 10, 1722, we can appreciate his fortitude and determination to succeed in his difficult commission of collecting against adverse circumstances. Says Catesby:

At the middle of September 1722 I was siezed with a swelling of the cheek which impostulated and was cut and by the ignorance of the surgeon, as I suspect, I have been confined within doors these three months in misery having my face twice cut and laid open with Teuls [14] [sic.] and injections every day.

I hope next summer if God gives me life and health to retrieve this lost time.

Thus amid these primitive and often painful conditions, scores of American birds first saw the light of scientific record and many Latin and vernacular names instituted by Catesby can be traced to him if we take the trouble to hunt back through the history and synonymy of orni-thological nomenclature.

We understand now as no one in Catesby's time could, that birds in a given region, say Charleston, may be dif-ferent in greater or less degree from the birds, of New England, and Florida for instance, although they might appear superficially identical. As modern ornithologists have studied specimens from the various regions, they have found that many birds should be divided into geo-graphical races and have accordingly placed subspecific names upon them. This has resulted in several varieties of the common birds that Catesby described being recog-nized as distinct subspecies. Now we have no way of knowing exactly where Catesby collected his birds, whether, for instance, when he painted his red-winged starling, he had the Florida race or the northern race of the red-winged blackbird in mind. So it has come about that though we might wish to preserve Catesby as the

authority for his descriptions, it is not always possible to do so. Dr. John Zimmer comments: "There are a fair number of cases where we have done so, sometimes by arbitrarily specifying a locality for his birds, in a few cases by judgment of the characters shown on the plates." To those who may be interested in a fuller dis-cussion of this subject, it is suggested that they study Dr. Witmer Stone's interesting article, "Catesby and the Nomenclature of North American Birds," *The Auk,* Volume 46, No. 4, October 1929.

It is hoped that further study may eventually unfold new details of this naturalist's career both in our south-ern states and abroad. Mr. O. A. Stevens, writing in the *Wilson Bulletin* for September, 1936, has tabulated the birds described by various early authors, and to Catesby he ascribes fifty-nine species which served as the bases of Linnaeus' descriptions of American birds.[15] If we could but discover Catesby's trail through the Carolinas and Georgia, where he collected these speci-mens, we would have one of the most important chapters in the history of American ornithology.

IX. AMERICAN ORNITHOLOGY UNDER EUROPEAN COMPILERS

ELEAZAR ALBIN

After Catesby we enter upon a period of several dec-ades when American birds were studied only from afar. There was no one who came here to collect or paint them in any numbers nor even any botanist who achieved dis-tinction in the observation of birds. Birds were, how-ever, studied and descriptions were compiled by several English and continental naturalists who were in com-munication with botanical collectors in various parts of eastern and central North America. There were also occasional opportunities to view a few forlorn dried specimens that went over with the numerous shipments of plants, and now and again a live specimen was held at some tavern or coffee house in London to help the keeper in his business of attracting the public.

This period was dominated by George Edwards, but one of his contemporaries, Eleazar Albin (1713–1759), whose publications preceded his should be included first as a contributor.

Albin was a younger man than Edwards, his birth date being set around 1715 and he is entered in the *Dic-tionary of National Biography* as "a naturalist and teacher of water-colour." In the preface to his *Natural History* he tells us that he taught his daughter, Eliza-beth, "to draw and paint after the life" and many of the plates are signed with her name. Apparently another daughter assisted.

His *Natural History of Birds* was published in Lon-don the same year (1731) as Catesby's *Natural History of Carolina, Florida and the Bahama Islands,* and was

---

[13] Catesby letters in manuscript, Roy. Soc. of London, folio 166.

[14] "Tools" no doubt intended.

[15] For recompiling and rechecking the Catesby list with the A. O. U., *Check-List of North American Birds,* I am greatly indebted to Dr. Arthur A. Allen.

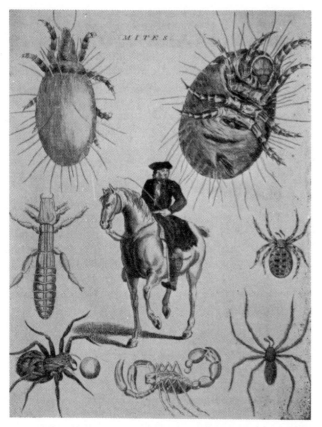

FIG. 26. Eleazar Albin (1713–1759), English writer on birds and bird parasites. From his *Natural History of Spiders* (1736).

illustrated with 306 "curiously engraved and exactly coloured" copper plates.

Albin never visited America nor other foreign lands, but to facilitate his work with exotic birds, he solicited presents of curious birds which he asked to have sent to him "in the comfortable vicinage of the Dog and the Duck" in Tottenham Court Road. The author shows a tincture of complacency about his work which perhaps predisposes the reader to some dissatisfaction with it, but it was moderately instructive in its day, and frequently amusing. After the test of time it is seldom mentioned but it contains a few plates of American birds which are interesting for the fairly skillful execution of the coloring and for the whimsical remarks passed by the author. He often gives, also, the source of his specimen and not infrequently refers to stomach content or internal structural details, which were a novelty in Albin's time.

The first American bird pictured by Albin is the New England Partridge (p. 28) the same species that attracted his contemporary, George Edwards. Albin secured some of these birds from William Lydal, a poulterer, who had bought them of a New England captain. Albin kept them alive and fed them on wheat and hemp seed, and later gave them to the Right Honourable Lord Trevor, who had them a long time with his pheasants.

He next takes up the red-winged starling. This is our red-winged blackbird, although it was shot near London, and was probably an escaped cage-bird. Its gizzard contained grubs, beetles, and small maggots, and from stomach content the author jumps to the nest construction which he says is arched over "to secure it from wet." He attributes this statement to Catesby, saying also that it flies in companies and is destructive. Inaccuracy and carelessness both are evident here, as well as in his description of the bill and eye. The bill, according to Albin, is edged with crimson at the base, and the eye has a black pupil and white iris, both of which statements are false.

In contrast to this, he gives an accurate description of the male and female red grosbeak or Virginia nightingale, our cardinal grosbeak, *Richmondena cardinalis*.

He then descends to ignorant superstition, saying of the house swallow, "a stone found in the stomach of a young swallow, taken at the full of the moon and bound to the arm or hung about the neck of young children is said to cure falling sickness."

Of the goosander or merganser Albin makes some interesting remarks on internal structure as follows:

It hath a huge bony labyrinth on the windpipe just above the Divarications, and besides the windpipe hath 2 swellings one above the other each resembling a powder puff. It hath a gall bladder and the blind guts were three metres long and full of excrements.

The flesh is not wholesome having a filthy unpleasant taste.

The Canada goose, golden-eye, sea pheasant or pintail, the Virginia groas beak, the great sea loon from Newfoundland, and the batt or flutter mouse conclude this author's account of American birds.

The "Virginia groasbeak" is probably intended for our rosebreasted grosbeak although the "hen" is depicted with a black face and back, and wings of reddish-brown, the breast and belly being "more dilute." According to Albin these birds were trapped in North America, much as the larks in England are caught by sweeping away the snow and baiting the place with Virginia wheat etc.

At that time several had been so curious as to try to breed them in England but according to Albin, "to no purpose."

In addition to Albin's account of several species of American birds, with considerable amusing notes on the efficacy of birds for medicinal use, we should call attention to his interest in the external parasites of birds. He published on this in his *Natural History of Spiders*, London, 1736, adding an appendix on the lice that are found on birds. The text of this matter was written by Doctor Hooke, F.R.S., and the plates were done by I. Carwitham Sculp. It is rather surprising to see the interest displayed in these bird parasites at such an early date and to note the number of birds that had been examined. The following kinds of birds were examined and parasites from each illustrated: buzzard, faulcon, pidgeon, crane, tame hen, coot, magpie, more hen, heron, cormorant, teal, crow, wild goose, peacock, swan, turkey, starling. Says the author:

Farther it is remarkable that the bigness of each bird's fleas bears not adequate proportion to the bigness of the birds they are found upon; but amongst the larger kind of birds may be found a lesser and larger sort of fleas of a different kind; and I remember that I have seen fleas upon a black bird as large as those found upon a swan.

Altogether Albin was a comparatively prolific writer on birds but his work is loose and unsystematic, "curious" but seldom accurate even according to the low standard of his day. Many of his plates were copied from an inferior artist of whom George Edwards, Albin's eminent contemporary, said "a very mean performer which Albin has not thought proper to confess."

Despite the stigma of superficiality that stamps Albin's work, it is noteworthy that this author envisaged a scientific goal toward which he aspired. The following quotation from Joseph Addison (1672–1719) (Spectator No. 121) appears at the beginning of Albin's *Natural History of Spiders:*

I could wish that out of several writers, some one would take each his particular species, and give us a distinct account of the frame, and texture of its parts, and particularly those which distinguish it from other animals. This would be one of the best services their studies could do mankind, and not a little redound to the glory of the all wise creator of them.

GEORGE EDWARDS

The Father of British Ornithology is the distinguished title often given to George Edwards (1694–1773). He was as earnest and as thorough in his ornithological study as was Mark Catesby and he had an advantage over Catesby in being naturally talented. He was a skillful draughtsman and a good observer of the living bird, while in making studies of prepared specimens he used an exactness worthy of a modern scientist. With these several abilities to equip him for the study of birds, and his complete freedom from entangling obligation to botanical study, it is probable that, if Edwards could have studied and collected in America, the science of ornithology in this country even in those early years, would have made very important progress.

For his early education George Edwards was placed under the tuition of two clergymen, first a Reverend Hewitt of Leytonstone and later under one of the Established Church at Brentwood. This master was exceedingly kind to him and his great learning in the classics perhaps helped to divert the young Edwards from the commercial life for which his father planned to prepare him. Edwards did serve an apprenticeship, however, under a merchant in Fenchurch Street, and, while living in London he, quite by chance, came under a strong natural history influence.

It happened that a large collection of natural history materials, sculpture, paintings, and antiquities, belonging to an eminent Doctor Nicholas in Covent Garden,

was moved at his death to a flat occupied by George Edwards. At this time Edwards was serving his apprenticeship, but at this eventuality, he became so interested in reading and studying among these treasures that he gave up the idea of going into business and devoted all his leisure time to art and natural history.

In 1716, at the age of twenty-two, the young naturalist shipped to Holland and, returning to London, was unemployed for two years, during which time he probably worked again at his art and natural history studies. He then went to Norway where he wandered through the haunts of sea birds, and it seemed to him the sun in its short dim hours set only to rise again.

He intended to go to Sweden also but this was at the time of the Swedish war when Charles XII (1682–1718) besieged Frederickstadt and all strangers were under suspicion and many were arrested. Edwards often travelled disguised as a beggar to avoid the importunities of the needy people whom he met, and this led to his arrest by Danish police on suspicion of his being a spy. After his release which promptly followed upon the necessary identification, Edwards returned home just at the time when an edict was issued to procure vagrants for America. Thus he narrowly escaped a western sojourn which indeed might have been much to his liking, if we may judge by the effort he later made to become familiar with American birds. In 1720 he went to France and undertook two one-hundred mile journeys on foot to Champagne and Orleans. This must have given his love of nature ample opportunity to develop and when Edwards went back to London he seriously took up the study of birds, purchasing some excellent portraits which he copied. This was the beginning of his ornithological self-education and he was so successful that several wealthy men offered to support his studies. The first of these patrons was James Theobold of Lambeth.

Edwards' work improved rapidly but he felt that he should become familiar with the originals of the great art centers on the Continent, and in 1731 accompanied by two members [1] of his family he visited Brussells, Antwerp and Utrecht.

On his return to London, Edwards became acquainted with Sir Hans Sloane who was then President of the Royal College of Physicians, and he was offered the position of Librarian of this learned body. He accepted this post in 1733 and was given apartments there.

This opened the way for him to become acquainted with the most learned men of the day, and several of the nobility and wealthy gentry became his patrons, in particular Sir Hans Sloane, the Duke of Richmond, the famous Doctor Richard Meade (1673–1754), and Martin Folkes (1690–1754), President of the Royal Society of Antiquaries.

Edwards' association with Sir Hans Sloane no doubt intensified his natural history interest, for Sloane is described primarily as a collector and only secondarily as

---

[1] Little is known of Edwards' family, but he had two sisters who may have been the relatives who accompanied him.

a physician. Though his practice was large and finally brought him the title of first physician to George II in 1727, his publications on medicine were few and unimportant. As early as 1701 he acquired the large cabinet of William Courten (1642–1702) and in 1712 he purchased the Manor of Chelsea where was located the famous botanical or Physic Garden, an enterprise in which he was always deeply interested and which he finally bequeathed to the Apothecaries' Company.

Edwards became one of Sloane's principle aids. From B. Jaeger's *The Life of North American Insects* (1859), containing a life of Sir Hans Sloane,[2, 3] we read on page 12, Edwards' own statement regarding his work for Sloane:

Sir Hans Sloane employed me for a great number of years in drawing miniature figures of animals after nature, in water colours to increase his very great collection of fine drawings by other hands; which drawings are now all fixed in the British museum for the help and information of those in future generations that may be curious or studious in natural history.

With regard to his own drawings for his publications he speaks as follows:

And if my things fall short of nature, and they certainly must, it is not for want of care in me or proper subjects to work from; but because there is an infinite difference between the great Creator of natural productions and the presumptuous weak creature who dared to essay an imitation of the works of the Omnipotent. Sometimes being for a moment thoughtless of the Great Source of nature, I have vainly fancied my faint imitations of her works in some degree complete; but on the least recollection, a slow aweful, majestic voice seemed to reprove me thus: vain and presumptuous wretch! dost thou imagine, thy faint endeavors can bear the least comparison with the works of Him that created Thee and all things?

We can see that Edwards felt very earnestly drawn to a life devoted to natural history and it was during his early years as Librarian of the Royal College of Physicians that he produced his first work, the *Natural History of Uncommon Birds* in four volumes. The first volume he dedicated to the President and Fellows of the College of Physicians and it appeared in 1743 with sixty fine bird plates many of which are American; a French translation was brought out in 1745.

The second volume, with one hundred and four plates, one hundred of which are birds, was dedicated to his particular friend and benefactor, Sir Hans Sloane, and appeared in 1747. The third volume, with fifty-nine birds figured on fifty-two plates, appeared in 1750 and the fourth and last volume, with thirty-nine birds on thirty-seven plates, came out in 1751. The last volume he considered his best; it contained also sixteen plates of serpents, fishes, and insects, and was dedicated to the "God of Nature." Edwards himself was the engraver of the

[2] Sloane's bird collection (birds and their parts), eggs, and nests of different species, 1172 specimens.

[3] Consult also Sweet, 1935: 49–64; 97–116; 145–164.

FIG. 27. Title Page of George Edwards' (1694–1773) *Natural History of Birds* (1743–1751). Courtesy of the Trustees of the British Museum.

plates and likewise the colorist of most of them, and in this new endeavor he was aided by Mark Catesby of whom he speaks as follows:

I was discouraged upon first thinking of this work, at the great expense of engraving, printing and other things, which I knew would be a certain cost attended with very uncertain profit, till my good friend Mr. Catesby put me on etching my plates myself as he had done in his works; and not only so but invited me to see him work at etching and gave me all the hints and instructions to proceed, which favour I think myself obliged to acknowledge.

It is interesting for the American ornithologist to go through Edwards' *Natural History* to see the great amount of work that he did on American birds. A careful description accompanies each plate and at the end of this the author usually tells where he had an opportunity to see the bird or from whom he received it. Two very helpful collections to which he had recourse were Dr. John Fothergill's (1712–1780) at Upton and Captain Raymond's at Valentines, Ilford.

The following list of American species in *The Natural History of Birds* is taken from the edition of 1802 kindly loaned me by the American Museum of Natural History, New York. Edwards' names appear at the left, and the modern approved common names at the right in so far as the drawings can be identified.

Volumes I and II of the *Natural History of Birds*

1. White-tailed Eagle	Gray Sea Eagle
3. Spotted Hawk	Duck Hawk (1st yr.)
4. Black Hawk	Northern Duck Hawk (adult)
38. Red-throated Hummingbird	Ruby-throated Hummingbird
46. Coot-footed Tringa	Northern Phalarope (winter plumage)
50. Spotted Greenland Dove	Mandt's Guillemot (imm.) or winter plumage
53. Ash coloured Buzzard	Rough-legged Hawk
60. Great Horned Owl	Great Horned Owl
61. Great White Owl	Snowy Owl
63. The Whip-poor-will or Lesser Goatsucker	Nighthawk
71. Brown and spotted Heath Cock	Spruce Grouse (female)
72. White Partridge	Willow Ptarmigan
78. Lesser Mock Bird	A variety of the Eastern Mockingbird
80. The Small American Redstart	American Redstart
93. The Pelecan of America	Brown Pelican
95. Red-Breasted Gousander	Red-breasted Merganser
97. Red-throated Ducker or Loon	Red-throated Loon
98. Great Black and White Duck	Northern Eider
99. Dusky and Spotted Duck	Harlequin
100. Little Black and White Duck	Bufflehead
101. Summer Duck of Catesby	Wood Duck

It should be pointed out that in the 1802 edition used in this description Volumes I and II are bound together and no division between the two volumes is indicated. However, from notes on the first edition which I examined in London, it appears that Plate 60 of the great horned owl concludes Volume I and Plate 61 of the great white owl (snowy owl) begins Volume II.

The following list of American birds appears in Volume III of Edwards' *Natural History of Birds* (1743–1751).

Volume III of the *Natural History of Birds*

107. Ring-tailed Hawk	Marsh Hawk
114. Three Toed Woodpecker	Arctic Three-toed Woodpecker
115. American Kingfisher	Belted Kingfisher
117. Long-tailed Grouse from Hudson Bay	Sharp-tailed Grouse
118. Black and Spotted Heath Cock	Spruce Grouse (male)
120. Great American Martin	Purple Martin (female)
122. Black and Yellow Creeper	Bahama Honey Creeper
123. Greatest Bulfinch—Cock	Pine Grosbeak (male)
124. The Greatest Bulfinch—hen	Pine Grosbeak (female)
126. Snow bird from Hudson's Bay	Snow Bunting
130. Painted Finch	Painted Bunting
Lower figure "not yet perfect"	Lower figure Indigo Bunting
132. Hooping Crane from Hudson's Bay	Whooping Crane
133. Brown and Ash coloured Crane	Little Brown Crane
135. Ash coloured Heron from North America	Great Blue Heron
136. Bittern from Hudson's Bay	American Bittern
137. Greater American Godwit	Marbled Godwit
138. Red-Breasted Godwit	Hudsonian Godwit
139. White Godwit from Hudson's Bay	Avocet
Lower Fig. White Redshank	Albino Yellow-legs
140. Spotted Plover	Golden Plover
141. Turn-stone from Hudson's Bay	Ruddy Turnstone
142. Red coot-footed Tringa	Red Phalarope
143. Cock coot-footed Tringa	Northern Phalarope (breeding plumage)
144. Little American Water Hen	Sora
145. Eared or Horned Dobchick	Horned Grebe
146. Speckled Diver or Loon	Pacific Loon
147. Northern Penguin	Great Auk
148. Arctick Bird	Long-tailed Jaeger
149. Arctick Bird	Parasitic Jaeger (imm.)
Lower fig. Tropic bird	Red-billed Tropic-bird
152. Blue-winged Goose	Blue Goose
153. Laughing Goose	White-fronted Goose
154. Grey Headed Eider	King Eider
155. Great Black Duck	Surf Scoter
156. Long-tailed Duck from Hudson's Bay	Old Squaw
157. Little Brown and White Duck	Harlequin (female)

Fɪɢ. 28. The Great White Crane (Whooping Crane), by George Edwards. From his *Natural History of Birds* (1743–1751). Courtesy of the Trustees of the British Museum.

Volume IV is a miscellany of birds, mammals, lizards, turtles, and fishes—of interest to American readers chiefly for its plates of American mammals—but there are no American birds.

Summarizing Edwards' contribution to American ornithology as seen in his *Natural History of Birds,* we find fifty-seven species described and drawn with a few showing the male as well as the female. Of his method of work he made this statement:

I have endeavored to finish my figures with such exactness both as to drawing and colouring, that the prints themselves may give a tolerable idea of the subjects exhibited on them and save such curious persons as have not leisure, the trouble of reading their descriptions.

His descriptions, however, are most meticulously drawn up and are well worth reading by the modern ornithologist. Edwards was likewise exceedingly particular about his plates; he is said to have made several drawings in many cases before he was satisfied with the pose and plumage. He was also insistent about seeing the bird in life if possible, going long distances through London and its environs, now to Stepney where Dr. Massey lived; now to Mill Hill to see Peter Collinson, to Upton to see something at Dr. Fothergill's, to Valentines, Ilford, to see some bird held captive by Captain Raymond. Even the royal midwife, Mrs. Sidney Kennon, had a considerable interest in birds and more than once furnished him with a sight of some new species.

GLEANINGS OF NATURAL HISTORY (1758–1764)

Several years passed by between the conclusion of the *Natural History of Birds* and the *Gleanings of Natural History.* These *Gleanings* are acknowledged by the author to be an afterthought, for he had not planned to continue publishing, as, in his own words, he "waxed in years and infirmities." During the preparation of his *Natural History of Birds,* Edwards had enjoyed "the great honour, happiness, and pleasure of being patronized by four gentlemen who were the greatest promoters of learning, science and arts of any in the present age," but, to use his own words again, "inexorable death deprived me of them all in a very short time."

It was therefore a much more difficult task to complete the *Gleanings.* The volumes are given over to mammals as well as to birds and relate mostly to species outside of England, among which the author has presented a number of plates and accounts of American birds. Modern names are in parentheses as follows:

Volume I
Maryland Yellow-throat
Blue Jay
Summer Redbird (Summer Tanager)
Chatterer of Carolina (Cedar Waxwing)
Golden-crowned Thrush (Oven-bird)
Blue Flycatcher (Black-throated Blue Warbler)
Olive-colored Flycatcher
Golden-crowned Wren (Golden-crowned Kinglet)
Ruby-crowned Wren (Ruby-crowned Kinglet)
Yellow-rumped Flycatcher (Myrtle Warbler)
Yellow Red-Poll (Probably the Palm Warbler)
American Red-start (American Redstart)
Ruffed Heath Cock (Ruffed Grouse)

Volume II
The Painted Bunting
The Gold Finch (Goldfinch)
The Spotted Tringa. (Spotted Sandpiper)
Pine Creeper (Pine Warbler)
American Water Rail (Virginia Rail)
Long Tailed Duck (Old Squaw)
Marsh Hawk
Reed Bird (Bobolink)
Little Thrush (Hermit Thrush)
Lark from Pennsylvania (Pipit)
Golden-crowned Flycatcher (Myrtle Warbler)
Golden-winged Flycatcher (Golden-winged Warbler)
Black throated Green Flycatcher
    (Black throated Green Warbler)
Black and White Creeper (Black and White Warbler)
Red-throated Flycatcher, male and female
    (Chestnut-sided Warbler)
Little Blue-grey Flycatcher, cock and hen
    (Blue-grey gnatcatcher)
Spotted Sandpiper
Crossbills
White-throated Sparrow
Worm-eater (Worm-eating Warbler)

Volume III
Scarlet Sparrow (Scarlet Tanager)
Round crested Duck (Hooded Merganser)

FIG. 29. The Ruffed Grouse of Edwards' *Natural History of Birds*. The first American bird to be the subject of a paper before the Royal Society (1754). Courtesy of the Trustees of the British Museum, Natural History Department.

Looking through Edwards' presentation of American birds in the *Gleanings,* one is impressed with his skill as a draughtsman, yet he failed to catch the spirit and personality of the birds even though in many instances he saw them in life. The yellow red-poll which was his name for our palm warbler, a bird he had studied at the home of Mrs. Kennon, and the crossbills which he had received from a whale fisherman and kept in a cage at his home, are not well done. The same is true of his portrayal of the painted bunting and two captive American goldfinches. However, his interpolation of notes on life history and the various sources of his information make his accounts interesting. Of the goldfinches he tells that he kept them in separate cages. The male soon died, but he had the female for over a year and in that time she moulted twice "in March and in September and in winter her body was wholly brown but the head, wings and tail were the same colour they were in the summer." Edwards included with his drawing of the goldfinches a picture of the egg which this captive laid in August 1755—"a small pearl coloured egg without any spots."

He received many notes for his accounts from John Bartram of Philadelphia. This famous Quaker botanist was known to the whole coterie of London naturalists who frequently consulted him and also received consignments of American plants, and sometimes other specimens from him. He had furnished Edwards with nesting notes on the oven-bird, *Seiurus aurocapillus,*

saying it always chose the south side of a hill for its nest which was "a hole in the leaves lined with dry grasses." This bird Edwards called the "Golden Crowned Thrush" (a name still heard today), but he remarked that it was smaller than the "Little Thrush" (hermit thrush) described by Catesby.

The most outstanding feature of the three volumes of *Gleanings* is Chapter 38 of Volume I which the author devotes to a thorough account of the ruffed heath cock, our ruffed grouse (*Bonasa umbellus*). Edwards had been corresponding with John Bartram on the subject and he conceived the plan to assemble all information on this interesting species for inclusion in his new work the *Gleanings* and also for presentation to the Royal Society of London. This was the most learned body of the time, and Edwards' paper which was presented on January 17, 1754, was the first dissertation of its kind on an American bird to be given. Notes on the coloration, local abundance and scarcity, behavior of young, the strange drumming of the male, and even some early attempts to hatch the eggs under hens were included. A drawing by Edwards of the bird in display from a specimen sent by John Bartram was exhibited. This early study of the grouse caused considerable comment in 1754 and it gathers new interest today in the light of the intensive modern investigation of this species.[4, 5]

Like all observers of his time and many subsequent ones, Edwards attempted to explain the rolling thunder of the male bird. The "thumping or drumming," according to him, "is produced by the birds clapping their wings against their sides and the sound of the drumming is the means by which the hunters discover them and shoot them in great numbers." According to Baron Lahontan whom he quotes, it is made by clapping one wing against the other and the drumming that ensues serves to call their mates and can be heard a quarter of a league. The startling flight of the grouse had always attracted the attention of Indians and travellers; but the drumming was an enigma, and though observed and discussed for hundreds of years, was never satisfactorily explained until Dr. A. A. Allen, of Cornell University, through his analysis of individual frames of his motion pictures of the drumming performance expounded it step by step. In short, it is produced as the bird, braced with its tail upon the log, fans the air very rapidly with forward and upward strokes of its concave wings.[6]

A second American bird was featured by Edwards in another paper before the Royal Society—the red phalarope (*Lobipes phalaropus lobatus*) called then the coot-footed tringa because of its lobed toes. A drawing of this bird by Edwards appeared as an inset in a larger plate depicting a new species of phalarope from Yorkshire and Edwards used this method to emphasize the difference between two related forms of widely separa-

[4] Allen, Arthur A., 1929: 3–21.
[5] Allen, Arthur A., 1934: 180–199.
[6] Bent, 1932: 142–147. See account of courtship by A. A. Allen.

ted localities. Thus American birds slowly were claiming attention in Europe, and scientists were beginning to find that New World birds were in many instances quite different from those of the Old World.

In the *Gleanings* Edwards presents thirty-five species of American birds which, with the fifty-seven in the *Natural History* make a total of ninety-two figured and thoroughly described, nearly as many as Catesby presented. These two men were contemporaries, Edwards being about twelve years Catesby's junior and they published about twenty years apart. It is obvious that Edwards was the better draughtsman, but Catesby had the advantage of having studied American birds in their natural habitat. In comparing these two men either as artists or as scientists, we should remember that they worked under very unequal conditions and were also unequally equipped. While Catesby's education eludes us completely and we feel that he became an ornithologist under great odds, Edwards' education, at least in so far as natural history is concerned, was largely in his own hands and early in life he was able to indulge his passion for bird study. This took the form of extensive travel into other countries, also practicing bird portraiture from standard bird drawings; later he studied famous originals in the great art galleries of Holland and lastly he took up the engraving of birds with the idea of accurate portrayal as his goal.

During the fifty odd years that he worked at natural history he accumulated nine hundred drawings of birds, mammals, and other forms all done by himself, but the bulk of his work was ornithological. This entire collection was eventually purchased by the Earle of Bute (John Stuart, 1713–1792) a very important character in the reign of George III who was a patron of literature and a student of agriculture and botany.

Before parting with his collection, however, Edwards arranged to place a copy of all his works with the four principal learned bodies in London, the Royal College of Physicians, the Royal Society of London, the Royal Society of Antiquaries, and the British Museum. This great institution had its origin in the purchase by the Nation of Sir Hans Sloane's vast collections of art, sculpture, minerals, manuscripts, drawings, and objects of natural history. It is interesting to conjecture what American specimens might have been in this nucleus of the British Museum. Certainly they could not have survived long for the taxidermy of those days was very crude. The head and wings of birds were never skinned out. Instead these parts with the brain and musculature intact received a few injections of "preserving fluid" and then the bird was wired and twisted and set up in a ghastly semblance of life. Flat skins were unknown and the more rare and difficult to obtain the specimens were, the more insistent were the authorities that they be displayed conspicuously for the delight of the public. Sun dust, and human hands added to the ravages of time and insect and we can readily understand that trophies from distant America must have been short lived. We know

from Doctor R. Bowdler Sharpe's (1847–1909) *History of the Collections in the British Museum* (1906) that a few American species stood in solemn array at the opening of that great institution.

According to his estimate, an approximation of 1,117 birds and their parts, nests and eggs were in the original collection of which the following are the more interesting American species mentioned with the current names:

> California vulture (California condor)
> Scarlet or Virginia grosbeak (eastern cardinal)
> Rose coloured spoonbill (roseate spoonbill)
> Several hummingbirds (hummingbirds)
> Crested California quail (California quail)

We may imagine that Edwards who had been so long associated with Sir Hans was a bulwark of strength to him after he retired from active life at the age of eighty years. Sloane then lived quietly at the Manor House in Chelsea but became very infirm, only able to get about in a wheel chair, the last years. Many requests for aid came to the aged benefactor of science and it was apparently Edwards' task to investigate the applicants who too often were the "decayed branches of noble families" and advise with Sir Hans as to the worthiness of each case. Saturday afternoons it was Edwards' custom to come and take coffee in the garden with his friend, and talk over the affairs and publications of the scientific world.

Sloane died on January 11, 1753, six years before the removal of his precious collections to their new vast quarters in Bloomsbury. His statue stands in the center of the Chelsea Botanic Garden which was one of his most cherished interests, and Sloane Square in Chelsea was named after him.

At the time of Sloane's death, Edwards himself was about sixty years of age. He still had another decade of active service and writing, but at the age of seventy his sight began to fail and his hand became unsteady. In 1771 he brought out his new edition of Catesby's work to which had been added the Linnean generic index of the animals and plants. This is a two volume edition of folio size and modest cloth binding, thus emulating Edwards' idea of appropriateness, for apparently he disapproved of Catesby's elegant and expensive edition. The type is a little clearer and the editor has omitted many of the capitals used by Catesby, since the custom of excessive capitalization was going out at this later date. A trace of Edwards' more cultivated diction is discernible in his consistent replacement of Catesby's "em" for "them." But the same quaint remarks which serve to lighten Catesby's ponderous tomes for the modern reader are retained, for example, the parrot of Carolina, of which he says "Their guts are certain and speedy poison to cats" and of the purple jack daw (the purple grackle), "They have rank smell; their flesh is coarse, black, and is seldom eat."

No further publications by Edwards came out during his lifetime but a paper on the *Emigrations of Birds* was published posthumously in 1781 and extracts from his *Gleanings* were put out under the title *Essays on the Natural History of Birds* in 1805.

The last years of Edwards' life were spent in retirement at a little place called Paistow. Blindness, caused by cancer, was creeping upon him and he died on July 23, 1773, leaving directions that he be buried in his native parish at Westham with only a simple epitaph to mark his resting place. A simple stone was erected but according to the *Essex Naturalist* [7] has long since disappeared.

We cannot call Edwards a prolific writer. Seven volumes are all that he published, except a few articles in the *Philosophical Transactions* of the Royal Society which may be read in the 48th, 49th, 50th, 51st, 53rd and 56th volumes. In recognition of his publication of the *Natural History of Birds* he was awarded in 1750 the Godfrey Copley (d. 1709) decoration given annually on St. Andrew's Day (November 30) for the most outstanding work of art or book on nature. This honor was followed by others, Edwards being elected to the Royal Society in 1757 and somewhat later to several leading learned academies of Europe. On February 13, 1773 he was made a member of the Royal Society of Antiquaries, just a few months before his death.

An interesting detail of his scientific career and one that has eluded his biographers, I chanced upon in London a few years ago. Soon after the publication of the first volume of his *Natural History of Birds,* Edwards was a candidate for election to the Royal Society in 1744. His several patrons sponsored his name and Peter Collinson, Mark Catesby, and other members indicated their approval. It was customary in the Royal Society to read the proposed names at ten consecutive meetings prior to balloting for the candidate.

But a week later Edwards sent word that he wanted to withdraw his name. Careful reading of the minutes of the Society failed to give any explanation of Edwards' action.

Knowing that he was an extremely pious and conscientious man, one is led to wonder whether he deemed himself unworthy at this stage of his career for the distinction of membership in the Royal Society. This, however, seems unlikely for he had already published one volume of his *History of Birds* in 1743; and other volumes were in preparation. Neither does it seem that the reason could have been financial for the dues at this time were only a shilling a week. But be that as it may, there lies in this chance finding a story to be told when some delver in the biographies of early naturalists has the good fortune to uncover it.

Edwards was a man of middle stature inclined to stoutness. Other than his faithful friendship with Sir Hans Sloane we know little of his private life but we recall that he was always helpful to younger ornithologists and he had a class for young ladies in the art of portray-

[7] Avery, 1903–1904: **13**: 343–348.

Fig. 30. Linnaeus (1707–1778), famous Swedish botanist who stimulated the study of all fields of natural history by his revolutionary system of binomial nomenclature. Courtesy of the Trustees of the British Museum.

ing birds and making flat mounts from the birds' plumages.

LINNAEUS

Although Linnaeus (1707–1778) had worked out his principles of classification with plants, he was able to apply them also to animals. A story of his early experience with birds suggests how he came to his great work.

We must go back to Linnaeus' university years to see the factors that entered into his later career. He went one year to the University of Lund, but transferred to Upsala, and in 1730 was invited to live in the home of Professor Olof Rudbeck, Jr. (1660–1740) as tutor to his younger sons. In this way Linnaeus had access to the excellent Rudbeck Library and the once beautiful botanic gardens that had been laid out by the elder Rudbeck, but it still showed the ravages of the disastrous Upsala fire of 1702.

It was, nevertheless, a joy to him to work and study in the garden describing the plants and arranging his descriptions according to his ideas of relationship. In this post Linnaeus had an excellent contact, for Rudbeck was a broadly trained scholar, having in addition to his medical learning a valuable botanical background through his father, with whom he had collaborated on the monumental work on plants, the *Campus Elysii*. The greater part of this important treatise was destroyed in the aforementioned fire, and young Rudbeck leaned more and more to his language studies.

However, an interest in birds from his early youth had never left him, and indeed at one time he envisaged a work on birds of the scope and perfection of the *Campus Elysii*. By 1695 he had painted a considerable collection of birds, which was viewed by King Charles XI on his visit to Upsala, and the King at once recommended that Rudbeck continue his art work, and include a trip to Lapland for the study of plants and birds. For this he received a stipend, which enabled him to travel, and he spent part of 1695 in the north of Sweden making collections of plants and birds, many of which were new to him.

Rudbeck's father died soon after the great fire, having overtaxed his strength in heroic efforts to save the fifteenth-century Upsala Cathedral and the Rudbeck Observatory adjacent it. The son then was appointed to his father's professorship, and became the lecturer in anatomy, botany, zoology and pharmacology. It was in this period that the Rudbeck paintings of birds came into real service in a small course in ornithology, which he gave over a period of years; just how many is not clear. At any rate, after 1720, according to Einar Lönberg, he was relieved of regular lecturing in order to devote himself to his great work, entitled *Thesaurus Linguarum Asiae et Europae harmonicus.*

However, he apparently was asked to renew his bird lectures, for in the spring of 1728 Linnaeus and a number of other students attended three lectures on birds of prey (de avibus rapacibus). Rudbeck lectured, also, on the birds of the Bible and a few other lectures were given in 1729 on Swedish birds. For this group Professor Rudbeck used his own paintings to demonstrate his talks and from the few notes by him still in existence it is possible to gain some idea of the scope and quality of his knowledge of birds. His notes contain many observations on habits and he was acquainted, also, with considerable morphological details. It may be that he had some plan of formulating a system of classification, for he expressed disagreement with Aldrovandus and other professors, but, if so, he never put this plan into writing. Only the drawings and a few notes remain, and these never passed beyond the manuscript stage, except for a few reproductions of the bird paintings, which Dr. Einar Lönnberg included in his articles on Rudbeck.

We may imagine that Linnaeus' natural interest in birds must have been considerably stimulated by this association, and indeed, there is ample proof of this for he was quietly working on an ornithological manuscript at this time. It seems that he kept it a secret and on the occasion of Professor Rudbeck's seventieth birthday in 1730, he presented it to him—a slender manuscript put together like a book, and entitled *Methodus Avium Sveticarum*. In this he had set forth the descriptions of many birds. This manuscript is still preserved in the Carolina Rediviva, but has become much larger, since Linnaeus

took it with him on his journey to Lapland and on other expeditions, and interleaved it with additional notes. Based on Professor Rudbeck's drawings this booklet became the foundation of Linnaeus' *Fauna Svecica* published in 1746 and in the tenth edition of the *Systema Naturae,* which was the first time that he used binomial nomenclature throughout, he often quotes the previous authority of *Fauna Svecica*. Rudbeck's drawings, from which Linnaeus first became acquainted with many species of birds, are still in the nature of type specimens of some present day species. And the following birds of the *American Check-List* still have as their types certain drawings described by Linnaeus from the unpublished bird portraits of the Swedish ornithologist, Olof Rudbeck: [8] *Buteo lagopus* (rough-legged hawk) ; *Larus hyperboreus* (glaucous gull); *Stercorarius longicaudus* (long-tailed skua) ; *Colymbus stellatus* (red-throated diver). Of the considerable group of other Swedish birds, which are also species of the American Check-List, and which Rudbeck included in his portfolio of bird paintings, we may cite several of our northern birds, for example: willow ptarmigan, raven, magpie, old squaw, Arctic loon, European cormorant, snowy owl, fish hawk, great black-backed gull.

These are only a few of the many species in this interesting group of Rudbeck originals, which inhabit, also, the western hemisphere.

After this rather lengthy digression to call attention to Linnaeus' introduction to ornithology under Professor Rudbeck, let us follow his career subsequent to 1730.

Early in his university course, he had attracted the attention of the Dean, Dr. Olof Celius (1670–1756), by his paper, *Preliminaries on the Marriage of Plants,* (1729). Under this arresting title he set forth his exposition of sex in plants, their physiology and the method of generation. In short, a true analogy of plants with animals was concluded. His obviously thorough understanding of botany also led Professor Rudbeck to ask his assistance in the lectures and demonstrations that were given in the garden. Linnaeus acceded proudly, but with surprise to the flattering offer, and was successful, for he drew an audience of from two to four hundred listeners. So great, indeed, became his popularity that envious competitors sought to put a stop to his teaching because he had not yet obtained his medical degree. This will show how closely the study of botany was tied to the medical curriculum in this period of natural science.

The Consistory of the University recognized the irregularity of Linnaeus' position, yet saw in him such genius that he was permitted to follow his own plans temporarily at least, and to continue his lectures and demonstrations which gradually changed from the more or less popular talks to more scientific and technical lectures upon his personally thought-out theories. Indeed, his lectures here were later enlarged and reconstructed

---

8 Lönnberg, 1931: 302–307.

to form his *Philosophia Botanica* as published in 1751. So matters went on until Professor Rudbeck, returning from a vacation and with less of a teaching burden upon him because of his age, wished to continue his lectures in botany. At this point, Linnaeus feeling that he was no longer needed and further calumniated by a woman in the Rudbeck household, decided to leave and make a collecting trip into Lapland (1732).

Such a perilous journey was not lightly decided upon. He sought his parents' counsel and applied to the university for a travelling stipend of 600 dalers ($75) but only after months of waiting did he receive word to proceed. As for his parents' consent, his mother remained firm against his entire scientific career, having never ceased to regret that he would not devote his life to the Church, but his father gave his blessing and told him to trust in God who was ever present even in the wildest Lapland fells.

Good fortune, but many adventures attended him ere he safely returned in six months with stores of new botanical, zoological, and mineralogical material. Although he went entirely alone on this his maiden journey, poorly equipped, short of money, and still but a youth, he emerged upon civilization again a mature scientist learned in many fields and meditating the subject matter of many future writings.

After his return to Upsala other journeys lay ahead, some with Dr. Celsius, some with Dr. Rudbeck, some to the rich mining country around Falun, where he met his future wife, and another with a group of students through Dalana on which expedition Linnaeus mentions particularly collecting the three-toed woodpecker, *Picus tridactylus* (now *Picoides tridactylus*). He had by this time been a student for seven years and still had no degree and no assurance of a permanent position at Upsala for he sensed definite opposition from other aspirants. Moreover, he was unable to publish his scientific treatises in Sweden. Thus, considering all these factors he made the break and went abroad to Holland in 1735 intending to take his medical degree at the University of Harderwijk and, if possible, to begin publishing.

So many honors and strokes of good fortune came to Linnaeus on the Continent that we can mention only a few, a decisive one being his meeting with the Dutch Senator and botanist in Leyden, Jan Frederick Gronovius (1611–1671), to whom he showed his *Systema Naturae* then in manuscript. So impressed was Gronovius with the rationality and lucidity of Linnaeus' binomial system of naming plants and animals that he sent it to press at his own expense and that of Isaac Lawson, a wealthy Scot.[9] It was well received and interested the famous Doctor Herman Boerhaave (1668–1738) who invited Linnaeus to his arboretum. We may judge of the great doctor's opinion of the young scientist by his offer to sponsor a two-year trip to the Cape to collect plants for the University garden at Leyden, and after-

wards to go to America. The offer no doubt was tempting but several ties, his parents, his betrothed Sara Moraea, in Falun, and his friendship for Dr. Celsius dissuaded him, and in lieu of the longer voyage it was decided that he should go to England where he would meet many famous botanists.

By other good fortune Linnaeus became acquainted with the President of the Dutch East India Company, George Clifford, a wealthy banker who owned a beautiful botanic garden and menagerie near Leyden. Through the sponsorship of Clifford, Linnaeus was able to begin publishing several of his early works; he was invited to live in the palatial Clifford home and to prepare a Hortus hartecampensi, Hartcamp being the name of the Clifford garden. In his dedication to Clifford Linnaeus writes

your menageries delighted me, full of tigers, apes, wild hounds, Indian deer and goats, South American and African swine; with these mingled flocks of birds, American hawks, various kinds of parrots, pheasants, peafowl, American capercailzies, Indian hens, swans, many sorts of ducks and geese, waders and other swimming birds, snipe, American crossbills, sparrows of divers kinds, turtle-doves with innumerable other species which made the garden re-echo with their noise.

All this wealth of bird and mammal life in addition to the fascinations of one of the world's most famous gardens lay before him. When finally he entered the "truly royal residence" and beheld the extensive museum and the herbarium he expressed his feelings in these simple words: "My earnest wish was that I might lend a helping hand to their preservation." And so he gave himself ardently to the arrangement of the herbarium, adding many new specimens; to the cultivation of many rarities in the garden, and the study and management of the menagerie.

While here he met again his countryman, Peter Artedi (1705–1735), newly come from England, whom he had enjoyed so much at Upsala when Artedi was beginning his work on fishes and Linnaeus was busy mostly with plants, birds and mammals. Artedi needed work, and Linnaeus was able to put him in touch with the wealthy apothecary, Albert Seba (1665–1736), of Amsterdam, then engaged in a work on fishes. So it was that Artedi's excellent knowledge of fish was turned to good advantage by Linnaeus but how short lived it was; for a few weeks later Artedi, walking home late at night, fell into a canal and was drowned. Linnaeus completed and published in 1738 Artedi's *Ichthyologia sive opera omnia de piscibus,* ascribing to him the honor of founding a useful scientific system of fishes.

No doubt Artedi's accounts of England and scientists there quickened Linnaeus' desire to meet some of these eminent men and it was arranged that he be spared for some two months from the work he was doing for Clifford. Sir Hans Sloane, Doctor J. J. Dillenius (1687–1747) of Oxford, William Sherard are some to whom he had letters of introduction and he met also Peter

---

[9] Jackson, 1923: 142.

Collinson, Philip Miller (1691–1771), administrator of the Apothecaries' Garden in Chelsea, Dr. Cromwell Mortimer (d. 1752), and Mark Catesby recently returned from America.

By this time Linnaeus had published in Holland his *Bibliotheca botanica* (1736), *Fundamenta botanica* (1736), and the very important work *Genera Plantarum* (1737), and we may be sure that the English botanists met Linnaeus with mingled feelings of respect and misgiving for his reforms in the classification and nomenclature of plants. Peter Collinson whom he visited tried to interest his botanical friends, and was perhaps more than half convinced of the new system's merits. In a letter to John Bartram who was shipping many American plants to England at that time, he wrote: "The Systema Naturae is a curious performance for a young man but his coining of a new set of names for plants tends but to embarrass and perplex the study of botany. . . . Very few like it." John Stuart, third Earl of Bute (1718–1792), Secretary of State under George III and a botanist by avocation, said he could not forgive the barbarous Swedish names and further he declared "I am surprised to see all Europe suffer these impertinences." On the whole, however, the English criticisms were less acrid than those of the Germans, and Linnaeus, though somewhat coolly received at first, won many followers in England and was given many plants from the Chelsea garden when he left.

It would be somewhat extraneous to Linnaeus' contribution to ornithology to go into the various encomiums and overtures that awaited him on his return to the Continent. Suffice it to say that Holland, Spain, and France all wished him to make that country his home but, true to his fatherland and having received his degree in Holland, he returned to Sweden in 1738, set up a medical practice in Stockholm and married his bride in 1740. Of the medical profession he was soon glad to be freed, and on the death of his former benefactor and professor, Dr. Olof Rudbeck, in March 1740 the King appointed him Professor of Medicine and Botany at the University of Upsala, to take office in 1741.

This was the post for which he had long hoped and he entered upon his epoch-making teachings which lasted for thirty-seven years.

The annual registration at the University of Upsala increased from 239 to 1,500 during his incumbency. Scientists from all over the world came to study with him, some remaining several years. Then they left to take up their duties in other universities, or, in some cases, they went as collectors to foreign lands. The specimens accruing from these expeditions, including plants, birds, mammals, reptiles, and minerals, were sent back to Linnaeus for description.

Apparently Linnaeus in addition to his great learning had many pleasing personal qualities which endeared him to his students—friendliness, humor, and his practice of combining field work with his teaching brought his students into close understanding. Eight places

around Upsala were visited for plants, birds, and other specimens, and when the party was large (sometimes two or three hundred) Linnaeus delegated certain jobs to certain members: one to take down notes from his dictation, one to gather plant specimens, one to shoot birds, and, when the party regathered after recess periods, Linnaeus lectured a short time on the more interesting things that the students brought back. These trips lasted all day from 8 A.M. to 9 P.M. and on the home stretch they often sang student songs as we do today.

One of the great professor's rules of life that he liked to offer his students was "mingle your joys sometimes with your earnest occupation." Another proof of his friendly relations with students is found in these words, "a professor can never better distinguish himself in his work than by encouraging a clever pupil, for the true discoverers are amongst them, as the comets amongst the stars." Thus his students became his apostles and were glad to keep contact with him and build up his great collections from their expeditions. Peter Kalm was one of these in whom Linnaeus took particular satisfaction. The story is told that Linnaeus was suffering from a severe attack of cholera followed by gout when Kalm returned from the American Colonies in 1751 but so welcome was he and so interesting were his collections that Linnaeus was promptly cured.

Now in what way may Linnaeus be said to have influenced ornithology? We have seen that his first publication on birds contained some American species which are found also in Sweden but it is not the description of the individual birds that is significant; it is rather the simple and clear method of classifying and naming birds that is important. In the words of Fredrick A. Lucas (1852–1929),[10]

But Linnaeus did much more than devise a scheme of nomenclature: he systematically defined each and every group of plants and animals with which he dealt, giving their chief characters in a few brief words; and the small groups, or genera, he combined into large divisions termed "orders." It matters not that the genera of Linnaeus have since been divided and subdivided many times, the underlying principle of assigning certain definite characters to each animal remains the same.

Previous to Linnaeus it was customary to use Latin phrases to describe every plant and animal but each worker followed his own idea or he attempted to follow the method of some predecessor. If he found this difficult to do or thought his specimen slightly different he changed the description to suit his particular specimen. It became very difficult and finally impossible to be sure of the identity of any given specimen from these loose descriptions. It was at this point that Linnaeus stepped in and made order out of confusion. In place of cumbersome phrases he substituted succinctness by giving every species of plant and animal a terse description consisting of the genus in which he placed it, plus a specific

10 Lucas, 1908: 52–57.

name which was sufficiently inclusive to apply to all the individuals of that kind. His scientific appellations consisted of a generic name, and a specific name—each a single word—the genus in his day, as now, always capitalized, while the specific name was written usually with a small letter, unless it was derived from a proper name. Botanists and zoologists have deviated from each other on this point, botanists commonly using capitals in specific names derived from proper names, while zoologists, including the ornithologists, rarely accept such capitalization.

According to Dr. John T. Zimmer, Curator of Birds at the American Museum, Linnaean bird genera approach in scope the modern bird families of today, and although the included forms of some Linnaean genera have shifted to other genera, as further study has made clear their true affinities, Linnaeus still holds the honor of having worked out a usable system of classification for the entire plant and animal kingdoms.

This system of classification is promulgated in his *Philosophia Botanica* (1751), and is put to use in the *Systema Naturae* of Linnaeus. There have been thirteen editions of this epoch-making work, but the tenth edition, of 1758, has been accepted by the scientific world as the beginning of scientific nomenclature. No scientific name published prior to this date is citable even, though it may be a binomial one.

However, it is clear that in 1758 a large part of the flora and fauna of the world was still undescribed, and it became necessary to set up a committee on nomenclature, whose function it was to formulate an International Code,[11] based on Linnaeus' binomial system. General attempts were made at standardizing the rules of nomenclature during the next hundred and twenty-five years. But the first one that met with anything approaching international acceptance was presented at the First International Zoological Congress in Paris in 1889 by Raphael Blanchard (1857?–1929), a French zoologist. In 1901 at the Fifth International Zoological Congress a committee of fifteen presented a revised code that approximates the code currently in use.

The intricacies of this important tool of classification need not concern us here, but, before leaving Linnaeus to take up his successors in the study of birds, we should glance at the state of nomenclature in America in his time.

At that date there were thought to be about 790 species of birds, of which 260 were American. According to Frederick A. Lucas, the American Check-List of birds, as early as 1889, had increased to 729 species and sub-species, and of these 202 were named by Linnaeus, and only thirty-three by Audubon.

Dr. Alfred Newton (1829–1907), the great British ornithologist, points out for us some interesting facts relative to the Linnaean genera.[12] The term "type

specimen" was not known to Linnaeus but the principle evidently was in his plan for he designated as the "type" of his genus "that species to which the name he adopted as generic, had formerly been specifically applied." He was conservative; he seemed even averse to inventing new names, preferring to retain old names when possible "thus building on ancient foundations," and he was careful to cite the authors from whom he borrowed. According to Newton he invented only the following twelve genera: Ramphastos, Buceros, Procellaria, Diomedea, Phaëthon, Palamedea, Mycteria, Cancroma, Parra, Didus, Numida, Pipra.

The rest of the seventy-eight genera for which he is responsible he adapted from his predecessors, chiefly Gesner, Aldrovandus, Belon, John Johnstone (1603–1675), Paul Moehring (1716–1792), Carolus Clusius (1526–1609), Jacob Klein (1685–1759), and Mathurin Brisson (1723–1806). This is shown by his reference to their works in his own publications.

It is easily understood that Linnaeus could not see in life, nor even as prepared specimens, all the birds that he described. Frequently he based his descriptions on drawings, as he had done in his *Methodus Avium Sveticarum,* and asked for descriptive notes compiled by other observers. The words of George Edwards in a letter to Linnaeus elucidate the probable manner in which Linnaeus was enabled to describe many birds for which he is the authority. Edwards writes:[13]

As it will be some months before I can publish a work I have now in hand, and knowing your thirst for the earliest insight of what is going forward in natural history, I have herewith sent you 75 prints in full confidence that you will make no use of them to my disadvantage. I believe before the next winter is over, the letterpress will be ready to be delivered, with the sets of prints I am now colouring; yet I thought this small present of black prints might be acceptable to you in the meantime.

To this Linnaeus wrote a letter of thanks and said in part:

Nothing can more conduce to the advancement of solid natural knowledge, than such beautiful and excellent figures accompanied by such exact descriptions. . . . I shall subjoin in an appendix to the second volume, whatever I can collect for the advancement of science from these plates.

Linnaeus concludes his letter with appreciation of Edwards' portrait that hung in his study and finally he states that "your Long-tailed Duck (Old-Squaw) *Clangula hyemalis* is frequent with us all winter long."

In another letter to Edwards, Linnaeus refers to 68 species of stuffed birds he had received apparently from J. Kramer who had just published a small bird book, *Flora Austriae inferioris,* in which he showed himself very proficient in ornithology. Many of these birds were already known to Linnaeus but he refers particularly to

---

[11] International Code of zoological nomenclature, *Proc. Biol. Soc. of Washington,* 39: 75–104, 1926.

[12] Newton, 1876: 94–105.

[13] Smith, J. E., *Correspondence of Linnaeus,* 2: 496, 1759–1828. Edwards' letter is not dated but Linnaeus' reply, written three days after he received Edwards' is dated Upsala, March 20, 1758. Also *op. cit.* 2: 501–502.

FIG. 31. Thomas Pennant (1726–1798), English naturalist, author of *Arctic Zoology* (1792). Courtesy of the Trustees of the British Museum.

a small species of grouse similar to *Tetrao alchata* called by Kramer *Practincola*. Linnaeus remarked with surprise "the nakedness of the thighs above the knees." (*T. alchata* of Linnaeus is a sand grouse which is feathered to the toes. The practincoles have long naked legs like shorebirds.)

Concluding a letter to Edwards written from Upsala April 13, 1764 Linnaeus pays tribute to Edwards with the following remarks:

> I congratulate you on the acquisition of such beautiful and innumerable rare birds, beyond what any other person has seen, or is likely to meet with; still less is any other hand likely to equal your representations in which nothing is wanting to the birds but their song.

THOMAS PENNANT

Many will recall Thomas Pennant (1726–1798) as the friend and correspondent of the Selborne naturalist, Gilbert White (1720–1793), whose famous volume, *The Natural History of Selborne* (1789), ranks as a classic of field observation. In the eighteenth century, this book set forth a new and growing method of natural history study. Aldrovandus, in the late sixteenth century, had aspired to it; Ray and Willughby, in the latter seventeenth century, had practiced it to some extent in their joint expeditions through England and the Continent; Catesby and Edwards more palpably sensed and understood the proper methods of observation of the living bird, but even they, with all their keen interest in the habits and characteristics of birds, lacked the literary touch which White and Pennant and, later, William Bartram diffused through their writings.

In Pennant's writings, therefore, we may look for certain warmer currents than we have found in the conscientious recording of facts by previous observers.

Thomas Pennant came of a very old Welsh family, one branch of it going back to Richard Plantagenet, Duke of York (1460). The name Pennant was not taken for many years. It is derived from the Welsh, Pen, meaning a head, and nant, a dingle or tree-clad dell, which was the type of location of the ancient family property at Downing in Flintshire. His father is described as a plain and worthy English gentleman of the old landed type, his mother the third daughter of Richard Mytton, Esq. of Halston, also an old family.

The old mansion at Downing which had come into the Pennant family through the marriage of a son, Hugh Pennant, with the heiress of the Downing estate, was built in 1600 and, while rich and elegant with ancient carvings, it bore the mark of stern Christian living in this motto over the front of the house:

Without God nothing, with God enough.

In this beautiful retreat, surrounded by many square miles of woods, fields, and glades, Thomas Pennant was born on June 14, 1726 and was immediately turned over to a young wet nurse who in deference to her new charge renounced her husband's name and took the name of Pennant.

There are few details of Pennant's early education. He went to school at Wrexham but a more important event in his development was a gift of Sir Francis Willughby's *Ornithology* from his kinsman, John Salisbury, when Thomas was only twelve years of age. Studying over these volumes during the next impressionable years, young Pennant acquired a lasting love of natural history and at twenty years he began a series of tours and travels that made him a famous and popular writer. First to Cornwall through the mining country; next to Ireland, but his journal of this trip he never published, because as he said, "such was the conviviality of the country, that the journal was not fit to give to the public."

On the death of his father in 1763 Thomas Pennant came into possession of the estate at Downing with a rich mine of lead ore which enabled him to make great improvements in this ancestral seat. His wife died soon after this and Pennant toured the Continent in 1765. Up to this time his principal natural history publication was the *British Zoology* (1766) with 132 plates, mostly by P. Mazell (*ca.* 1755–1797), P. Brown (fl. 1766–1791), and with a few by George Edwards. He had likewise submitted several papers to learned societies and in recognition of his account of a certain shell (*Concha anomia*) from Norwegian waters he was made a member of the Royal Society of Upsala. This was on the recommendation of Linnaeus who was then at the crest of his fame. Pennant ever regarded this as his greatest literary honor.

In 1769 Pennant issued the first part of a proposed work on Indian zoology. Its twelve plates and three unpublished ones were then turned over by him to J. R. Forster (1729–1798), that versatile professor and traveller, and were published in 1781 together with notes and drawings in which Sydney Parkinson (*ca.* 1745–1771), J. G. Loten (1710–1789, formerly governor of Ceylon), and the native Indian artist, P. C. de Bevere (*ca.* 1722–?1781), had cooperated. This is a rare publication and the distinguished American ornithologist, Dr. J. A. Allen (1838–1921),[14] has expounded the importance of Pennant's contribution (even though he never completed the projected series), because all the species are treated under scientific names.

A few years later Pennant issued another book on birds which despite its slender size and obscurity casts an interesting light on his ornithological concepts. The *Genera of Birds* (1773) he calls "a trifle" which he prepared for a friend, Dr. Robert Ramsay, Professor of Natural History at Edinburgh, who was giving a course in ornithology. A snow bunting is vignetted on the title page, showing the various feather areas blocked in and labelled as follows:

1. Bastard wing
2. Lesser coverts of the wing
3. Greater coverts
4. Quill feathers
5. Secondary feathers
6. Tertials
7. Coverts of the tail (uropygium)
8. Vent feathers (crissum)
9. Tail feathers (rectrices)

The preface of this little book is an elementary text on birds, starting with a definition of ornithology, then a definition of a bird followed by an exposition of external parts. A few pages on nuptials, nidification, and the eggs of birds form the next part while the main body of the book is concerned with the description of ninety-five genera.

Apparently Pennant planned to figure an example of each genus, but the appearance of John Latham's *General Synopsis of Birds* (1781–1785) discouraged the project. His friend, Dr. Ramsay, printed the book first in 1773 without plates but it was reissued in 1781 with fifteen plates.

This appears to be a forerunner of the modern laboratory notebook for the study of birds and shows its author striving to give practical aid to the layman.

The *Arctic Zoology* (1784–1785), in two volumes, is Pennant's most important work. Volume 1 is an account of the arctic world with special reference to the quadrupeds but a general account of arctic bird-life likewise is given. It contains eight plates. The second volume is concerned solely with birds and contains fif-

teen plates. It was published in 1785 and is generally regarded as of great significance in American ornithology. Doctor Elliott Coues (1842–1899) attributed 511 species of American birds to Pennant's *Arctic Zoology,* but he failed to recognize the fact that the first 85 numbers belong to mammals. This leaves 426 birds,[15] numbered 86–510 in the general volume, and one addition, 175a, in the supplement.

Although Pennant had used scientific names in his previously published *Indian Zoology* the birds of his *Arctic Zoology* are described under vernacular names, the scientific names of the species being listed only in the synonymies. His whole assemblage of birds in Volume 2 contains numerous inaccuracies, some of the birds being only subspecies, according to modern classification, while some are foreign birds erroneously believed to be American. Others, such as the Norton Sound bustard, represent the fancy of some ignorant traveller who thought the Canada goose for example, a representative of the European bustard family. There are numerous references to bustards in America, to be found in the old chronicles, all of which are referable to the Canada goose or its allies.

Although we cannot accept Pennant's listing of species as usable today, we must credit him with careful treatment of a large part of our present check-list, and his descriptions, in the same way that Catesby's and Edwards' were used, were the source of many binomial names later formulated by Johann Gmelin (1748–1804), the tireless editor of Linnaeus' works.

While preparing his *Arctic Zoology*, Pennant had the cooperation of several arctic explorers—Morten Brünnick (1737–1827), Otto Müller (1730–1804), and the Reverend Otto Fabricius (1744–1822), author of the *Fauna Greenlandica.* He likewise corresponded with Samuel Hearne (1745–1792). Thomas Hutchins,[16] and Andrew Graham, all of whom lived and worked in the Hudson Bay region. Another cooperator of Pennant in the study of boreal species of North American birds was Humphrey Marten, author of an unpublished manuscript on birds in the Royal Society of London.

Several other cooperating associates located in more southern parts of America assisted Pennant by sending specimens. The most interesting one of these collectors was perhaps Ashton Blackburn who supplied Pennant with birds from New Jersey, New York, and Connecticut. Blackburn had a sister, Anna Blackburn(e) [17] (1740–1793), who holds a unique place with reference to American ornithology. Both spellings are used.

---

[14] Allen, J. A., 1908: 111–116.

[15] I am indebted to Dr. John T. Zimmer, Curator of Birds, Amer. Mus. Nat. Hist., for explaining Pennant's large list of birds.

[16] Hutchins, Thomas, see page 520.

[17] The blackburnian warbler, *Dendroica fusca,* is reminiscent of this name. Elliott Coues refers to this person as Mrs. Blackburn, leaving off the "e" and adding "Mrs." Since she is referred to as Ashton's sister, "Anne Blackburne," the married name, if she had one, must have been different. See Coues *Check-List of North American Birds,* p. 37, no. 121, note, 1882.

FIG. 32. Baltimore Orioles at nest from Pennant's *Arctic Zoology* (1784–1785). Courtesy of the Trustees of the British Museum.

It is known that she was a botanist of note and that she was a friend and correspondent of Linnaeus, but the fact that she maintained a museum of American birds at her home near Warrington, England, is apparently not recorded in American journals. Her brother, Ashton, lived continuously in America, and beside being a zealous sportsman was also a careful observer, interested in the habits of birds. He sent many life history notes with his shipments of specimens to his "worthy and philosophical sister."

Another one with whom Pennant had frequent correspondence was Alexander Garden of Charleston. This man is familiar to us already, as a collector of fish for Linnaeus, and we recall him unpleasantly as the author of a ruthless criticism of Catesby's work. Pennant was likewise in touch with John and William Bartram, both of whom sometimes sent specimens.

It is interesting that Pennant for a number of years contemplated visiting America. The earnest work of Mark Catesby over here as well as the plan of Sir Francis Willughby to study and collect here had inspired him with a zeal for American travel. For Pennant was almost a professional traveller and writer of travels.

While touring on the Continent again in 1767 he met several of the most famous and gifted men of his generation including the brilliant and prolific writer Albrecht Haller (1708–1777), the French philosopher, Voltaire

(1694–1778) and the famous naturalists, Comte de Buffon (1707–1788) and Dr. Peter Simon Pallas (1741–1811). He visited Buffon at his home in Montbard and seems to have admired him although with some reservations. To Pallas, however, Pennant was immediately drawn by mutual understanding and community of interest. They discussed a cooperative work on quadrupeds based on Ray's classification, but Pallas at the invitation of Catherine II (1729–1796) of Russia accepted a professorship in St. Petersburg and almost immediately set out on his six-year expedition into northern Russia and Siberia. Thus it was that Pennant's *History of Quadrupeds* came to be executed, as he said, "by his own inferior hand."

The loss of his collaborator and the oncoming American Revolution caused the American scene to lose its glamor and by the time the Colonies emerged from war he felt he no longer had the same right to call himself zoologist of the New World. He expressed his change of heart as follows:

I thought I had the right to attempt, at a time I had the honour of calling myself a fellow subject with that respectable part of our former great empire; but when the fatal and humiliating hour arrived, which deprived Britain of power, strength, and glory, I felt the mortification which must strike every feeling individual at losing his little share in the boast of ruling over half of the New World. I could no longer support my clame of entitling myself its humble zoologist; yet unwilling to fling away my labors do now deliver them to the Public under the title of the Arctic Zoology. I added to them a description of the Quadrupeds and Birds of the North of Europe and of Asia from latitude 60 to the farthest known parts of the Arctic World, together with those of Kamtschatka, and the parts of America in the last voyages of the illustrious Cook.———— Whatever is wanting in the *American* part I may foresee, will in time be amply supplied. The powers of literature will soon arise, with the other strengths, of the new empire, and some native Naturalist give perfection to that part of the undertaking by observations formed on the spot, in the uses, manners and migrations. Should, at present no one be inclined to take the pen out of my hand, remarks from the other side of the *Atlantic*, from any gentleman of congenial studies, will add peculiar pleasure to a favorite pursuit and be gratefully received.

The exchange of letters in those more contemplative days was a fruitful source of information and a stimulant to more careful study. Though the correspondents in many cases never met, their expressions of intellectual sympathy lighted the torch of friendship that united the far corners of the earth. Pennant's *Arctic Zoology* teems with personal observations of a large and varied group of collectors and travellers which the author has compiled into readable accounts of each species. Furthermore he shows that he was entirely conversant with the old authors, citing each one in his synonymy so that the reader gains an historical picture of each bird as it presented itself to many recorders during early scientific observation. As early as Pennant's time that now rarest of North American birds, the ivory-billed woodpecker, was becoming scarce, from its persecution by the Indians

FIG. 33. Woodcock and Eskimo Curlew from Pennant's *Arctic Zoology*. Courtesy of the Cornell University Library.

who used their white bills to make coronets for their sachems and warriors. One bill was worth two or three buck skins, said Pennant. Though the ivory-bill was said to dig a deep spiral hole to protect its nest, it has not been able to withstand this exploitation nor the encroachment of civilization upon its forest home, and it is doubtful whether it can be saved, but a sanctuary has been established for two birds recently found in northern Florida and all lovers of birds are hopeful that it can be saved from complete extermination.

Interesting details such as this and his reflections on the bobolinks of Cuba (Vol. 2, p. 260) commend Pennant's volumes to the seasoned ornithologist. The early edition of 1785 was illustrated with engravings by P. Mazell (*ca.* 1755–1797), executed from drawings done by Moses Griffith (1749–1809) and P. Brown (fl. 1766–1791). A de luxe edition was issued in 1792 with 170 water colors of birds and scenery of the arctic regions. Some of the illustrations adorn the wide margins of the text. The arists were Mercatti and Moses Griffith (1749–1809 or later), who worked from sketches made in many cases by Pennant himself.

Looking back on Pennant's career, we see him in several different walks of life: as a law student [18] at Queen's College, Oxford, as a traveller and antiquary, as a business man, as a man of letters and as a naturalist. Perhaps his interests were too diverse to carry him to the top rank of ornithologists.

---

[18] Pennant prepared in Law but did not obtain a degree.

JOHN LATHAM

A century, lacking only three years, was the long lifetime allotted to John Latham (1740–1837), the eminent British ornithologist of the late eighteenth and early nineteenth centuries. He was born at Eltham Kent on June 27, 1740, the son of Doctor John Latham, a practicing surgeon and druggist. His mother was of the distinguished family of Sothebys in Yorkshire. Young Latham attended the Merchant Taylors School and later studied anatomy under the radical surgeon, John Hunter (1728–1793). After finishing his medical education at London hospitals Latham opened a practice at Dartford in 1763.

Natural history, and birds especially, were his abiding interest and early in life he began to build up a museum of natural history objects. We find him in the early 1770's launching upon friendly zoological correspondence with the leading scientists of the day, very much as Linnaeus, Dillenius, Sherard, and others were engaged in exchanging their views on botany. Thomas Pennant and Latham were well acquainted. Pennant upon hearing Latham's favorable criticism of his *British Zoology* wrote to express his appreciation and invited Latham's correspondence. This correspondence lasted for many years and the two friends cooperated on the revision of Pennant's *Indian Zoology* in 1793, Latham doing the more laborious part on insects, while in the posthumous edition of the *British Zoology*, issued by Pennant's son, David, he edited and enlarged the section on ornithology.

FIG. 34. John Latham (1740–1837), leading English Ornithologist of the Eighteenth Century. Courtesy of the Trustees of the British Museum.

Sir Ashton Lever (1729–1788), founder of the Leverian Museum,[19] was another of Latham's correspondents and they were accustomed to exchange specimens as we see by the following letter:

Dear Latham—Having plundered Amsterdam, Leyden, Haarlen, the Hague, Rotterdam, Delft, Maesensluys, the Brill and Helvoetsluys, I am now returned to England, and in consequence of the above voyage shall have more duplicates for you. You should see me soon, as I have wonderful things to tell you.—Yours, with compliments to Mrs. L., Ashton Lever.

Others in his circle of friends were Sir Joseph Banks (1743–1820), Sir James E. Smith (1759–1828), John Edward Gray (1800–1875), and many others. In fact, Latham as a leading scientist himself was well known and liked by the large active group of London savants of the late eighteenth century. He was deeply interested not only in his chosen profession from which he amassed a fortune, but he was engrossed in natural history, architecture, and antiquities. He was elected to the Royal Society of London in 1775; other honors followed, and he was invited to join the Royal Society of Stockholm, the Natural History Society of Berlin and in 1788 he took part in the founding of the Linnean Society of London.

His first ornithological work was the *General Synopsis of Birds* in three volumes with 106 plates all executed by himself. It was published in 1785, a time when ornithology was coming very much into the foreground of public interest. Many expeditions to Australia and the South Seas, and explorations in Africa served to augment ornithological knowledge. Two famous bird collections, that of the British Museum and the Sir Ashton Lever collection at Leicester House, were being founded. Much ornithological work was likewise being done on the Continent notably by Mathurin Brisson (1723–1806), Georges Louis Leclerc, Comte de Buffon (1707–1788), and Peter Simon Pallas (1741–1811).

The Synopsis of Birds contained many new genera and species, but the author was reluctant to adopt binomial nomenclature, although he was a great admirer of Linnaeus. However, he included Linnaean names together with their various vernacular names under each species. Two supplements to the *General Synopsis* were written by Latham, the first published in 1787, but the second did not appear until 1801. During this interim he was at work on his *Index Ornithologicus* in two volumes, which also is considered supplementary to the *General Synopsis*. This was published in 1790 and is written in Latin, with binomial names based on the Linnaean method. It has been suggested that this was done in deference to the thirteenth edition of Linnaeus' *Systema Naturae,* which appeared in 1788.

---

[19] Sir Ashton Lever first collected live birds, later, stuffed birds, shells, fossils, and savage costumes and weapons. His museum was moved to London in 1774 and in 1788 was won by lottery by James Parkinson (1730–1813).

As with several previous authors, the Latin names and descriptions of many of Latham's birds have not stood in their original form, but they have been valuable and basic to the more formal nomenclature, as worked out by Linnaeus' editor, Johann F. Gmelin (1748–1804). It may be interesting to glance at the plan of Latham's work, as followed in the *Synopsis.*

The two principal divisions are Land Birds and Water Birds; and Latham follows, in the main, the system of John Ray as he applied it to his friend Francis Willughby's posthumous ornithology, which had come out about a hundred years before. This would seem to put Latham's work rather out of date, but it is still a valuable text to systematists. His conception of the arrangement of birds with the characteristics on which he framed his classification is set forth in the following outline:

Division I. Land Birds

Order I. Accipitrine
Order II. Pies
   a. with legs made for walking
   b. with climbing feet
   c. Feet made for Leaping
Order III. Passerine
   a. with Thick Bills
   b. with curved bills upper mandible bent at tip
   c. with Bills leaving the upper mandible emarginated near the tip.
   d. Simple-billed—Bill strait, integral attenuated
Order IV. Columbine
   Bill sharpish on the edge, nostrils gibbous covered with an obsolete membrane.
Order V. Gallinaceous
   a. with four toes
   b. with three toes
Order VI. Struthious
   a. with four Toes
   b. with 3 toes, placed forwards
   c. with 2 toes placed forwards

Division II. Water Birds

Order VII. Waders.
   a. with 4 toes
   b. with 3 toes placed forwards
Order VIII. with Pinnated (lobed) feet
Order IX. Web-footed
   a. with Long Legs
   b. with short legs.

Latham is best known and remembered for his third treatise on birds, that monumental work, *A General History of Birds* (1821–1828), in ten volumes completed in 1824 while the volume of index was published in 1828. It is remarkable not only for its comprehensiveness but also for its 193 colored plates all of which are Latham's own handiwork. In this treatise, Latham reverts to the English tongue for the running text, preserving only the Latin names listed in the synonymies. The *General History of Birds* contains a number of American species of which may be mentioned in Volume 1, the boat-tailed grackle, and in Volume 3, the roseate spoonbill, the oystercatcher, the horned grebe, the American avocet, and the flamingo.

Latham's works are entirely in the nature of reference books and are best appreciated by the taxonomist. The layman, though he may not grasp the scientific learning nor the literary quality of Latham's writing, will surely remember him for some of the whimsical epithets employed in his vernacular names. Among them are the following: the frivolous thrush, the respected kingfisher, the plaintive eagle, the foolish sparrow.

Latham is the first ornithologist who achieved anything like completeness in treating of the birds of the world known at that time. A large proportion of his new descriptions are Australian owing to the intensive colonization of this vast territory by the British beginning in 1788. Indeed Latham is regarded as the founder of Australian ornithology and many of his original descriptions are included in the work of Governor Arthur Phillip (1738–1814) published in 1789, while the five hundred twelve original watercolors by the artist T. Watling (fl. 1788–1792) furnished the types of a great many new species.

These drawings and certain letters regarding them did not come to light until the mid-nineteenth century and many scientists had been puzzled by the vast number of new species with which Latham was credited. However, through an article it is revealed that Latham discussed this group of birds and gave full credit [20] to the artist who made the drawings.

A strange story attaches to him. It appears that T. Watling was convicted by a Scottish jury for forgery and was sentenced to deportation. He left England in the *Pitt* in July 1791 but escaped at the Cape and was at large for a month. Upon capture he was kept in prison for seven months waiting for a ship to take him to Sydney, the seat of the new penal colony, and arrived there October 7, 1792. Watling was obviously an artist already and not one who just took it up as has been intimated; he was also a man of culture. The details of his alleged crime are not given, but in writing to a friend he said, "My present position is owing to the low revenge of a certain military character now high in office." In an advertisement which he proposed to use he called himself the principal limner in New South Wales and suggested making a set of "highly finished water colours to depict picturesque description done faithfully on the spot to include views, natives, groups, and if possible curiosities in Ormithology [*sic*] and botany." This letter is dated May 12, 1793. Watling was permitted to turn his talent to the uses of the expedition and produced the large set of drawings which are referred to above and of which Latham made use in his books. Some dried specimens also were prepared by Watling and notes on the birds were added to the drawings he made. His paintings are signed T. Watling and are housed in the British Museum as "Watling Drawings." The work of two other artists is among them

Fig. 35. Roseate Spoonbill, a colored plate from Latham's *General History of Birds* (1821–1828). Courtesy of the Cornell University Library.

but Watling's can be recognized not only by his signature but also by his annotations on the habits of the birds.

Latham's undaunted activity in his very old age, especially his gigantic work, the *General History of Birds*, is thought to have been an effort to offset some of his great financial losses, but apparently his heroic labor though successful as a scientific work never raised him out of poverty. Instead he was faced with further calamity, the loss of his sight; yet he continued untiringly at his work and was held in high esteem by his fellow scientists.

Despite his three thorough-going texts on birds, however, he does not seem to have inspired the warm regard that Edwards and Pennant enjoyed. This may be due to the fact that he represents the cold and laborious compilation of a scientist and lacks the more mellow reflective quality of the general naturalist. There is also this to be considered, that Latham stands, so to speak, at the parting of the ways and the turn of the century, his predecessors, Catesby, Edwards, and Pennant, representing the comparatively simple study and exploration of new regions, while he has assembled and classified myriad facts from all parts of the world at a time when zoological data were increasing with almost modern speed.

He kept up with all the modern development of ornithology and as late as 1831, when he was ninety-one,

---

[20] Gray, George R., Some rectifications of Australian birds, *Ann. and Mag. Nat. Hist.*, **11**: 189–194, 1843.

spoke of revising his *Index Ornithologicus* [21] which had appeared in 1790 but he was troubled by the petty conceit of the then modern ornithologists.

On this subject he wrote to Sir William Jardine (1800–1874) from Winchester 9 September 1831 as follows:

I sh[d] however, most readily admit a new Nomenclature, where modern authors agreed to adopt one standard name for each Subject but everyone being desirous to form one of his own, often to the amount of three or even four, creates undesirable confusion. A second edition of the Index Ornithologicus is now wanted and indeed I have completed one of my old systems, but the new names multiplying so fast, have so puzzled me, that I have laid it on the shelf.

This entire letter of which the above is a short excerpt is well worth the perusal of every young ornithologist, as an invitation to scholarly work in ornithology.

But though Latham's grand passion was undoubtedly birds he proved himself competent in antiquarian study and completed seven volumes [22] on the history and architecture of the Romsey Abbey. Latham lived in Romsey between 1796 and 1819 but then, with his second wife, went to live at the home of his daughter, a Mrs. Wickham in Winchester. His wife and daughter both died in 1835, leaving Latham, fast becoming blind, at the age of ninety-three, with only his grandchildren.

According to Dr. J. E. Gray (1800–1875), writing in a letter [23] to Sir William Jardine, dated April 3, 1837, Latham was at work on the second edition of the *Indian Ornithology* at the time of his death and in the preparation of this work borrowed many ornithological books from Gray and General Hardwicke (1751–1835), so that he could go through and correct and improve his Synopsis. Further than this, according to the same letter, Latham etched and colored a drawing of a certain Indian pheasant for Dr. Gray within a year of his death.

We cannot doubt the statements of this letter, amazing though they are, and must therefore question the reliability of the article in *The Naturalist* (Vol. 4, 1937) in which it is definitely stated that Latham was blind. Certainly his eyesight was greatly impaired, yet it is obvious that he continued to the last in his work, vigorous and clear in mind and finding his greatest satisfaction in being able to help young ornithologists.

Certain manuscript letters by Dr. Latham give definite information as to his failing sight. In 1948, while working at the British Museum, I examined twenty-three letters [24] by Latham (Add Mss. 29533) and in several he mentions his condition. Folio 222 of this manuscript, dated July 3, 1833, reads in part: "my sight is very imperfect so as to disable me from making a sketch or drawing of any bird. I can, indeed, read the newspaper with

difficulty, but as to handwriting, if not written very plain, I cannot often decipher it."

Another letter, dated November, 1835, folio 223, reads in part: "I am thus explicit—as my eyesight is so dim that I shall soon not be able to write at all." He was now ninety-five years of age.

In addition, he published a thorough discussion, with plates, of the tracheae of birds,[25] depicting the diverse shapes and positions and muscles of the syringes, or voice-producing mechanism of birds. Several other papers came from his pen as follows: *"A Plan of a Charitable Institution intended to be established upon the Sea coast for accommodation of Persons afflicted with such deseases as. are usually relieved by bathing,"* 1792; *"Rheumatism and gout,"* 1796; *"Observations on the Limax";* [26] *"Facts and Opinions concerning Diabetes,"* 1811. Latham died peacefully on February 4, 1837 and was buried in the Abbey Church of Romsey to which he had devoted years of study.

It is sometimes helpful to the biographer in his search for the more personal details of the life he is investigating to consult articles and testimonials on the deceased that were written shortly after his death. In this instance the article in *The Naturalist* just referred to mentions Latham's early love of birds and a portrait of him owned by his family in which the great naturalist at ten years of age is painted with a bird upon his hand. Here, also, we may read of the very personal interest combined with actual manual labor that he gave to his museum; that he stuffed and set up almost every animal in his extensive collection and built with his own hands many of the cases in which they were displayed.

Another portrait lithographed by Day and Haghe was presented in 1835, by Latham to his friend Neville Wood, the author of *British Song Birds*. According to this article this book was read to the venerable ornithologist by his grandchildren "after he had become blind."

It is of special interest to American ornithologists that Latham was actively in touch with several collectors in this country, among whom may be mentioned two who did considerable work on birds. These are Dr. Thomas Hutchins,[27] who lived for many years as surgeon at York Factory, Hudson Bay, and John Abbot,[28] naturalist of Georgia, author and artist of American birds, whose large collection of plates of the birds of Georgia has never been published.

From Latham's preface to Volume 1, we gather that Hutchins gave Latham a large volume of observations on the birds of Hudson Bay, while of John Abbot, referring to his cooperators, Latham says, "I have also the satisfaction of naming Mr. Abbot, of Savannah, Georgia who, I trust, yet lives to continue to furnish faithful observations on the birds of his vicinity as well as speci-

[21] Mathews, 1931: 466–475.

[22] Latham, John, Unpublished MS., British Museum, on the History and Architecture of Romsey Abbey.

[23] *Ibis,* ser. 13: 474–475, 1931.

[24] Latham, John, MS. letters, British Museum, add. MSS 29533: folios 222 and 223.

[25] Latham, 1797: read July 4 and Nov. 7, 1797.

[26] *Ibid.*: 85–58; read Feb. 7, 1797.

[27] For an account of Hutchins, see this work, Chap. XI, p. 520.

[28] For an account of Abbot and his work, See Allen E. G., *Auk,* **59** (4): 563–571, 1942.

mens." In Volume 2 of Latham's *Synopsis of Birds*, Latham refers apparently to a letter from Abbot in which he, Abbot, had discussed the tyrant flycatcher, or kingbird, *Tyrannus tyrannus;* and in Volume 3, page 369, Latham referring to the ivory-billed woodpecker says, "Abbot has never found this species in Virginia." This is significant as pointing to Abbot's probable period of residence in Virginia, a question that has not been answered until recently.[29]

It is of further interest to know that Latham, as the leading ornithologist of his day, identified the large collection of Abbot's drawings, known as Egerton manuscripts 1137 and 1138 of the British Museum, at the time when Abbot, through John Francillon, was trying to sell them in England. Research on John Abbot, recently completed by the present writer, has uncovered the history of these drawings.

These are only fragments of the hidden story of European participation in the development of American ornithology, but they help to make the modern ornithologist aware of the vigorous study of birds under very difficult conditions that went on a hundred and fifty years ago. Ornithology's American critic, Elliott Coues, regards Latham as one of the six great workers on birds of the eighteenth century. His collaborators in the century are Catesby, Edwards, Forster, Pennant, and Bartram and among these Latham is by far the greatest.

The following American birds derive their first descriptions from him: sooty shearwater, white pelican, least bittern, surf-bird, bristle-thighed curlew, wandering tattler, great horned owl, Merrill's pauraque, scissor-tailed flycatcher, Steller's jay, varied thrush, Barrow's golden-eye, red-tailed hawk, coot, wood thrush, veery, dickcissel, white-winged crossbill, Savannah sparrow, sharp-tailed sparrow, vesper sparrow, song sparrow, LeConte's sparrow, swamp sparrow.

NATURALISTS FROM THE CONTINENT

Ere we turn once more to ornithological work actually undertaken in America, we should pause for brief consideration of a few of the Continental naturalists in order to see the more definite position that ornithology was beginning to assume. No longer were birds just a secondary matter. They were rapidly earning their votaries in every country and, with the improvements in illustration, birds with their fascinating color patterns, and grace of form, furnished the ideal subject matter to delight both artist and public.

A prominent figure on the Continent in the ornithological field in the latter eighteenth century was Mathurin Jacques Brisson (1723–1806), a French scientist who published in 1760 a six-volume work with 261 plates and 4,000 pages of text. The title was in the customarily lengthy form of that day, as follows: *Ornithologie, ou Méthode contenant la division des oiseaux en ordres, sections, genres, espèces et leurs variétés.*

A laquelle on a joint une description exacte de chaque espèce, avec les citations des auteurs qui en ont traité, noms qu'ils leur ont donnés . . . & les noms vulgaires. Ouvrage enrichi de figures en taille-douce.

This contribution was the most thorough study of birds that had until then been made; yet it was two-thirds printed before Brisson had opportunity to study Linnaeus' classification of birds in the tenth edition of the *Systema Naturae* of 1758, which was generally regarded as a very important ornithological treatise. Brisson had used the sixth edition but this obviously was a superficial study, the birds occupying only seventeen octavo pages. In the tenth edition the bird matter was increased to 116 pages and birds were divided into fifty-one genera, which served somewhat in Brisson's more modern study. Brisson was one of the first ornithologists who had a keen appreciation of the taxonomic affinities of the birds of the world, and he soon formulated his own ideas on classification.[30]

Volume 1 of his six-volume work opens with a good preface on ornithologists, in which he mentioned the contributions of Hernandez, Marcgrave, Frisch, Albin, Catesby, and Edwards.

He then goes on with a discussion of the class Aves, under the chapter heading "Le Regne Animale," followed by the included forms in each of twenty-six orders, giving the number of toes, type of foot, and the characteristics of the beak. The text is in Latin and French in parallel columns. Seven plates of heads and feet accompany this matter with an explanatory table. There are no colored illustrations in Brisson's work, but his drawings make clear his descriptions, for his heads are done with a technique that brings out the individuality of the birds, similar to the modern portraiture of Louis Agassiz Fuertes (1874–1927).

Mathurin Jacques Brisson was born April 30, 1723 at Fonteney-le Compt and died June 23, 1806. He was a member of the French Academy and of the Institute; he held the chair of physics at the University of Navarre but later in life devoted himself to birds and mammals.

Brisson was a personal friend of M. René Antoine Ferchut de Réaumur (1683–1757), the famous physicist and naturalist who had a large cabinet, or collection, of birds, from all parts of the world. Brisson's work was therefore greatly furthered by his study of the specimens constantly being added to this collection. He likewise had access to the large collections in the Paris Museum and the museums in other principal cities of Europe; and his scrupulous exactness may still be an inspiration to modern ornithologists. Most of the descriptions were made from bird specimens that he actually handled, while the balance he took from the descriptions of others, adapting the phraseology to his own diction. He listed the specimens with their describers, specifying those which he did not actually see, himself, and he was careful to name the country where each bird

[29] Remington, 1948: 28–30.

[30] Zimmer, 1926: **1**: 94.

was found. In the case of the specimens in the cabinet of M. Réaumur, he mentions the name of the correspondents who had collected and sent them. Brisson represents the most exemplary workmanship and his descriptions are still very helpful to the modern student. Indeed, his work is so careful and his grouping of birds so rational that many of his genera were accepted by the British Association Code of Nomenclature in 1842, even though Brisson established them prior to 1766, the date of the twelfth edition of the *Systema Naturae,* which the Association selected as marking the start of binomial nomenclature. Thus Brisson's work, although it is not strictly binomial in character, is sufficiently accurate to have stood the test of time, and to serve as a model of method in observation and description to modern ornithologists. It is the tenth edition, 1758, that is the standard today, and many of Brisson's genera are still accepted as valid.

In glancing through the volumes, it is interesting to recognize several New World species, which indicate that American birds, through collectors who were sent to America, were taking their places in foreign cabinets.

The following American species are among the birds portrayed by Brisson: ruffed grouse, whip-poor-will, waxwing, crossbill, red-breasted nuthatch, white-breasted nuthatch, cardinal, pileated woodpecker, yellow-bellied sapsucker, red-headed woodpecker, red-bellied woodpecker, killdeer, stilt, several sandpipers, roseate spoonbill, three species of merganser, pintail, wood duck, shoveller, Canada goose, eider, baldpate, avocet, flamingo.

Contemporaneously with Brisson, another continental ornithologist was preparing his studies in natural science in Germany. Peter Simon Pallas (1741–1811), though a native of Berlin, transferred his residence to Russia following Catherine II's invitation to him to become Professor of Natural History at the Imperial Academy of Science in St. Petersburg. The same year, 1768, he was appointed naturalist of the extensive expedition through Russia and Siberia, mentioned previously, which lasted for six years. Thus he became acquainted with many North American birds of circumpolar distribution and, in American ornithology, he is the authority for the Alaska Hermit Thrush, *Hylocichla guttata guttata* (Pallas) and he described many other birds. These are: short-tailed albatross, pelagic cormorant, lesser snow goose, Stellar's eider, rufous-necked sandpiper, curlew sandpiper, sanderling, Caspian tern, Cassin's auklet, paroquet auklet, crested auklet, least auklet, rhinoceros auklet, tufted puffin, hermit thrush, Aleutian rosy finch, golden-crowned sparrow.

This expedition, which was instituted to study the transit of Venus (1769), resulted in a richly illustrated work that was translated into an English edition of three volumes in 1812. Pallas also brought out the work of Johann Anton Guldenstadt (1745–1781), who with S. G. Gmelin (1743–1774) and Ivan Lepechin (1737?–1802) were also members of the same expedition.

Pallas was one of the most learned and versatile men of his generation, for his researches took him into zoology, astronomy, and the philology of several languages. It was because of Pallas' acceptance of the post in St. Petersburg under Catharine II that Pennant changed his proposed cooperative zoology of the New World to *Arctic Zoology* which he executed alone.

Georges Louis Leclerc, Comte de Buffon (1707–1788), was the author of a more spectacular work in forty-four volumes and became a world figure in the long chronicle of natural history. This remarkable series took over half a century to produce and Buffon had long since died when publication was at last concluded in 1804. It is a great storehouse of biological information, comprising birds, mammals, fish, reptiles, and plants, and it bears the comprehensive title, *Histoire Naturelle —avec la description du Cabinet du Roi.* It has served as the basis of almost innumerable later editions which represent parts of the original enlarged and republished, or the whole work revamped, enlarged, and further embellished. A reference to the catalogue of any large library owning the set, and a perusal of the various collations of Buffon's works constitute a very appreciable lesson in the naturalists and iconography of the late eighteenth century. Suffice it for our present purposes, however, to mention in some detail only Buffon's work on birds, his *Histoire Naturelle des Oiseaux* [31] (1770–1786).

This was based on the nine original bird volumes (23–31) of his *Histoire Naturelle Generale,* begun in 1749, and is more in the nature of true natural history than mere descriptions of specimens because it emphasizes the habits of birds. The birds are referred to by their vernacular names, but many were given Latin names in later editions. The publication of these bird volumes extended over the years 1770 to 1786, and during this period the younger Daubenton (E. L.) (1732–1795), whose father, Louis Jean (1716–1799), had collaborated with Buffon in the *Histoire Naturelle Generale,* began in 1765 the publication of a series of 1,008 plates of which 973 are birds engraved by the artist, F. N. Martinet (1731–?). P. G. de B. Montbeillard (1720–1785) also collaborated with this work. It is this series to which Elliott Coues refers in his Historical Introduction to the *Key to North American Birds* (5th Ed. 1903), as the Planches Enluminées of Daubenton.

These plates do not represent any consumate skill in bird portraiture, nor is the series particularly laudable from the scientific point of view, the names being vernacular (and therefore permitting of error), and the written matter amounting to a few words of description, but no real text. They are, however, of considerable interest in that they foreshadow the great popularization of ornithology, which was to take place a century later, and they are suggestive, if somewhat crudely so, in their general format of the modern sets of bird plates without

[31] Wood, 1931: 267–268.

FIG. 36. Georges Louis Leclerc, Comte de Buffon (1707–1788), French compiler of Zoology. Courtesy of the United States National Museum.

text, for example the *Birds of New York* and the *Birds of Massachusetts* of the present day.

These 1,008 plates were issued in 42 sections in two sizes, without any planned sequence, and the whole series lacks a definite title. Nevertheless, they achieved great popularity and were generally known as the *Planches Enluminées*.

The Comte de Buffon whose unadorned name was Georges Louis Leclerc was to France, in a measure, what Linnaeus was to Sweden. They were born in the same year 1707 and both achieved royal favor as evidenced by having titles bestowed upon them for their important contributions to science. Buffon, however, was more inclined to enjoy the ostentatious and his spectacular books with their sumptuous illustrations bear this out. He lived in a period when France and England were engaged in more or less rival exploration of the world and Buffon availed himself of much material from the circumnavigating expedition of Louis A. Bougainville (1729–1811), and his collector, Philibert Commerson (1727–1773), to the South Seas. England, though she had no naturalist at this time comparable to Buffon or Linnaeus, was eager to amass information and specimens by the Cook voyages round the world.

In this era of exploration and exploitation Linnaeus

remained mostly at home in the professorial chair at the University of Upsala but he made his revolutionizing contribution by classifying and describing the thousands of animals and plants that accrued from these expeditions, according to his binomial system of nomenclature.

Buffon rose rapidly to fame and social prominence, not only by his scientific writings but by his mastery of style and the commanding presence he maintained in the cultured circles of Paris. Voltaire (1694–1778) described him as a "man with the mind of a sage in the body of an athlete" while David Hume (1711–1776) said that he had the "bearing of a marshall rather than a writer." The general public was not concerned over Buffon's loose treatment of the systematics of ornithology. He candidly maintained that short cuts in bird description are allowable and says as follows (Nouvelle Edition 1824 Oiseaux Tome I, p. XXI):

. . . au lieu de traiter les oiseaux un à un, c'est-à-dire par espèces distinctes et séparées, je les réunirai plusieurs ensemble sous un même genre, sans cependant les confondre et renoncer à les distinguer lorsqu'elles pourront l'être ; par ce moyen, j'ai beaucoup abrégé, et j'ai réduit à une assez petite étendue cette histoire des oiseaux qui serait devenue trop volumineuse, si d'un côté j'eusse traité de chaque espèce en particulier en me livrant aux discussions de la nomenclature, et que d'autre côté je n'eusse pas supprimé, par le moyen des couleurs, la plus grande partie du long discours qui eût été nécessaire pour chaque description.

Buffon believed that there were between fifteen hundred and two thousand different kinds of birds in the world, and eagerly kept in touch with expeditions, acquiring specimens for the Cabinet du Roi, of which he was the keeper, and also new material for his books. There were several editions of Buffon's *Histoire Naturelle des Oiseaux*—the earliest started to come out in 1749 and completed publication in 1804. Another edition known as the Deux-Ponts edition appeared between 1785 and 1791, and includes fifty-four volumes. Another edition by C. S. Sonnini (1751–1812), an engineer of the French Army, came out with Buffon's original text, but with also numerous additions to the text and footnotes by various other writers. Sonnini spent three years in South America, returning in 1775, and provided many new birds for Buffon's series of ornithological volumes.

Buffon died in 1788, but his books continued to be popular, owing to the wealth of material they contained and the large number of writers and artists who continued to work on subsequent editions. The general influence of Buffon, it must be admitted, however, was the popularization of a loose kind of bird observation, which was primarily productive of numerous composite sets of plates, in which several artists and writers collaborated. But most of these sets are inadequate as an aid to accurate description.

It should be mentioned that the German zoologist, Peter Boddaert (1730–ca. 1796), prepared for his own use a table, in which he gave the Latin names of the bird figures by Daubenton. He later (1783) had fifty copies printed under the title, *Table des Planches enluminéez d'histoire naturelle*. The work is exceedingly rare, but in 1874 W. B. Tegetmeier (1876–1912) published a reprint of it. There are many errors in the *Table*, and most of the Latin names are taken from earlier authors, but in some cases Boddaert supplied names of his own creation, the first that had been given to the birds in question, and some of these are still in use.

Since both Daubenton's plates and Boddaert's *Table* (or its reprint) are necessary to establish and identify the names, both works are of considerable ornithological importance. The student should consult Zimmer and Mathews on this rare list.[32]

A swing to more careful bird observation and ornithological publication was accomplished by some of the Italian and German ornithologists of the late eighteenth century.

The most important name in Continental ornithology of this period is that of Naumann,[33] a German family which contributed fundamentally to our knowledge of the birds of central Europe. Father and son, Johann Andreas Naumann (1744–1826) and Johann Friedrich Naumann (1780–1857), began to publish a work on the natural history of the birds of Germany in 1795, *Naturgeschichte der Land-und Wasser-Vögel des nördlichen Deutschlands* . . . in four volumes with 192 colored plates. Owing to political unrest in central Europe the publication of this work was not completed until 1817. Five years later the Naumanns began to bring out a better and more complete edition, but because of the father's death in 1826 the entire series of *Naturgeschichte der Vögel Deutschlands* was not completed until 1844. This remained a standard for many years, being a thoroughgoing twelve-volume set, illustrated with some 300 plates. These are of special interest for their careful portrayal of the various seasonal moults of many species, and for the simplicity of the written descriptions. A thirteenth supplementary volume was begun by the son and after his death (1857) was completed by Blasius, Baldamus, and Sturm, carrying the date of final completion to 1860.

From the earnest ornithological labors of the two Naumanns sprang also the important though short-lived bird journal *Naumannia, Archiv für die Ornithologie, vorzugsweise Europa's*. It was edited by the versatile August Karl Edward Baldamus (1812–1893), author of some German fairy tales about birds (*Vogel-Märchen*, 1876), and a practical handbook on cage birds and domestic fowl, *Illustriertes Handbuch der Federviehzucht* (1880). This author wrote also on the habits of the European cuckoo and other parasitic birds, *Das Leben der Europaischen Kuckucke* (1892). Naumannia be-

gan publication in 1851 and continued through 1858. In 1860 it was merged with the *Journal für Ornithologie* which continues to the present. *Naumannia* in its brief span published 31 colored plates. It was the third exclusively ornithological journal of Europe, the first being *Ornis*[34] published at Jena 1824–1827 and the second *Rhea*[34] published at Leipzig in 1846 and 1849. The Germans have consistently shown keen interest in their fauna and many great ornithologists have been German born.

One other German writer on birds should be mentioned in this eighteenth-century period, not because of any one large piece of work but for his numerous small publications including translations, travels, and general lists. I refer to Johann Reinhold Forster[35] (1729–1798), whose first publication was concerned in part with North American birds. This was the first attempt to cover American fauna and of birds alone he mentions 302[36] kinds not described nor even named accurately, but nevertheless a long list which served to impress European scientists with the wealth of bird life in America. This book is now exceedingly scarce, although a reprint of it was put out by the Willughby Society in 1882.

X. BIRD OBSERVATION RESUMED IN AMERICA

JOHANN REINHOLD FORSTER

It seems that the work of Johann Reinhold Forster may serve as a bridge to introduce us to a consideration of American ornithology once more. In addition to the rare volume just referred to, this author published also *An Account of the Birds Sent from Hudson's Bay: with Observations Relative to their Natural History; and Latin Descriptions of some of the most Uncommon*.[1] It is concerned with fifty-eight species, and occupies some fifty pages describing several birds new to the American list. Among them are the white-throated sparrow, the blackpoll warbler, and the Hudsonian curlew. Many of these fifty-eight species pass through the United States on migration and some remain here to breed, so that we can see a substantial contribution made by Forster to our sum of ornithological information at that time.

Forster is interesting from another point of view, for in his earlier publication, the *Catalogue of the Animals of North America*, he appends a section entitled *Directions for Collecting, Preserving and Transporting all Kinds of Natural History Curiosities*. This is a forward step in the progress of ornithological study and one that was greatly needed, for in this period the men who went on expeditions were entirely untrained and learned by the costly trial and error method.

[32] Mathews, G. M., and T. Iredale, *Austral Avian Record*, **3** (2): 31–51, 1915, for discussion of additional names applied by Boddaert in this rare reprint.

[33] Review Baldamus of Naumann's Vogel Deutschlands, *Ibis*, 45–58, 1862.

[34] Anker, 1938: 42.

[35] Forster, 1771. See Wood, 1931: 346.

[36] Coues, 1903: **1**: XV.

[1] *Phil. Trans. Roy. Soc., London*, **42**: 382–438, Art. 29, 1772.

In one of William Sherard's letters to Mr. Richardson dated London February 23, 1722/3 there is a reference to a Mr. More who was collecting in New England at the same time that Catesby was in Carolina. Says Mr. Sherard:

Mr. More has been very diligent for the short time he was in the country (America) before the ship came away, but most of what he gathered were common, and spoiled in coming over by his fault, for he put in the same box with all the dried plants, Fruits and Seeds, Limes, Gourds and such like trash and to fill it up, put sea weeds atop. I took him for a better philosopher, and shall give him orders how to pack for the future.[2]

This gives some idea of the crude and ignorant mistakes that were often perpetrated in the name of botany, and it is certain that zoological collecting fared no better. Indeed after reading what was considered the correct method of preserving specimens, one is constrained to wonder what the less finished process was like. Forster's directions the original tract of which is in the Alfred Newton Ornithological Collection at Cambridge, England, follow:

Birds must be opened at the vent, their entrails, lungs and craws taken out, washed with the preparing liquor, strewed with the preparing powder, stuffed with the oakum or tow; their plumage kept clean during the operation, sewed up with thread steeped in the preparing liquor; the eyes taken out, with the tongue, both places washed with the same liquor; the mouth must be filled with prepared tow in the great birds, the eyes filled up with putty and when dry, painted with oil-colour after the natural colour of live birds, of the same species, and then dried in an oven; however, as there is all the meat on the bird left, care must be taken not to take too plump or too fat birds, and dry them slowly under the same precautions as mentioned No. I (Quadrupeds). The operation must be repeated until the bird be perfectly dry. The attitude may be given to the bird before he be put in the oven, by wires that are sharp on one end and thrusted through the birds legs body breast and neck and others going through the wings and body. Small birds are likewise well-preserved in brandy rack or rum, and when arrived in their place of destination they must be washed and sweetened in fresh water for several times and lastly dipped in the preparing liquor, the plumage laid in order, the attitude given to the bird by wires and dried.

Birds were always mounted in those days, and the more rare or noteworthy the specimen, the more was it displayed in a bright light for the pleasure of the public. It would be interesting to trace the change in treatment of specimens and the evolution of the meticulously perfect bird "skin" as we know it today.

Forster included also directions for labelling but these were not always carried out even at a much later date for inexperienced or careless collectors often omit all data on the skins although the skins may be well made.

On this subject Forster continues:

. . . and in general to all the specimens must be fixed lead tickets by means of a wire and a number on the lead scratched in; which must be referred to in a paper where under the same number the collector would be pleased to write the name by which the animal goes in his country or among the various tribes of Indian nations, with the food, age, growth, nature, manners, haunts, how many young or eggs it brings forth, in what manner it is caught, what it is used for etc., etc.

Forster divides American birds into land and water groups, naming 183 land birds and 118 water birds; many of these, he acknowledges, were previously described by Pennant, Catesby, Linnaeus, Brisson, Edwards, and a few were marked N.S.[3] by Forster.

Johann Forster is known also for his *Indische Zoologie* written in German and Latin in parallel columns. This, however, is largely a translation of Pennant's *Indian Zoology*. He likewise rendered into English, Peter Kalm's *Travels into North America* which was first written in Swedish.

Forster and his son, Johann Georg Adam Forster (1754–1794), are frequently confused, because both father and son accompanied Captain James Cook (1728–1779) on his second voyage round the world and both collaborated in writing their combined observations which were published in 1777. It is interesting to know that the younger Forster made some drawings [4] of North American birds on this expedition (although he was primarily a botanist) which can be seen in the Natural History Museum, in London.

The elder Forster was born in 1729 at Dirschau, near Danzig, Germany. Generally regarded as a naturalist and traveller, although he was educated for the ministry, he served, for a number of years, as pastor of a church at Nassenhuben, near Danzig. He devoted most of his time to mathematics and natural history, and, in 1765, was invited by the Russian government to inspect Russia's new colonies on the Volga. His irritable temperament involved him in disagreements with the government and the following year saw him in England teaching natural history at Warrington, in Lancashire.

Apparently Thomas Pennant took an interest in Forster, for he introduced him to his friends in London, and states that "at my [Pennant's] persuasion and by my encouragement" Forster translated Peter Kalm's *Travels into North America*. Forster also added a second volume to his Translation of Bossu's *Travels in Louisiana* with a *Life of Peter Loefling,* one of Linnaeus' favorite pupils. These translations were sponsored by Pennant and procured Forster sufficient funds until he went with Captain Cook on his second voyage round the world in 1772.

Few ornithologists have had the wide learning that the elder Forster possessed for he had a good knowledge of modern and ancient languages, antiquities and natural science. Yet he was not successful, being always handicapped by a quick temper and lack of tact as in his account of his experience with Captain Cook which was derogatory to the British Government and necessitated his leaving England.

---

[2] Nichols, 1812–1815: 1: 384.

[3] New species.
[4] See Chapter XI.

In 1780 he returned to Germany and became Professor of History and Mineralogy at Halle where he probably remained until his death in 1798. There were many factors in the late eighteenth century that made for a compelling interest in America and Forster's writings on the American fauna certainly played some part, at least in scientific circles, in fostering interest in North American exploration.

The indomitable hope that a northwest passage would be found was still a passion of the British people while the growing nationalistic feeling in the Colonies which produced the American Revolution kept the New World in the foreground of European thought. After the war had broken, many French officers and soldiers came to the aid of the Colonies, and travellers, adventurers, and refugees from the threatening French Revolution sought deliverance from tyranny on American shores.

In contrast to these disturbing influences, we should mention the hundreds of Jesuit missionaries who toiled across Canada and parts of the American Colonies, in the hope of converting the Indians to Christianity. The records they have saved for us are ample proof of their charity and industry.

CHARLEVOIX

It is to one of these that we turn now, the French missionary and traveller, Pierre François Xavier Charlevoix (1682–1761), who had already spent the years from 1705–1709 as a professor of languages and philosophy in Quebec, and who came again in 1720, at the request of the Duke of Orleans, to gather information on the "western sea," then supposed to be not far from the Mississippi River. Many are familiar with him no doubt, for his scholarly six volume work, *L'histoire et Description Generale de Nouvelle France,* but it is his much less known two volume *Journal of a Voyage to North America* in a series of letters to the Duchess of Lesdiguierres (1761), that contains the natural history notes in which we are interested. It is significant that he quotes from Nicolas Denys, then not yet forgotten, when considering the extent of the Newfoundland Banks and he shows a touch of humor when he inveighs against the contrary winds that detained them on the "frontiers of the empire of the codfish."

Having been hopelessly seasick for five of the eleven weeks spent in crossing, Charlevoix's enthusiasm for the letters he had promised the Duchess had considerably waned, but admitting that he "was incapable of refusing her anything," he manfully kept his word.

We gather that Father Charlevoix had no leanings of the true naturalist although in fairness to his task he treats briefly of all branches of nature. But said he,

it is something extremely shocking not to be able to stir out of doors without being frozen and wrapped up in furs like a bear, to behold one continuous tract of snow which pains the sight . . . and what can a man think who sees the horses with beards of ice a foot long?

In letter number IX we may read his brief account of birds. This is strongly reminiscent of Nicolas Denys, for he speaks in the same words of the three kinds of grouse; and, of the owl of Canada, he believes with Denys that it stores away live mice, breaks their legs to prevent their escape and feeds them carefully until they are fat. At this date (1720) Denys' admirable work was less than twenty-five years old and probably widely read.

We are led to believe that Father Charlevoix did not have a sensitive ear for bird music. "The thrush of Canada," says he, "is much the same with that of France as to shape, but has only half his music; the wren has robbed him of the other half." Yet this was written in the breeding territory of that marvelous singer, the hermit thrush, a bird surpassed by none, not even the nightingale according to many ornithologists who have heard both. However, the American naturalist is pleased to note the good friar's approval of that diminutive brown creature, the winter wren, also a breeding species of the Canadian woods with a song of wild ringing quality. The song of the goldfinch Charlevoix could not judge as he had never seen it in a cage!

But the cardinal and the hummingbird seemed to stir this worthy Jesuit to real enthusiasm. He had seen the cardinals as cage birds in Paris and remembered their sweet whistles and the brilliancy of their plumage, while of the hummingbird or flybird or l'oiseau mouche, he says, "were its pipe as grateful to the ear as his outward appearance to the sight, it would have the unanimous voice of every one." The male's plumage he describes as a perfect jewel, the back, wings, and tail of green like the leaves of a rose bush while specks of gold scattered all over the plumage add a "prodigious éclat" to it. The mate of this amazing creature Charlevoix describes as "nothing striking" of a tolerable agreeable white under the belly, and of a bright grey all over the rest of the body. He knew of hummingbirds having been kept for short periods and fed on sugar-water, and had even kept one himself for twenty-four hours and believed that frost, coming the next morning, had killed it. This account of the hummingbird is the best of Charlevoix's ornithological descriptions but he fails completely at the end by saying the eggs [5] are the size of a pea with yellow spots on a black ground and number three and sometimes five!

A running comment on hawks, eagles, snipes, woodcocks, ravens, and the vast multitude of wild ducks, which he had heard, includes two and twenty species, of which the canard branchus (wood-duck) is the most beautiful, and brings Charlevoix's number of birds up to a fair average. Like several other writers, he includes bustards, a European species, which he must have confused with the Canada goose.[6] Swans, turkey cocks,

---

[5] Regular complement two white eggs.

[6] Johann Reinhold Forster, translator of Bossu's *Travels through Louisiana* (see preface, p. viii) "The French word outarde signifies commonly a bustard but in North America

water hens, woodpeckers, "an animal of extreme beauty," and cranes of two colors, some quite white and others a light grey, conclude his list. We observe that the whooping crane, now nearly extinct, was still common in Charlevoix's time but his final remark that they "make excellent soup" helps to explain the inexorable passing of this noble species.

Upon arriving in Quebec in September 1720 Charlevoix went up the St. Lawrence proceeding west to Michilimacinac then down the Mississippi in a small boat to New Orleans. He suffered a shipwreck in the Bahamas, visited Santo Domingo and returned to France in 1772. His *History of New France* and his *History of Paraguay* are his principal works. He was primarily an historian and a teacher but his American Letters even though not the work of a lover of nature are well worth a naturalist's perusal.

According to Elliott Coues' *Bibliographical Appendix*, Charlevoix's *Journal of a Voyage to North America 1761* is quoted by Field as being a translation of the third volume of the *Histoire de la Nouvelle France* but this it obviously is not, since it opens with a discussion of the origin of the American Indian and proceeds from this to the letters to the Duchess of Lesdiguierres, sixteen of which are in Volume 1 and fourteen in Volume 2.

LE PAGE DU PRATZ

Another French writer, but one who cannot be recommended, is Le Page Du Pratz, a planter who came to Louisiana in middle life and remained here for some fifteen years. He was an overseer and director of public plantations and thus should have been familiar with a large part of the country. He traversed the territory of the Natchez Indians with dog and gun and ten Indians and gave his readers a simple account without aiming to impress by wonderful stories. However, the account in his first three-volume French edition of 1758 is too long and too wordy with personal anecdote and inconsequential detail. Accordingly, the English translation of 1774 was condensed to one volume although the matter on birds remains very much the same as in the French version.

The birds are discussed in Chapter VII *Of Birds and Flying Insects* and occupy pages 271–283. In general, the account is unreliable, many of the birds being erroneously described, but now and again the author presents some good observation which comes as a surprise to the ornithologist; for instance, the barbs on the woodpecker's tongue. Too often he remarks that the birds are the same as in Europe, as the woodpecker and the nightingale which latter bird never occurs in America. He had obviously never observed the flicker feeding on ants or if he had, he did not realize that it was a wood-

pecker, for he takes to task a modern author who had observed this "woodpecker" feeding upon them.

Some of his local names of birds are interesting in that we have not previously found them used:

The Pope [scarlet tanager?] is a bird that has a red and black plumage. It has got its name perhaps because that name makes it look somewhat old, and none but old men are promoted to that dignity; or because its notes are soft, feeble and rare; or lastly because they wanted a bird of that name in the colony, having two other kinds named bishops [possibly painted buntings or indigobirds] and cardinals.

Du Pratz has a good deal to say about wood pigeons [passenger pigeons] and ways of catching them, but the paroquets interest him little because they do not learn to speak easily. The eagle, according to Du Pratz, is white, the flamingo is grey, the kingfisher always goes against the wind even when its dead carcass hangs in the breeze, and the crane and the spatula [spoonbill] make excellent soup.

In spite of grossly inaccurate observation mixed with idle stories we note that Du Pratz was apparently the first writer to mention the frigate-bird and its habit of returning every night to the coast to roost. The "Draught Bird," which this writer says is similar to the frigate bird "with a chequered brown and white belly," we are unable to identify. It is interesting to know that Du Pratz sent two vultures to John Latham the English ornithologist which he kept in his garden.

Du Pratz is valuable mainly for his account of the Natchez and Mississippi tribes of Indians, but his method of writing lacks style and plan and the illustrations, a few of which represent birds and mammals, are poor.

CHASTELLUX

Several other French writers come to mind as contributors to the description of America in the late eighteenth century. Most of their accounts possess an insight into the American scene and a charm and piquancy of expression that make for delightful reading, even when written primarily from the soldier's point of view. This is particularly true of that pleasing and facile commentator, the Marquis de Chastellux, (1734–1788), a distinguished French gentleman who was one of the forty members of that learned body the French Academy. He was also a major general in the French army who came to America under the Comte de Rochambeau (1725–1807). The perusal of the American travels by this writer has been as a fair oasis in a wide desert of dull and factual description that characterizes many of the accounts, especially those of the eighteenth century. Still we cannot claim for Chastellux any place of rank among the early observers of birds for he made no list nor systematic account of them; only, we may remember with pleasure his few experiences with American game birds,[7] his account of Jefferson's experiment in raising

---

they give that name to a kind of goose." Forster had just been informed (1771) of this by a gentleman recently returned from America.

[7] Chastellux, 1828: 192–193 and note.

deer at his Virginia park, Monticello, his description of the pet wolf in the house of one of his friends, his pause of an evening to listen to two thrushes (probably our beautiful wood thrush), and his delightful appreciation of the mockingbird and the hummingbirds at the home of Mrs. Bird.

The Marquis of Chastellux, without being a trained observer, possessed that general culture which made him appreciate beauty intelligently whether he was contemplating feminine pulchritude or bird song, the glory of a primeval forest or the precision of a military manoeuver. He refers to the woodhen's [grouse] drumming as the "beating of their sides with their wings which may be heard above a mile"; he was eager to see his first heath hen; one of these an innkeeper had in his tavern, and his response to the evening song of two thrushes is worthy of John Burroughs. He writes as follows:

. . . I returned to the house, but stopped some time to hear at sunset, two thrushes which seemed to challenge each other to the song like the shepherds of Theocritus.[8] This bird in my opinion ought to be considered as the nightingale of America; it resembles those of Europe in its form, colour, and habits: but it is twice as large.[9] Its song is similar to that of our thrush but so varied and so much more perfect that if we except the uniform plaintive notes of the European nightingale they might be taken for each other. It is a bird of passage, like the mockingbird, and like it also sometimes remains through the winter.

As to the hummingbird, M. Chastellux devotes two paragraphs to his sheer delight in watching these tiny creatures. John Josselyn a hundred years previously had averred that they slept all winter and Chastellux harks back to this belief with some doubt but admits that he cannot understand their ability to cope with wind and weather in migration. He then speaks of an ingenious method of collecting the birds without damaging their delicate plumage, as practiced by a fancier of birds who had a "cabinet." "This method," he said, "is to load his gun with a bladder filled with water. The explosion of this water is sufficient to knock down the hummingbird and deprive it of motion."

Chastellux is remembered not alone for his charming book of American travels but also for a philosophical treatise, *De la Felicité Publique* wherein his generous ideas of philanthropy and freedom find expression. He is said to have been a favorite correspondent of the illustrious Pope Ganganelli. His democratic interest and concern for his fellow man is in one way evidenced by his participation in the early smallpox immunization experiments in France. When, only a youth of twenty years, he offered himself to be inoculated and after his recovery he declared, "Here I am safe, and what is still more gratifying to me is that by my example I shall be the means of saving many others."

[8] Greek pastoral poet, third century B.C.
[9] The wood thrush and nightingale are similar in size but a view of birds at close range always makes them seem larger.

He was born in Paris in 1734 of a distinguished family but he lost his father when still a child and entered the army at only fifteen years of age. In 1780 he came to America with the Count de Rochambeau's army remaining here a few years after which he returned to France and died in 1788.

HECTOR ST. JOHN DE CREVECŒUR

From an entirely different walk of life, we may cite Hector St. John de Crevecœur, also a Frenchman and one of noble birth, but one who became a farmer and lived close to the soil amid the simplest surroundings. Born at Caen in 1735 he was sent to England when he was a boy of sixteen years and thus mastered in youth the English language so that his *Letters of an American Farmer* were written originally in English and published first in London in 1782.

These letters dispensed an aesthetic appreciation as well as a practical knowledge of natural history, and after being translated by the author into French, and finding their way into many other languages also, they were widely read for nearly half a century.

The author had first come here in 1754 when only nineteen and settled in Orange County, New York, on a tract of one hundred and twenty acres, completely transferring his home and allegiance to the New World. Here he worked his ground with love of home and reverence for bird, plant, and every natural phenomenon. This constituted his fellowship with God. No longing for fame or wealth disturbed him in his quiet retreat, but, surrounded by his wife and children, who were real companions and helpers in his labors in the field, he worked out his simple yet satisfying philosophy which is embodied in his seven famous letters.

At this time the young country, newly become independent, was thoroughly engrossed with the strenuous aftermath of the Revolution. She had done little in literature, aside from her religious and political writings, except to engage in some rather perfunctory imitation of the English pastorals. Many of these may be read in the early American magazine, *The Portfolio*.

Therefore, de Crevecœur's letters were arresting for their new methods and their new subject matter, and they were timely in that they represented a response in America to the invigorating Romantic Movement in Europe which looked with favor on all fresh matter in literature. These letters did not, however, escape the English interpretation of being a pandering fabrication by their author to induce emigration to America. Nevertheless, the *Letters* were popular, perhaps more so because of the aspersive comment they called forth, and they certainly contained abundant proof of the author's keen powers of observation. His account of the kingbird which had been stealing his bees is a bit of investigation worthy of the Fish and Wildlife Service of today: After careful observation which seemed to prove the kingbird a serious menace, de Crevecœur shot the culprit and examined the contents of its stomach. He took out 171 bees, all drones, and of these fifty-four, after having been devoured, licked themselves clean and soon flew away. Here was the scientist; but his enjoyment of the morning chorus of birds bespeaks the real naturalist stirred by the reaction of the poet:

I generally rise from bed about that indistinct interval which properly speaking, is neither night nor day; for this is the moment of the most universal vocal choir. Who can listen unmoved to the sweet love tales of our robins told from tree to tree; or to the shrill catbird? The sublime accents of the thrush on high always retard my steps that I may listen to the delicious music.

Like William Bartram who was his friend and contemporary, de Crevecœur held a scientific and enquiring attitude toward external nature, but while Bartram combined the literary sense of the essayist with his science, de Crevecœur evinced more the emotional attributes of the poet, and although his writing took a prose form he showed many of the qualities of that modern personality, the poet-naturalist.

Many ornithological notes can be gleaned from de Crevecœur's letters and while his kingbird story cannot be surpassed for astuteness, his remarks on the hummingbirds perhaps appeal more to the general reader. In addition to an appreciative description of their gorgeous plumage, he gives an account of their irascible disposition which throws them into tantrums of anger when they fail to find the desired nectar in the flowers, or they may even engage in desperate combat with competitors in the flower garden.

De Crevecœur is the author also of *Voyage dans la Haute Pennsylvania* or *Travels through Upper Pennsylvania,* Paris, 1801.

This is a fanciful tale purporting to be based on an English manuscript found in the wreck of a vessel sailing from Philadelphia and bound for Denmark. It forms a skeleton around which a great body of authentic information on the country and the Indians and the new settlers is built. Here again de Crevecœur shows himself adept in the writer's craft, a bookish and imaginative man yet practical and objective in his attitude toward his adopted profession of farming and his chosen avocation of natural history.

BOSSU

Before leaving these eighteenth century French travellers we should briefly note Jean Bossu's *Travels through Louisiana* which was translated from the French by that indefatigible worker in science, Johann Reinhold Forster. Bossu was a captain in the French marines and is said to have made three voyages to America, the last one being reported in an account published in 1777.

The complete English title of the present work which covers Bossu's first two voyages reads, *Travels through that part of North America formerly called Louisiana* (two volumes) and is in the form of twenty-two let-

ters [10] addressed to the Marquis de l'Estrade, the first being written in February 1751 and the last in November 1762. The translation was brought out in London in 1771 and Forster must have undertaken this work before his departure on Captain Cook's second voyage.

The translator praises Bossu's usual adherence to fact and his unwillingness to quote from hearsay. However, Forster reasons very logically against Bossu's arguments for lions and elephants in America, pointing out the wrong shape of the grinder teeth referred to by Bossu, and the impossibility of the Indians using the lion as an example of bravery when the lion does not occur in the New World.

Bossu's references to birds include a dozen or fifteen kinds, some of which, as ducks and grouse, compass several species. Elliott Coues in his bibliographical appendix asserts that Bossu's bird notes are not of any value and it is true that the first part of them amounting to a mere paragraph to which the editor adds clarifying notes, is negligible. However, on pages 368 to 375 Bossu has a few paragraphs on birds that are worthy of note. The list is as follows:

1. Karaucro (carrion crow) Turkey vulture. Here he makes the curious misstatement that the bird is the shape and size of a turkey; he describes its flight and habit of waiting about in droves for the opportunity to descend upon a dying animal or a decampment of men from a hunting station and finally he refers to the downy feathers under the wings as being useful for stopping the blood.
2. Flamingo—end of wings black, back white, belly flame-colored.
3. Stares of two kinds, probably Red-winged Blackbirds and Grackles. The red shoulders of the former, according to Bossu, were used in ladies' dress linings.
4. Parrots and Parokeets
5. Jays
6. Magpies
7. Mockingbirds. His remarks on this bird show that he observed them accurately for he called attention to the mockingbird's mimicking ability and its susceptibility to other music saying it "appears enchanted and pleased when one plays on any instrument, and even joins the concert." This is exactly as mockingbirds behave when listening to their own music emanating from a loud-speaker.
8. Pope, the male of the Painted Finch

---

[10] It is necessary to note that Bossu is listed variously as "N. Bossu" and "Jean Bernard Bossu," the latter form being the correct one if we may judge by the Library of Congress Catalogue. It is likewise necessary to state that some emendation of the book has occurred, the title page of volume 1 being substituted for that of volume 2, at least in the sets examined in this study; and the last letter, which according to Sabin's (Sabin, Joseph, *Dictionary of books descriptive of America,* N. Y., author, 1868) collation is to be found in the second volume, is missing. This letter, according to the *Monthly Review,* **26**: 61, Jan. 1772, tells of a plan of Bossu to investigate, with some of his followers, the famous island of Bimini, where was to be found the Fountain of Youth. In Ponce de Leon's time (1530) this was attributed to Florida, but now its location was shifted to the Isle of Providence, one of the Bahamas, owned by the English. Bossu, hearing that a contingent of Spaniards failed to find it, did not go.

9. Cardinal. This bird he notes is a kind of sparrow that whistles like a blackbird. [Probably the European blackbird, a thrush.]
10. Bishop, a species of Tanager
11. Goldfinch, quite yellow with the tips of the wings black.
12. Harlequin, species not clear from the context.
13. Hummingbird.
14. Ducks—various kinds but the duck that perches on trees is the best for eating as it feeds on acorns and beech seeds.
14. Coot. On page 95, Bossu mentions also teals and divers.
15. Egrets. These are described as exceeding white and the ladies employ their feathers as aigrettes.
16. Pelican or Great-throat. The fat of this bird according to Bossu was useful for precipitating the paste of indigo, a dye stuff that was manufactured in Louisiana.
17. Spoonbill, having a bill shaped like a spatula, an apothecary's instrument.

Bossu closes his list with mention of the lancet-bill [species?], remarking that a full account of the birds would require volumes which were better undertaken during his time by his learned countrymen, M. de Buffon and Daubenton (1732–1785).

Far more interesting, however, than Bossu's list of birds with the few remarks on their uses and habits is the more or less random mention he makes of eagles and the Indians' method of capturing them. These birds which many early writers designated as "gripes" were valuable to the northern Indians because they adorned their calumets of peace with their feathers and these were called "feathers of valour." Only the old warriors were permitted to engage in the singular method employed for capturing these birds and it seems worthy of description in this volume as a contribution to our bird lore, by the North American aborigines.

The Indian warriors first studied the places where the eagles were wont to hunt and induced them to continue to come to certain areas by providing them with a sumptuous repast of flesh, entrails, and the like. The first bird was allowed to eat his fill and thus several others came and fought over the booty. Then the warrior, having skillfully estimated all difficulties and how to overcome them, dug a pit for himself, covered the opening with fagots of wood to which the bait was securely fastened. He then laid straw beneath the fagots, covered his hand with a thin leather mitten or sack and awaited his birds. When the eagle was busy eating, the warrior worked his hands up through the fagots and grasped the mighty flier by the tarsi; the eagle then powerless met an ignominious death in the Indian's oxhide. Sometimes five or six birds were caught thus by one warrior who was neither fatigued nor hungry upon his return for the baits were brought to him by his children, his victuals were prepared and sent to him by his women while he had had the sport of the hunt and the honor of bringing home the trophies of his unique vigil, which were valuable as articles of trade.

M. Bossu appears to have been successful with the first volume of this work, and received a substantial gratuity for it from the French king when it first came out in 1768. He was recalled during the writing of the second volume however, and apparently broke with his associates at that time. His future career seems to be unknown, but it is interesting to read of his adoption by the Arkansas Indians who amid wild rejoicings admitted him to their fold by the painful operation of drawing with great needles the figure of a stag upon his thigh.

PETER KALM

Much more important than the foregoing French travellers was Peter Kalm (1716–1779), a Swedish botanist and economist who visited America in the mid-eighteenth century. Like Catesby, he came here to study and collect plants suitable for introduction into his native country. He was a student of Linnaeus at Upsala, and he was also a graduate student at the University of Åbo, in 1735. Early in his college career he came under the influence of Bishop Johan Brovallius, also a naturalist, who directed Kalm into natural history. Another prominent man who took an interest in Kalm was Baron Sten Bjelke, who took him into his home for a time and then sent him to travel in many parts of Sweden. Kalm soon made a name for himself, going to Russia and part of the Ukraine in 1744 with his patron Baron Bjelke, and in 1747 was chosen the first professor of economics at Åbo.

After his trip to Russia there was talk among the scientists of Sweden of sending a naturalist to Iceland and Northern Siberia for boreal plants to be naturalized in Sweden. Linnaeus, however, favored America instead of Iceland, and so it was decided that Kalm should go to the English Colonies in America in the interest of Swedish agriculture. His appointment came the same year that he was given a professorship, hence it was necessary for Kalm to secure a leave of absence from his academic duties. This done, he was apparently delighted to go, and used the opportunity to record not only his scientific observations but also to write a literary description of new Sweden and the adjacent Colonies. His effort to include everything in his impressions considerably hampered the elegance of his style yet gave it a certain piquancy of expression that is very pleasing. Kalm's trip was supported by several agencies—the University of Upsala and the University of Åbo, the Academy of Science of Sweden, and the Board for Promoting Manufactures in Sweden. A joint subsidy of 1,000 plates (about 150 pounds sterling) was provided by the universities, and 300 plates (about 45 pounds sterling), were given by the Board for Promoting Manufactures. It appears also that Baron Bjelke and Linnaeus helped to finance the trip. Still Kalm was obliged to use his own salary and about 130 pounds of his private "fortune," so that he felt quite reduced in circumstances on his return.

En Resa til Norra America was the title of his journal, published in Stockholm between 1753 and 1761. It is an account of much more general interest than many of the early journals, and the ornithological matter, while not of great scientific value, is attractive and sincerely compiled.

Kalm was absent in America three years and eight months, leaving in October, 1747,[11] accompanied by his gardener, Lars Jungstrom, who was also skilled in drawing and mechanics. They set out from Gothenburg, stopping in London, where Kalm met Peter Collinson and other naturalists, and secured from Collinson an introduction to Benjamin Franklin, who at this time was turning his attention from business to scientific matters.

Kalm divided his time among three regions—Ontario, New York, and parts of Pennsylvania and New Jersey —and returned to his professorship at Åbo in 1751. While in Philadelphia, he was several times the guest of the Bartram family, who always were hospitable to visiting naturalists, and it is about his visit there that a slight atmosphere of unpleasantness seems to hover.

Kalm's breach of social etiquette appears in substance to be that he appropriated some of John Bartram's findings as his own, and, further, after visiting in the Bartram home, failed to write the customary letter of thanks. John Bartram wrote as follows in a letter [12] to Linnaeus:

Pray how doth our friend Kalm go on with his history of our country plants? He promised to send me one, as soon as printed, and that he would do me justice in mentioning what plants I showed him; but I never can get a letter from him since he left my house. I shall be very well pleased to see what he hath wrote of our plants.

Unfortunately, Peter Kalm was not a master of the English language nor was he familiar with American customs. Perhaps it seemed to the Bartrams a little inappropriate that he sent his servant ahead to Philadelphia while he (Kalm) awaited the development of certain seeds in Quebec, and in lieu of coming himself he wrote a clumsy letter to Bartram.

We should not, however, take these cumbersome letters as entirely reliable indicators of the American feeling toward Kalm. According to Adolph Benson,[13] Professor of German and Scandinavian languages at Yale University, Kalm was a welcome guest in the best circles in the Colonies and received many flattering courtesies and privileges from institutions both in Canada and the Colonies, which attest the people's confidence in, and liking for, him.

As for his relationship with the Bartrams and other prominent Americans, he felt great admiration for John Bartram, referring to him as the "attentive" Mr. Bartram, and, again he says (*Kalm's Travels*, vol. 1: 62. Benson edition):

---

[11] According to Spencer Trotter, (*Auk*, 20 (3): 254, 1903) Kalm had not spent a winter in America by October, 1748, but it seems definite that he left Sweden in October, 1747 and must have spent the winter of 1747–1748 in the American Colonies and Quebec.

[12] Not dated; probably 1753.

[13] Kalm, 1937: Introd. XI.

I also owe him much, for he possessed that great quality of communicating everything he knew. I shall, therefore, in this work, frequently mention this gentleman. For I should never forgive myself, if I were to omit the name of a discoverer, and claim that as my own contribution which I had learned from another person.

It is probable that Kalm may have been instrumental in the election of John Bartram to the Swedish Academy of Sciences in 1777. He considered John Bartram a greater botanist than his son William, although he expressed sincere admiration for him too. For Franklin, to whom he had a letter of introduction from Peter Collinson, he had the highest regard, and he enjoyed much hospitality in his home and apparently was occasionally in the field with him. Kalm had the capacity for enjoying all kinds of people, and hence, his travelogue is varied and readable throughout.

He was, of course, primarily a botanist, as were most naturalists of the eighteenth century. However, he included bird observations as an integral part of his daily journal, giving first the birds observed on the voyage, as petrels, shearwaters, tropic birds, gulls, and terns. The list observed after he arrived in America must be called small, but it is noteworthy that it shows a sensible grouping approximating present-day understanding of relationships, as cranes, partridges, turkeys, pigeons, followed by hummingbird and whip-poor-will. Next, all the woodpeckers known to him are described in a separate list, which is one of the earliest annotated lists of American birds. Even the ivory-billed woodpecker (*Campephilus*) is given as an occasional visitor to the dense cedar swamps of the Delaware River, but this seems not to have been likely even in Kalm's day—more probably it was the pileated that he saw. The various blackbirds also are discussed under the general name of "Maise thieves," which was the local Swedish name for redwings, purple grackles, and bobolinks. The last-named were further designated as the white-backed maize thieves. According to Kalm, these birds were guilty of attacking the grain "both publicly and secretly," and though they are very different in species "yet there is so great a friendship between them that they frequently accompany each other in mixed flocks." These birds are minutely described; his account of the purple daw (purple grackle), with references to the daw and stare of Europe, would be a credit to a modern ornithologist:

As these blackbirds are so noted for their misbehavior, I will here give a short description of them. Their size is that of a starling. The bill is conic, almost subulated, straight, convex, naked at the base, black, with almost equal mandibles, the upper being only very little angulated, so as to form almost squares; they are placed obliquely at the base of the bill and have no hair. There is a little horny knob, or a small prominence on the upper side of them. The tongue is sharp and bifid at the point. The iris of the eyes is pale; the forehead, the crown, the nucha, the upper part and the sides of the head under the eyes are dark blue; all the back and coverts of the wings are purple; the upper coverts of the tail are not of so conspicuous a purple color, but are, as it were, blackened with soot; the nine primary quill feathers are black; the other secondary ones are likewise black, but their outward margin is purple; the twelve tail feathers have a blackish purple color and their tips are round; those on the outside are the shortest, and the middle extremely long. When the tail is spread, it looks round towards the extremity. The throat is bluish green, and shining; the breast is likewise black or shining green, according as you turn it to the light; the belly is blackish, and the vent feathers are obscurely purple-colored; the parts of the breast and belly which are covered by the wings are purple-colored; the wings are black below, or rather sooty; and the thighs have blackish feathers. The legs (*tibiae*) and the toes are of a shining black. It has four toes, as most birds have. The claws are black, and that on the back toe is longer than the rest. Dr. Linné calls this bird the *Gracula quiscuta*.

The bounties placed upon these birds in that early time also are discussed by Peter Kalm and make us feel that the "bounty system" is truly an archaic and misconceived remedy, and that all modern applications of it should be abolished. Even the untutored agriculturists of the mid-eighteenth century soon learned that their threepence-a-dozen for dead maize thieves, according to the laws of Pennsylvania and New Jersey, did not work.

Benjamin Franklin expressed himself on the bounty as follows:

. . . by means of the premiums which have been settled for killing them in New England, they have been so extirpated that they are very rarely seen, and in a few places only. But as in the summer of the year 1749, an immense quantity of worms appeared on the meadows which devoured the grass, and did great damage, the people have abated their enmity against the maize-thieves.

Thus the bounty laws in the various states were repealed, for they merely involved the people in great expense to pay the premiums and gave the insect pests a better chance by removing their natural enemies.

Though Kalm could be scrupulously accurate in some ways, he showed himself unscientific and credulous in others, for, like nearly all the observers of his day, he believed in the hibernation of swallows and cited several authorities and personal experiences to justify his belief. It is strange that he apparently did not discuss this with Bartram, who did not believe this prevalent explanation for the disappearance of these birds and could, no doubt, have convinced Kalm, but said Kalm: ". . . I observed them for the first time on the 10th of April (new style); the next day in the morning, I saw great numbers of them sitting on posts and planks and they were as wet as if they had been just come out of the sea." What he has to say of the black snake attacking people, especially at its mating time, is equally credulous. He noted carefully the various species of swallows—those which nest in barns, in chimneys, and underground (the bank swallows)—and also mentioned the martins and the crude "houses" constructed for them by the colonists by affixing boards on the outside of the walls. Thus they served to warn of hawks and crows and were valued by the settlers. A particularly interesting bit of ornithology is recounted by Kalm, concerning a pair of barn swallows which nested in the barn of a lady of his acquaintance. She and her children had observed the male bird twittering near the nest for a long time, and, on investigation, found that the female had died while sitting on the eggs. On removing the female, the male took possession and sat for two hours, but, as Kalm said, "thinking the business too troublesome for him, he went out and returned in the afternoon with another female, which sat upon the eggs and afterwards fed the young till they were able to provide for themselves." This was undoubtedly true, as in nature the bird's entire concern is always for the successful upbringing of the young, despite the sentimental interpretations of bird-behavior which many bird-lovers seem to read into their actions.

Another excellent demonstration of Kalm's powers of observation lies in his remarks on the bluebird, in which he points out the errors made by Catesby in his plate of this bird. Kalm calls attention to the color of the tarsus, feet, and bill, which were quite black, and the particular shades of color in breast and back. The food, too, is remarked upon as containing plant substance as well as insects.

His description of the hummingbird is the most noteworthy ornithological matter of his *Travels*. This bird being limited to the New World always impressed the Europeans with its beauty and almost incredibly small size and Peter Kalm did full justice to it in a four page account of its iridescent plumage, its feeding habits and its nest. He speaks of a nest he had secured as follows:

. . . that which is in my possession is quite round, and consists in the inside of a brownish and quite soft down, which seems to have been collected from the great mullein or Verbascum thapsus. . . . The outside of the nest has a covering of green moss such as is common on old pales or enclosures and on trees; the inner diameter of the nest is hardly a geometric inch at the top, and its depth half an inch.

He had evidently not seen the tiny white eggs but reported that: ". . . they are said to lay two eggs each the size of a pea."

These careful observations compare favorably with modern field ornithology. And his reference to Bartram's having kept two hummingbirds for several weeks on a diet of sugar and water and his own comment that they would not be difficult to keep in a hot house foreshadow modern aviary practice. For many species of this large family of some five hundred kinds limited to South America and a few from North America are now successfully kept and raised in the Zoological Gardens of London and other large cities.

Beside Kalm's discussion of hummingbirds his descriptions of swallows, his annotated list of woodpeckers, and his account of the evils of the bounty on crows and blackbirds, there are brief accounts of other birds as follows: duck, crane, cardinal, snowbird, mockingbird, robin, ptarmigan, catbird and whip-poor-will, of which last bird he says: "Their note is not whip-poor-will but rather whipperiwhip, with the first and last syllables accented and the middle ones but slightly pronounced."

A few illustrations accompany all editions except the first one, a drawing of the mockingbird and robin occupying one plate, the purple jackdaw (purple grackle) and red-winged stare (red-winged blackbird) on another, and the migratory pigeon is figured above. The name of the artist is unknown, but the drawings were copied from drawings made in America or from birds recently (at that time) brought over.

Although the ornithology of Peter Kalm's *Travels* is slight in bulk, the quality of it is good, and if the writer's main duty had not been to botany he would probably have made a large contribution to our knowledge of birds.

Few travellers have written accounts so buoyant with interest and varied detail. With his ability to give equally well the minutiae of a bird's plumage or the manoeuverings of assembled women about a fire concealing their warming pans beneath their skirts, Peter Kalm recalls to our minds the Marquis de Chastellux, but of course Kalm's account of America is a far more meaty document.

In his journals covering nearly four years of American experience, he includes a wide range of general information: shipping news, with ships arriving, ships lost and goods imported; statistics of deaths by years, in so far as this could be determined from imperfect parish records; and living conditions in town and outlying country. In fact, nothing was without important meaning to him, even a quaint and novel food receipt could intrigue him, while throughout the entire journal the naturalist-reader is assured of copious botanical and zoological detail.

When Kalm had been in the Colonies only a few days he compiled a list of fifty-eight trees which he had identified and concludes: "The trees were full of all sorts of birds, which by the variety of their plumage delighted the eye while the infinite variety of their tunes was continually reechoed."

Peter Kalm was born during the reign of Sweden's beloved but unsuccessful King Charles XII (1697–1718), in March 1716 [15] in the province of Ångermanland, whither the family had fled during the king's wars. He was the posthumous son of a Lutheran clergyman of Österbotten, Finland, which then belonged to Sweden, and early in life he showed a leaning toward theology. Under the guidance of Bishop Brovallius, however, Kalm took up seriously the study of natural science. He always showed a preference for practical science and was quick to discern useful applications of his scientific findings. He was therefore considered particularly well qualified for the American expedition as we may judge

from a letter [16] of his master Linnaeus in which he speaks of Kalm's ability.

Kalm was elected to the Swedish Academy of Sciences in 1745 at the early age of twenty-nine or thirty years, and he was in his early thirties when he went to America. He approached his travels with an open mind, and was interested in all phases of the American scene —the fast developing urban life of Philadelphia and Albany, the private household of Dutch, Swedish, French, and English families, the many religious sects and the surrounding Indian tribes. Yet, by profession he was only a botanist and an agriculturalist. It is interesting to know that the title of "Docent in Natural History and Agriculture" was bestowed upon him in recognition of his knowledge of farm economy and in 1747 he was given a professorship at the Åbo Academy. Despite his rapid rise in this field he never relinquished his interest in the church and frequently in America he was called upon to preach in the Swedish Church at Racoon,[17] New Jersey, the pastor of which, the Reverend Johan Sandin, had recently died. This courtesy on the part of Kalm grew into personal interest as time wore on, for in 1750 he married the widow of the late Reverend Sandin, Anna Maghretta Sjönan.

The following year, 1751, Kalm returned with his bride to Sweden and began again his duties at the University of Åbo. He took the most assiduous care of his seeds and plants from America and he continued to publish frequent articles on America up until 1775. One of these articles was on the passenger pigeon [18] and it was reprinted in English together with Audubon's account (1831) of the same species in the Smithsonian Institution's Annual Report for 1911, Washington, 1912, pp. 407–424.

There were originally three sets of Kalm's botanical specimens, one of which went to the Museum of the University of Upsala. Another [19] in 1754 was in the museum of Queen Lovisa Ulrika at Drottningholm and from there passed to the Museum of Natural History at Åbo. This collection was mounted by Kalm himself and bore his notes on habitat, flowering season, etc., but it was probably destroyed by the great fire of 1827 together with a manuscript *The Flora of Canada* which is mentioned by Linnaeus in his Species Plantarum (1753). The third set found its way to the Linnean Society of London. The renowned Swedish systematist described some seven hundred species of American plants and in ninety cases Peter Kalm was the original collector. Of these ninety species about sixty were new to science. According to L. J. Chenon, Kalm brought home large collections of shells, insects, and amphibia in addition to his seeds and plants. He was the author of three genera

---

[15] The year of Kalm's birth is given by Adolf Benson in his edition of Kalm's Travels (1937) as 1716, but all the early authorities give it as 1715. The date appears not to be known.

[16] Fries, 1908: Del. **11**: 59, in Swedish.

[17] Now Swedesboro, located near the Delaware River opposite Wilmington.

[18] Beskrifning pa de vilda Dufvar i Norra America, *Svenska Vetensk. Acad. Handlingar,* 1759: 275–295.

[19] See *Proc. Acad. Nat. Sci. of Phila.,* **81**: 297–303, 1929.

of plants, *Gaultheria* (wintergreen), *Lechea* (Pinweed), *Polymnia* (Leafcup), and as many know, he is the one for whom our beautiful mountain laurel *Kalmia* was named. With justifiable pride Kalm remarks: "Dr. Linné, because of the peculiar friendship and kindness with which he has always honored me, has been pleased to call this tree, *Kalmia folus ovatis, corymbis terminalibus,* or *Kalmia latifolia.*" Kalm discovered also a new species of *Rhus.* He is remembered in Åbo for founding the Botanical Garden there.

XI. EARLY ORNITHOLOGICAL OBSERVATION AROUND HUDSON BAY AND OTHER BOREAL REGIONS

The riches of Asia were the driving force that impelled England to seek the northwest passage. Many years were consumed in fruitless quest and many lives were lost in that perennial search for an outlet to the southern and western oceans by way of some strait or river in North America. Martin Frobisher's (1535?–1594) *Voyages* were the first to recount these expeditions, and he went there himself in 1576 under the auspices of Ambrose Dudley (1528?–1590), Earl of Warwick.

Thirty years later Henry Hudson (d. 1611) after three voyages to Canada concluded there could be no strait across North America at an easy latitude. In 1610 he made his final attempt entering Canada by way of Hudson Strait and penetrating to what is now Fox's Channel beyond the Strait. Concerning birds he wrote, in his journal that "in one afternoon [he himself] killed so many as feasted all our company being 23 persons at one time onely with Partridges besides curlew, Plover, mallard, Teale and Geese." Returning through Hudson Bay he became ice bound in the southern part of James Bay and found himself at the mercy of his mutinous men who bound him and cast him adrift, in a small boat with his son and a few other seamen. The only account of the voyage was written by Hudson's cabin boy, Alucak Prickett, whose veracity and loyalty to Hudson are questionable. However, because of the perfidy of Hudson's men, England has sought to expiate his death and to honor him for his valorous exploration.[1]

Sir Thomas Button (d. 1637) was the next explorer who went to Hudson Bay (1612–1613) and discovered the Nelson River and Southampton Island, which he called Carey's Swan's Nest. He was followed by Robert Bylot (fl. 1610–1616), who had been with Hudson, and William Baffin (d. 1622), who penetrated farthest north of all the arctic voyagers of the late sixteenth and early seventeenth centuries. Though much was learned and charted about these arctic regions, little encouragement was offered of finding the long-sought northwest passage and the matter languished for some time for lack of support for further expeditions.

It happened, however, that one Captain Luke Fox (1586–1635), who had cherished the desire for twenty-five years, persuaded some London merchants to outfit the *Charles Pinnace,* which was loaned to him by his Majesty Charles I (1600–1649). Fox therefore, realizing his great ambition at last, his ship victualled for eighteen months, with a list of stores rivaling those of Admiral Byrd for his antarctic expedition, set sail from Deptford on May 5, 1631. Though Fox was a rough, untutored Yorkshire man, he was clever and conceited, and his narrative glows with his pleasure in his own accomplishments. The "North west Fox" he whimsically calls himself; and the sights he tells of are stirring if not always convincing. He did not find the northwest passage, but, by studying the tides as he cruised up Fox Channel clear into the Arctic, he says he convinced himself that "there was such an outlet." Frustrated in his main purpose, he nevertheless was undaunted and felt great satisfaction over "not having lost one man, Boy nor soule" and was gone only six months. Said he on his return "All Glory be to God!"

The bird matter of Fox's narrative is interesting. Rough and ready in diction, it lists a goodly number of some twenty species and the remarks on them are usually informing. Fox made apparently one of the earliest references to the whooping crane, a bird now all but extinct over its once extensive range. He describes it as follows:[2]

> They brought on board two goodly swans, and a young Tall fowle alive; it was longheaded, long neckt, and a body almost answerable. I could not discerne whether it was an Estridge or no, for it was but pen-feathered. Within 3 or 4 days, the legges by mischance were broken and it dyed.

Since Fox penetrated to the western part of Hudson Bay, discovering the strait and shore known as "Sir Thomas Roe's (1581?–1644) Welcome," it seems likely that it was the little brown crane (*Grus canadensis tabida*) rather than the sandhill crane (*Grus canadensis*) which he described, for the little brown crane formerly inhabited the great plains of western Canada, while the sandhill was and still is more southern in distribution.

Other birds mentioned briefly by Fox are the blackbird, cormorant, crow, duck, eagle, goose, gull, hawk, jay, owl, partridge, pheasant, plover, ptarmigan, raven, sea mew, stint, swan, teal, and thrush. Of the ptarmigan he quotes from Prickett's account of Hudson's voyage (1610–1611): ". . . how mercifully God dealt with them [the men] in this time for in the space of three months he [Hudson] had such store of one kinde of Fowle which were Partridge as white as milke, of which he killed at least one hundred dozen. . . ." In all these voyages food supply was the main concern of the voyagers, as it is of an army. Abundance of fowl, ptarmigan, and seabirds' eggs gave zest to Fox's narrative, so that, with all its flow of egotistical language, it is the

---

[1] Ewen, 1938: **2–3.**

[2] *Voyages of Fox and James,* **2**: 325, London, Hakluyt Soc., 1894.

most readable if not the most productive of information. After Fox returned, in October 1631, interest in arctic exploration rather flagged, and it was over a century before fresh enthusiasm kindled plans for new expeditions.

Then Henry Ellis, F.R.S. (1721–1806), hydrographer and mineralogist, and later a governor of Georgia and of Nova Scotia, went thither in 1746 and published, on his return in 1748, a more accurate treatise called *A Voyage to Hudson Bay by the Dobbs Galley and California*. He succeeded in dispelling the belief that the route to the northwest passage lay through Hudson Bay. His account includes a natural history of the country, in which there are descriptions of several species of birds with copper plates of the pelican, the heath cock, the horned owl, and the white-tailed eagle.

The pelican and the white-tailed eagle are not indigenous to the Hudson Bay region, the pelican belonging a thousand miles farther south and the white-tailed eagle being native to Europe. However, the heath cock and the horned owl are common birds, which this author describes with considerable detail. Speaking of the birds in general, Ellis says (p. 185):

The Indians live not only on the Flesh of Animals they kill in hunting but on that also of Birds of Passage; such as swans, wild Geese, Ducks, Plovers and many others of that Kind that go to the Northward in the Spring to breed and return to the Southward in Autumn, and others also such as Eagles, Crows, Owls, Hawks and Gulls, likewise upon Partridges and Pheasants which stay in the Winter. Their Flesh in general they boil and eat by itself and they drink the water it was boiled in, which they esteem very wholesome.

Speaking of conditions at York Fort on the eighteenth of April, 1746, Ellis describes a shower of gentle rain which was followed by an influx of "Fowls" which had not been seen for seven months. In addition to the abundance of wild fowl which are proper to that country there was likewise "a great flight of small Birds mostly of a dark unpleasing colour; but the sweetness of their notes sufficiently compensated whatever was amiss in their Plumage, and made their Company equally harmonious and agreeable."

These were very probably tree sparrows and others of the Fringillidae, possibly Harris's sparrows and white-crowned sparrows. Perhaps Ellis' best account of a single bird is his description of the ptarmigan, giving careful color values of all the feather areas, the bill, the skin above the eye, the legs, the toes and the peculiar "snow shoes" on their edges to help these birds to walk in the snow. These pectinations, however, he noted were absent from the hind toes.

We should cite also the Danish work of Hans Egede, 1686–1758, a missionary to Greenland for twenty-five years. From his long experience there he knew every phase of the Greenlanders' life and produced a full and authoritative account of their way of living, including dress, hunting, fishing, games, marriage customs, and so forth. His account of the land birds is comparable to Ellis', mentioning "Rypper" (ptarmigan), ravens,

eagles, falcons, owls, and "different sorts of little sparrows, Snow Birds, and Ice Birds and a little Bird not unlike a Linnent which has a very melodious Tune."

Egede's list of sea-birds contains about a like number, as eidder-fowl (eiders), three (other) kinds of ducks, one with a broad bill like tame ducks, one with a long pointed bill (merganser) and a bird he calls the wood duck, concerning which they had a strange belief, to be described at the end of this list. Beside these, this author mentions several sea mews (gulls), big and small, terns lundes (puffins), snipe and the lumbs or the sea-emms, "a Fowl of a large size with very small wings for which reason he cannot fly." This last bird was probably the now extinct great auk. Many of these various birds appear in the cuts illustrative of the Greenlander's activities in his daily life.

To return to the anomalous wood duck, this bird is not the wood duck (*Aix sponsa*) of our present check-list, but the barnacle goose (*Branta leucopsis*), for he said it was large and had a black breast and grey body.

These do not propagate in the common Way of Generation by coupling like other Birds; but (which is very surprizing) from a slimy matter in the Sea which adheres to old Pieces of Wood driving in the Sea of which first is generated a kind of Muscles, and again in these is bred a little Worm, which in Length of Time is formed into a Bird, that comes out of the muscle-shell as other Birds come out of Egg-shells.

By a long series of footnotes the author supports or refutes the varying interpretations of this belief and concludes as follows:

And although this may seem to exceed the ordinary Bounds set by Nature in the Procreation of other Birds; yet it is observed and confessed, that the sea produces many strange and surprising Things and even living Animals, which we cannot affirm to have had being from the First Creation; but that by vertue of the primitive Blessing, God gave the Sea to produce.

It is difficult to understand how this fantastic belief could survive into the middle of the eighteenth century, but as early as the twelfth century, and probably much earlier this strange theory gained credence, and folk tales of such antiquity have a strong hold on the people. According to the old writer, Giraldus Cambrensis (1147?–1220), learned Welsh topographer and ecclesiastic writing in 1187, these birds were produced from fir timber drifting in the sea. At first they are like eggs upon it, says he, and after hatching hang down by their beaks. Finally when clothed with feathers they either fall into the water or fly into the air.

Hans Egede was a Dane born January 31, 1686 and educated for the church by devout parents. For a time he was pastor of a church in Tronhjem, Norway, and it was probably there that he conceived the desire to go in search of the early Norse who emigrated to Greenland several hundred years before. In vain he tried to interest the Danish government in such a project and, failing in this, he induced several merchants to subscribe small sums toward the plan. With these, plus his personal property amounting to two thousand pounds, he purchased a small vessel and was preparing in 1721 for his Greenland expedition. The Danish king at last moved by his courage and determination appointed him pastor of the new colony with an annual pension of sixty pounds. He gave him also forty pounds for immediate needs and Egede with his wife and children and forty settlers left May 12, 1721 and arrived July 3 in Balles River. His mission was to teach the Greenlanders and to impart the Gospel of Peace. Christian VI, on his ascension to the throne, was unsympathetic and ordered the colony relinquished. But Egede with ten seamen stayed resolutely on, though many others returned. Although Egede in some accounts is said to have remained there for twenty-five years, it was apparently only fourteen, for feeling in ill health and waxing in infirmities, he returned in 1736 to Copenhagen, leaving his eldest son, Paul, in charge of the Greenland settlement. He

the topography and anatomy of the mallemuck, that strange seabird that gorges itself until it must cast up its food and then falls to and devours it again until it is finally tired. Anderson's description of the mallemuck occupies twelve pages (56–67) of the second volume.

Mollymoke, or mallemuck, is a term applied rather indiscriminately by fishermen to several members of the Procellariiformes, especially the fulmars and smaller albatrosses. This group is popularly known as the tube-nosed swimmers and, in this case, the mallemuck was probably the Atlantic fulmar, *Fulmarus glacialis* (Linn.), a bird nesting in the north of Greenland and wintering along the coast of America down to the Newfoundland Banks. The account by Anderson is remarkable for its detail, both of the living bird and of its anatomy, for it was obtained by Anderson in 1733 and kept alive, that he might observe its habits, and he later killed it for detailed study of its anatomy. The author even

Fig. 37. Bird life in Greenland as seen by Johann Anderson. From his *Histoire Naturelle de L'Islande du Groenland du Détroit de Davis, Et d'autre Pays situés sous le Nord* (1754).

continued to give time and study to the Greenlanders, however, and wrote a grammar and a dictionary of their language and translated the New Testament for them. He published his description of Greenland in Danish at Copenhagen in 1757 and died the following year.

Two other publications on Greenland during the mid-eighteenth century are of interest for their inclusion of certain birds that are found in North America. The first of these is Johann Anderson's (1674–1743) *Nachrichten von Island, Grönland und der Strasse Davis zum wahren Nutzen der Wissenschaften und der Handlung* (1746).

The same work under the title, *Histoire Naturelle de L'Islande du Groenland du Détroit de Davis, Et d'autre Pays situés sous le Nord,* which is the one used in this study, was brought out in Paris in 1754. In addition to the running comments on birds, it contains a large folding plate of birds and a detailed description of

arranged to have it drawn from life by an artist and took his pet to the home of a païnter, but the bird was unhappy and refused to eat until it was restored to its master and, as he said, "lui fit beaucoup de caresses & de demonstrations de joye de se retrouver en Pays de Connaissance."

After a careful observation of the bird in life, its method of feeding, food preferences, etc., told in entertaining language, the author tells of its external topography with measurements of its bill, eyes, feet, legs, tail, and the color of these various parts even to the front and hind toe nails; then the plumage and the peculiar enveloping skin, such as the pelican has for holding extra air and facilitating its rise and descent, and probably also to break the impact against the water when the bird dives. Next the musculature is described with the covering of fat that is necessary for birds of Greenland's icy wastes.

From these external features the author proceeds to an account of all the internal anatomy, including the tongue, trachea, lungs, heart, spleen, pancreas, intestines, kidneys, and gonads. The eye is mentioned as having the sclerotic hard and firm and the lens with the magnifying powers of a glass lens.

This account is unique among the arctic travels in being the work of a very learned and important citizen of the State of Hamburg. Anderson's father, Ammon Anderson, came of a great family of merchants of Gothenburg, Sweden. He settled in Hamburg and the son Johann, was born May 14, 1674.

From early youth he showed great aptitude in the study of languages yet he determined to study law, al-

useless dilations upon the crude and repellent customs of the natives with which some accounts are replete. The book in two volumes was originally written in German, translated into French by Gottfried Sellius, and published posthumously in 1754, Anderson having died the third of May, 1743.

The other publication on Greenland of about this period is David Crantz's (1723–1777) *History of Greenland,* a two-volume work published in London in 1767. Crantz was a missionary of the United Brethren for the Furtherance of the Gospel among the Heathen, and, though his work in Greenland was largely with the natives, he took rather careful cognizance of the natural history of the island.

Fig. 38. Falcon and Snowy Owl from *The History of Greenland* (1767) by David Crantz (1723–1777). Courtesy of the Cornell University Library.

though his father was a merchant devoted to the church. Johann spent a great deal of time also in the study of Greek and Natural Philosophy and in the course of years became an exceedingly erudite scholar. His training at the University of Saxony was interrupted by the death of his father and he returned to Hamburg in January 1697. From then on for several years he enlarged his horizon by many diplomatic commissions from his government which resulted in several trade treaties with neighboring states. So useful were his services that he was elected Bourgomestre in 1723 and from this progressed to more and more important posts. Just what events in his life brought about his travels into Greenland and Iceland is not clear but he showed in the writing of the natural history the scholarly and serious approach that he put into his other writings, omitting the

The bird matter is arranged under Book II, on the Beasts, Birds and Fishes. Sections 1 and 2 deal with land birds; sections 3 and 4 with sea fowl.

Land birds are few because of the scarcity of food, but he describes with great detail the appearance and habits of the Greenland partridge, or ptarmigan, and remarks its inherent wildness, which belongs to many feral creatures, saying that when caught it cannot be made tame but refuses all food and dies for grief in an hour or two. It is interesting to see the care with which he observed the ptarmigan's mode of changing its color. Says Crantz:

They are grey in summer and white in winter. Some people imagine that they keep their feathers, and only change their colour; but here we have taken strict notice that they cast their feathers every spring and autumn and get new ones; only the bill and the top of the tail-feathers remain grey.

Henry Ellis likewise was very particular in his observation of the ptarmigan's moult.

A number of small land birds are mentioned by Crantz. These in some cases are the same species as the birds in Norway but the Greenland fauna is more like that of northern America, than northern Europe; and many of the birds mentioned by Crantz had already been described by Erik Pontoppidan (1698–1764), Bishop of Bergen, in his *Natural History of Norway* (1755).

But, though Greenland has a small land fauna, the sea about teems with multitudes of birds in great variety. Crantz discusses them under four headings.

In the first group Crantz places the ducks and geese and discredits entirely the old belief about the barnacle goose, which his predecessor Hans Egede some twenty years before showed implicit faith in.

In the second group he places the auks, murres and puffins, while in the third group he puts the gulls, terns and jaegers. His discourse on the nourishment of sea fowl and their propagation constitutes his fourth division and is by far the most interesting part of this writer's bird-lore, for he carefully explains the various birds' adaptations for securing their food: the ducks feed on snails and sea weeds because of their short blunt bills; the auks pursue their diet of fish beneath water and pierce and bruise it with their sharp bills, while their short wings and tails are no impediment to them in diving. The third class, being equipped with long wings and well developed tails, are intended for sustained flight and therefore find their food while flying low over the water. Their hooked or sharply pointed bills, as in the gulls and terns, are useful implements for tearing their prey apart.

After describing these adaptations of sea birds for their mode of living, Crantz describes the eggs and nesting sites of many sea birds and sees in this

a wise providence for the preservation and vast increase of sea fowl in this particular that the eggs [by being hidden in rock clefts] are secured from the injury of cold, tho' the bird is frequently off her nest.

Speaking of life in the arctic, he says:

This would be a spacious field for a curious inquisitive mind, and he would often fall into pleasing and profound meditation, when he surveys and traces in thought, the nature and aim of all the inhabitants of the vast ocean from the minutest insect, scarce perceptible to the eye, to the monstrous whale, . . .

This is one of the earliest articulate musings of the true naturalist. David Crantz's work shows a high order of ornithological observation and should be known to all ornithologists with an interest in the historical development of their science.

When it was first published [3] it was criticized for be-

ing a compilation largely from Egede and Anderson and for the great amount of attention given to the Moravian Sect (called by the reviewer "Hottentots" of religion). The author, however, is given credit for his diligent observation of birds, animals, and general natural history.

The book was abridged, purged of fanatical phraseology, and unimportant detail, and republished in 1820, at which time it was more favorably received.

THE COOK VOYAGES

Exploration during the latter eighteenth century was considerably spurred by the impending Transit of Venus. This phenomenon of the planet becoming periodically visible against the sun had been observed several times since 1518 and was due to happen again in June 1769. As a means of computing the earth's distance from the sun, it was an important astronomical event and numerous expeditions were outfitted during the preceding months, and timed so that the passage of Venus could be observed from various parts of the globe.

At this time the famous English navigator Captain James Cook (1728–1779) was acting as marine surveyor of the coast of Newfoundland and Labrador. He had already published a chart of the St. Lawrence River from Quebec to the sea, and this together with his rising reputation as a mathematician and astronomer [4] made him the first choice of the British Admiralty to take charge of the expedition inspired by the forthcoming Transit of Venus and other problems needing study. This was the first of Captain Cook's three famous voyages round the world and in addition to studying the Transit of Venus which he observed on June 3 from Tahiti, he went in search of the great antarctic continent which then was believed to lie in the southern Pacific Ocean. We could dwell to advantage upon Cook's vast discoveries of islands and regions we have learned of in the recent war, but we must confine ourselves to the zoological and botanical aspects of his explorations.

His first expedition with ninety-six men on board, including, as botanists, Joseph Banks (later Sir, 1743–1820) and Dr. Daniel Solander (1736–1782), assistant librarian at the British Museum, set sail from Plymouth August 26, 1768. Banks had become acquainted, through James Lee (1715–1795), a botanist and nurseryman of Hammersmith, with the young Quaker artist, Sydney Parkinson (1745?–1771), a woolen draper of Edinburgh, and in 1767 had engaged him to make drawings at Kew Gardens. His work showed great talent and Banks then invited him to go, as draughtsman, on Captain Cook's first voyage round the world. But an ill-fated voyage it proved to be, for they lost thirty-eight officers and crew from disease and young Parkinson, after the most meticulous work upon his journal, collections, and drawings for nearly three years, finally succumbed to fever and dysentery the twenty-sixth of

---

[3] *Mo. Rev.*, **36**: 231, 1767.

[4] Cook presented a paper on the eclipse of the sun of the 5th of August, 1766, to the Royal Society, which was published in *Phil. Trans.*, **57**: 215–216.

FIG. 39. Sydney Parkinson (*ca.* 1745–1771), artist and naturalist of Captain Cook's First Voyage round the World (1768–1771). Courtesy of the British Museum of Natural History.

January, 1771. At this time the expedition was leaving Prince's Island bound for the Cape of Good Hope.

Parkinson is the artist of thirty-two unpublished drawings of birds now housed in the Natural History Museum, London, and of these four are American species, as follows: No. 16, *Puffinus elegans*; No. 21, *Puffinus griseus*; No. 22, *Ossifraga gigantea*; No. 25, *Diomedia exulans*.

Since methods of preserving [5] birds at this time were still so crude as to serve only temporarily, it was of prime importance to engage artists for all collecting expeditions and, also, to employ competent scientific workers who could be relied upon to describe the specimens accurately. Accordingly, when a bird or other animal was shot, it was given to the artist, who made a sketch of it with written notes on the locality where it was taken, its plumage, and the coloration of bill and feet. Sometimes color areas were washed on with the thought of doing a more finished drawing later. After the artist had made such preliminary sketches, the scientific worker wrote a detailed description, and then the specimen was given such imperfect "skinning" and poisoning as was in vogue, or, if edible, it was prepared as food. The drawings and descriptions made on this expedition were examined by John Latham soon after their arrival

in England, but no list of them was published until nearly a hundred years later, when Osbert Salvin (1835–1898), Strickland (1811–1953) [6] Curator of Ornithology at Cambridge, England, identified them. Dr. Solander's descriptions of the birds, which were made simultaneously with Parkinson's drawings, also are to be found in the Banksian Library of the British Museum. Although Parkinson's name was omitted from many of his drawings, he is now credited with a total of 955.

It is difficult to understand the dispute between Parkinson's sponsor, Joseph Banks, and his brother, Stanfield Parkinson, over the journal, specimens, and other effects of the young naturalist, Sydney Parkinson. But since some erroneous information concerning Sydney is extant, it seems advisable to give a few of the facts as gleaned from Sydney's journal, which, only after years of altercation between Banks and Stanfield Parkinson, was published by the latter in 1773.

According to the *Dictionary of National Biography,* Sydney is said to have quarrelled with his brother and for this reason was excluded from the log of the ship *Endeavour.* This dispute, however, occurred between Joseph Banks and Sydney's brother, Stanfield, after the return of the expedition. Banks regarded Parkinson's work and his generous supply of drawings, which were far in excess of what he expected him to do, with unqualified admiration.

It seems, however, that Sydney left a will before he sailed, bequeathing his effects, collections, journals, etc. to his brother, and Stanfield insisted on having them. But John Hawkesworth (1715?–1773) was at work upon another report of the expedition and wished his account to be published first and, by way of retaliation toward Stanfield, omitted Sydney Parkinson's name from the report; likewise his name was omitted from drawings of which he was the artist. This gave new fire and determination to Stanfield to accomplish his purpose of publishing Sydney's journal in order that justice might be done at last to his unfortunate brother, who so needlessly and tragically perished at sea.

The journal, as brought out by the brother Stanfield, assisted by a Doctor Kendrick, was not published until Stanfield after becoming insane had died. It was, however, published in 1773 and is a faithful account of the trip, with a portrait of Sydney Parkinson the youth surrounded by drawing materials and specimens, as the frontispiece. This portrait was done by Dr. James Newton (1670?–1750), who kept a private lunatic asylum and studied botany to divert his mind. Other of Sydney Parkinson's original drawings, consisting of

<hr>

[5] Common practices were drying by heat, preservation in alcohol, or even dipping in varnish.

[6] Strickland, Hugh Edwin, authority on zoological nomenclature, author of *Ornithological synonyms* (1855) and *The dodo* (1848). His fine general collection of birds was presented to Cambridge University by his widow, and was to be housed in the same room with the Swainsonian collection. According to the *Ibis,* 383–384, 1867, these two collections probably contain more type specimens of birds than any museum of the United Kingdom except the British Museum. The Strickland Curator is in charge of the Strickland Collection.

plants, costumes, villages, and the like, may be found in the British Museum Additional Manuscripts 23920 and 23921, and there are three articles in the *Gentleman's Magazine* concerned with him: July, 1773, p. 342, August, 1784, p. 603, and January, 1785, p. 52.

On his second voyage round the world, in 1772–75, Captain Cook was accompanied by Johann Reinhold Forster, and the famous Swedish explorer, Anders Sparrman (1748–1820). The English landscape painter, William Hodges (1744–1797) also was with him, and, since another one of the artists engaged to go was unable to do so, it fell to Forster to select some one in his place. Reinhold Forster had already published, in the previous year a catalogue of the animals of North America, which gave him prominence, and he was well versed in several languages, so that he could select from a wide circle of friends and associates. He did not seek far, however, but chose his son Johann Georg Adam Forster, who was with him in England. Young Forster was then a youth of only eighteen years, but he was quite talented in drawing.

It was customary to take even younger boys on such expeditions, for it is related that Isaac Smith, who was a cousin of Captain Cook and who later became an admiral, went on this same expedition when only "a youngster." In his old age, harking back to that adventurous experience of his childhood, Admiral Smith made a list of the birds of which George [7] Forster had made the drawings. Of course this list is too inaccurate to be depended on, having been compiled from memory, but it gives some idea of the birds seen.

It is unfortunate that such casual methods prevailed and that no list was made at the time when the birds were drawn.

Georg Forster is said to have made many duplicates and to have had about thirty of them redrawn in London by a more accomplished artist so that he could present them to King George III. Many others of the lot went to Cook's cousin Smith, already mentioned, and are now in the Australian Museum, at Sydney. They include a variety of sea-birds, such as gulls, terns, boobies, petrels, albatrosses, and fulmars, but no North American species. According to Tom Iredale, from whom the above Forster notes were extracted, two of the birds from the British Museum set by Georg Forster were published in the *Penny Cyclopedia*, Vol. 18, 1840. But these were not of American species.

Georg Forster apparently was not employed by the Government but, through private arrangement, by his father, who engaged him to make natural history drawings.

It appears that the elder Forster had a plan of using his own notes and his son's drawings in a complete account of the voyage, but he was not permitted to do this except as father and son collaborated in some general

Fig. 40. Johann Reinhold Forster (1729–1798) and his son Georg Adam Forster (1754–1794) who accompanied Captain Cook on his Second Voyage round the World (1772–1775) as naturalist and artist. Courtesy of the United States National Museum.

"Observations" in which birds are hardly mentioned. Instead J. R. Forster's complete manuscripts went to the Berlin Museum, and many years later, in 1844, Heinrich Lichtenstein (1780–1857) edited them. Georg Forster, on the other hand, wrote in two volumes *A Voyage Round the World in H. M. Sloop Resolution,* which is described as an "excellent narrative," [8] with references to birds occurring throughout.

These publications of the Forsters were not illustrated, but, according to Joseph Henry Maiden's book on Sir Joseph Banks (1909), the drawings done by Forster Jr. came to the Banksian Library by purchase,[9] the paintings numbering 168. It was customary to make duplicates of the sketches, but no duplicates of Forster's work were found until recently, when a set of fifty-three drawings at the Australian Museum was identified as his work. These are described in an article [10] in the *Australian Zoologist*.

Like many other naturalists of the eighteenth century, Georg Forster was primarily a botanist, as we may judge by the fact that he wrote the *Flora of the South Seas* and for this was elected a member of the Royal Society in 1775, when he was only twenty-one.

In 1784 he was made Professor of Natural History at Cassel; in 1787 he accompanied his father to Russia,

[8] Wood, 1931: 346.

[9] From a journal note by Sir Joseph Banks (see Maiden, J. H., *Sir Joseph Banks,* 54). Banks bought both J. R. and Georg Forster's drawings for 400 pounds.

[10] Iredale, 1925–1927: **4**: 48–53.

and, altogether, gave promise of becoming a prolific scientist and writer. His career was early ended, however, for in 1794, while he was preparing to leave for East India, he died very suddenly in Paris. In addition to his scientific publications, he wrote several literary works; his letters to his wife, Theresa,[11] also were published, in 1829. He is of special interest to us in this study for his contribution to American descriptive ornithology. There are two American species included in a group of unpublished drawings by Georg Forster in the British Museum, No. 93a *Ossifraga gigantea,*[12] the giant petrel labelled by the artist "Procellaria," and No. 108 *Pelecanus plotus,* which is the same as *Sula sula* (Linné). These drawings furnish an interesting link in the growing chain of contributors to American ornithology.

WILLIAM W. ELLIS, BIRD ARTIST

The third voyage of Captain Cook was productive of a very considerable amount of work on American birds. This expedition was undertaken in the two ships *Resolution* and *Discovery* and left in 1776 with the purpose of attempting once more to find the northwest passage by sailing across North America from the Pacific. While cruising in the Pacific, Cook discovered the Sandwich Islands[13] in 1778, and during the following year charted the Pacific coast of North America as far as Bering Strait and Norton Sound. The next year he went back to Hawaii intending to explore the group of islands further but hostile natives stole one of the *Discovery*'s boats, and Cook, with his customary bold policy, took the king of the island prisoner. This expedient failed, however, and in the ensuing fight Cook was overpowered by a crowd of natives and killed in the Bay of Kealakekua on February 14, 1779.

The natural history artist and draughtsman of this expedition was William W. Ellis, a figure in this colorful period who remains entirely unknown except for his drawings made on Cook's third voyage. These are in the Natural History Museum, London, and number one hundred fifteen, thirty-six of which are apparently of American birds. They are known as Banksian Manuscript No. 33; and below the press number and, apparently in the artist's own hand, there is the following inscription: "115 original water colour sketches of animals made by W. W. Ellis on Cook's third voyage— 1776–1780." All the drawings are signed and bear the words "ad vivum delinquum et pinx," with the date. Many of the subjects are familiar birds of our Pacific coast and, from the point of illustration, are an important contribution to American ornithology of the late eighteenth century.

[11] By remarriage, "Huber."

[12] According to Peters's *Check-List of Birds of the World,* 1931, this species was again called *Procellaria gigantea* Gmelin *Syst. Nat.,* **1** (2) : 563, 1789, and became *Macronectes giganteus* Gmelin, by Richmond, *Proc. Biol. Soc., Wash.,* **18**: 76, 1905.

[13] An earlier name of the Hawaiian Islands, so named by Cook in deference to Admiral Sandwich (John Montagu, 1719–1795).

Fig. 41. Varied Thrush and Western Robin by W. W. Ellis, artist of Captain Cook's Third Voyage round the World (1776–1780). From an unpublished drawing from Banksian Manuscript 33. Courtesy of the Trustees of the British Museum of Natural History.

Some of the more interesting birds of the Pacific coast which Ellis included are the following: red-backed sandpiper, northern phalarope, red-shafted flicker, American three-toed woodpecker, Hudsonian chickadee, pileolated warbler, varied thrush, Lapland longspur.

These drawings are suggestive of the careful work of George Edwards and the later unpublished bird drawings of John Abbot, naturalist of Georgia, for they are finely delineated, show considerable detail in the plumage, and the contours are delicately wrought. External parts, such as bills, feet and eyes, which even today are not always accurately executed, are drawn with great care, some of the sheets showing preliminary pencil sketches of these parts in addition to the birds. Commenting on the whole series of Ellis' drawings in his account of the British Museum collection of birds, R. Bowdler Sharpe (1847–1909) says:

It is tolerably certain that all the artists who accompanied Banks on Captain Cook's voyages, Parkinson, Georg Forster and Ellis, were in the habit of drawing an outline, sometimes colouring the bill and feet from the freshly shot bird, but much of the colouring was left to be filled in at home from the actual specimens and in many cases this was never done.

It is interesting to know that Doctor Sharpe, with fitting historical sense, perpetuated Ellis' name in the scientific name of an extinct shorebird, the white-winged sandpiper, *Prosobonia ellisi*. This bird is No. 65 of Ellis' drawings and came from Eimeo, or York Island, one of the Society Isles, where the bird was called Te te.

HUMPHREY MARTEN

In addition to these published accounts and manuscript drawings of birds emanating from Cook's expeditions, in the latter eighteenth century many observations were made on the birds of Hudson Bay by two writers, who should be of some interest to students of American ornithology, even though their accounts remain unpublished.

These men, Humphrey Marten (b. 1729?) and Dr. Thomas Hutchins, were both employed by the Hudson's Bay Company and they collected and observed birds for many years in the arctic and sent their notes and specimens to Thomas Pennant and John Latham.

I am indebted to Mr. H. W. Robinson, recent Librarian of the Royal Society, for showing me the Marten manuscript. It is not known how the Royal Society acquired the manuscript, since Marten was not a member of that body and little could be learned about the man. However, "A Short Description of the Birds in a Box," as it is called, is a beautifully penned piece of writing bound with coarse greyish paper covers, which are attached with a heavy stained string to the included sheets. There are fourteen sheets on nine of which Marten wrote his observations while the other five are blank. Twenty-six specimens are described, mostly under native names, and though we cannot accept the identifications nor the statements throughout, it is worth while to consider the writer's sincerity and care for detail as he prepared the manuscript. The following excerpt on the swallows seems to offer a clear conception of Marten's method of observation and the keen interest he felt in the birds about the Fort.

No. 1 a cock Swallow, no. 2 a hen Ditto, no. 3 the Nest with Their Eggs in it. These are Birds of Passage, They visit us between the 10th and 20th of May, begin Building in June, finish their Nest in about 8 Days more or less as the Weather is foule or fair, have generally 5 Eggs though sometimes but three, sometimes 6, the Time of Incubation from 17 to 24 Days, the Cock & Hen sit Alternately, from the breaking of the shell to the flight of the Young Birds a lunar month nearly according to the goodness or badness of the Weather, about 7 Days before the Young can fly the Old Ones take them out of the Nest between Their Claws, Carry them 30 or 40 yds to Exercise them, and regularly bring them back to the Nest every Night, or at the approach of a Storm, about 7 Days after the Young are grown Strong They all go away to the Northward, return on the first approach of bad Weather, Stay a Day or two at the Fort and then farewell untill the nest Season. I never heard that either Swallows or Martins lurk in Rocks, or were found in this Country under Water, but I have Seen them Several times mount in Circles very high in air, then Dart away to the Northward, during the time the Cock is off the Nest, he Sings very pleasingly a fine Open Note, his Eyes are a Jet

Black and Exceedingly Brilliant, as are those of the Hens; They are not as shy Birds, and when you approach too near Their Young will dart full at you with a Squeeking noise, They are fond of Building in Our Guns or Loop holes, and have for 2 years past Built in Boxes which I fixed up about the Fort for that purpose, when the Cock treads the Hen, he mouths her as doth the common Poultry, They are not numerous, both the Swallow and Martin Skim in Flight/ Except when going away, When they have a darting waving motion, both sorts Young & Old, feed on small Worms grubs and flys found by the sides of the River.

Although several misstatements occur in this passage, particularly the exaggerated incubation period and the carrying of the young in the claws, we note many evidences of good observation: the spring arrival, the number of eggs, the alternate setting of both birds, the singing of the male, the color of the eyes, the way of defending the young and the food; and it is noteworthy and indicative of Marten's type of observation, that he built bird-boxes for the swallows which they occupied. We notice also Marten's disbelief of the popular fancy that swallows hibernate under water.

Following No. 26, the concluding description of the manuscript, the author writes as follows:

I hope those Gentlemen that inspect the afore written history of Birds will Observe that I do not absolutely declare all I have Set down to be a Truth, Except in what regards the Swallow and Marten, as to those Birds I was a Constant Eye Wittness as were messrs Favell and Kitchen, to what I have related, for more than 2 years. As to the Others, as to Numbers of Eggs, Food and the difference between Male and Female, I was Obliged to have the best Indian Intelligence I could get, I trusted not to the assertions of any single Person, let his Age or Experience be what it would therefore hope that I am near the Truth, if not quite so. I could have wished that when I received Orders from my masters to make a Collection of Birds etc, that the naturalists' Journals, as also the Brittish Zoology had been sent to me, for which I would have Paid with Thanks; fine Seed Shot, Bird lime, Glass Bottles with ingredients for making the preparing Liquor, would have Enabled me to have given more satisfaction to the Gentlemen Concerned as well as myself than it is possibly for me now to do. Wire and Beads of all Sizes and Coulers that resemble the Eyes I presume should have been sent as not a Soul I Believe in Hudsons Bay knows anything of Painting either in Oile or Water Coulers.

Another feature of the manuscript is the section of two pages with the heading "answer to the Queries," in which he answers questions on various subjects, the swallows, stags, the rabbit, the Aurora Borealis, the depth of the snow and how deep the rivers are frozen, concluding with

wishing all possible success to the great and good work the Gentlemen have in hand and am with great respect Their most Obedient Humble Servant.

Humphrey Marten.
P. S. I beg to add that it was impossible to give satisfactory answers to the [ques]tions now received as time would not permit it, but as far as a willing mind and weak ability can answer them, I shall endeavour to do by the next ship.

Humphrey Marten was in the service of the Hudson's Bay Company in various capacities from 1750 to 1786, at which latter date he was about fifty-seven years of age and considered himself a very old man. He was born about 1729; the date of his death is unknown, but when he returned to England, because of ill health in 1786, he was still suffering the consequences of a severe burn in the left kidney, which he sustained in 1779, when helping some men with a large vat of scalding water, and it is doubtful that he lived long after his return.

In 1750, when he came over from England, he was stationed at York Factory, as clerk and steward, about mid-way between Cape Henrietta Maria and Rolls Welcome, on the west coast and about one hundred miles south from Churchill. His various duties took him between Moose Factory at the southern end of James Bay, Albany Fort, and York Factory. While on a trip to England, some time about 1758, he was presented with twenty guineas for a model of Albany Fort which he had made.

Little else can be learned about Humphrey Marten; but, on writing to Hudson's Bay House in London, where I thought some of his letters and manuscripts might be found, I was kindly referred to the Journals of Samuel Hearne and Philip Turnor published by the Champlain Society in 1934. This was obtained in the Rare Book Room of the Library of Congress; and in the fine print of the appendix, on pages 592 through 597, a few additional facts were gleaned.

Marten had a son by an Indian woman, of whom, at her death, he wrote in his journal on January 24, 1771: "At 10 minutes before 3 o'clock this morning departed this life the Indian woman called Paw Pitch daughter of the Captain of the Goose Hunters by whose death my child becomes motherless."

After the accident to Marten's back in 1779, he was confined for eight weeks and had to endure constant pain. His fortitude and his deep affection for his associates at York Factory may be felt in the following words by him:

I love and esteem the men and in return they love and revere me to see the poor fellows when I am in great pain with deep sorrow on their faces and to be informed of the heartfelt prayers offered up for my recovery melts me in the tenderest manner and makes me desire not to be parted from them.

A copy of the Humphrey Marten manuscript labelled "(2)" also is preserved with the original, but the handwriting is obviously different and no suggestion of the time when the copy was made is given.

The absence of data on Humphrey Marten is explained in part by a footnote in Samuel Hearne's account. Referring to the collecting done by Mr. Andrew Graham and Mr. Thomas Hutchins, *Journey to the Northern Ocean,* 1795, p. 446, Hearne says:

It is, however, no less true that the late Mr. Humphry Marten, many years Governor of Albany Fort, sent home several hundred specimens of animals and plants to complete the collection; but by some mistake nothing of the kind was placed to his account. Even my respected friend Mr. Pennant, who with a candour that does him honour, has so generously acknowledged his obligations to all to whom he thought he was indebted for information when he was writing his Arctic Zoology (See the Advertisement,) has not mentioned his name; but I am fully persuaded that it entirely proceeded from a want of knowing the person; and as Mr. Hutchins succeeded him at Albany in the year 1774, every thing that has been sent over from that part has been placed to his [Hutchin's] account.

It should be remembered that although the publication date of the above note is 1795, Hearne wrote it probably in 1771 or 1772. These collections were sent to the Royal Society.

THOMAS HUTCHINS

Closely associated with Humphrey Marten in the Hudson's Bay Company for a number of years was Dr. Thomas Hutchins (?–1790). He entered the service in 1766 and was employed for seven years as surgeon at York Factory. From 1774 to 1782 he was in charge at Albany Factory. In 1776 he was directed by the Governor and Committee to send expeditions inland from Moose and Albany Factories to intercept the "Pedlars" who offered great competition to the Hudson's Bay Company in supplying goods to the natives.

Hutchins became a very keen observer and collector of birds and mammals while he was resident in Canada, and he is the author of one of the twelve manuscript volumes of Observations on Hudson Bay, now in possession of the Company. John Latham tells us in his Preface to his *General Synopsis of Birds* that Thomas Hutchins sent in numerous specimens of birds from Hudson Bay and also gave him "a large manuscript volume of Observations on the birds of that climate." Whether this is the same one owned by the Hudson's Bay Company, I have not been able to learn, but it would be interesting to glean from the Hudson's Bay Company archives a full understanding of Hutchins' knowledge [14] of American birds.

According to Miller Christy writing in the *Journal of Botany,* Vol. 60, 1922, p. 239 and 336–337, some birds collected by Hutchins long stood in the bird galleries of the British Museum. Mr. Christy also tells that a volume of Hutchins' observations, probably the same one referred to above, belonging to the Hudson's Bay Company, was made ready for publication by him with the aid of his friend, Ernest Thompson Seton (1860–1946), at about the time of the First World War. The book appears, however, not to have come out, and Professor John Macoun, of Ottawa, who identified the plants, is since deceased.

It is possible at this time only to describe briefly a manuscript written by Hutchins on American birds, which I saw recently at the Royal Society. It is filed with the Humphrey Marten manuscript and opens as follows:

---

[14] It was the author's plan to do this while in London, but the political tension in Europe prevented research of this kind.

To The Honourable Hudson's Bay Company, The following remarks intended to improve Natural History of their Territories are respectfully addressed by

Their obedient humble servant

York Fort　　　　　　　　　　　Thomas Hutchins
August 1772　　　　　　　　　　Surgeon

In the recess of better employment, the time which is bestowed on study, if even attended with no other advantage, serves to occupy with Innocence the hours of leisure and set bounds to the pursuit of ruinous and frivolous amusements. (Ferguson on Civil Society)

Following this worthy sentiment, Hutchins gives several paragraphs of explanatory notes, from which we gather that he was collecting for Thomas Pennant and was in some way under the direction of a Mr. Andrew Graham.

Says Hutchins of his list of birds:

The Indian name is inserted throughout both in compliance to Mr. Pennant's direction and, also, because very often I knew not the proper European Epithet.

Of his descriptions he says:

In pursuance of Mr. Graham's advice, I have described the plumage of the Birds, but as my knowledge of the variety of colours is very small, consequently the description must be very imperfect. The intent was to preserve an Idea of the plumage after it had faded by keeping or preserving.

Hutchins was assisted in this work by a young apprentice, of whom he wrote as follows:

The following check were not wrote by one who is skilled in Zoological affairs but by a young person seeking after knowledge, and improvement who would think himself extremely happy to be of service to the Learned, and is proud of every opportunity of demonstrating his gratitude for favours received from the Hudson's Bay Company.

York Fort
28 August 1772

The manuscript is divided into Quadrupeds, pages 2–39; and Birds, pages 40–104. These, in turn, are divided into migratory birds, which are described on pages 40 to 90, while stationary birds are discussed on pages 91–104. The birds are described mostly under Indian names of great length and unpronounceability, while the comments upon them lead one to surmise that this manuscript may be in some measure the work of Hutchins' apprentice referred to above.

On page 44 we read:

wekissew (Eagles) There are several species of this kind of bird in Hudsons Bay, but we have not been able to procure specimens. They are the earliest of the migratory Tribe visiting us in March, the nest are built in Trees, they bring forth two young ones in May and leaves us in Autumn. One of the upland Indians had a small bag made of one of the skins. . . .

Hutchins returned to England in 1782 and became secretary of the Company in London. He likewise was awarded a gold medal for his scientific work by the Royal Society and many of his plants, which he sent to Sir Joseph Banks, are preserved in the Herbarium of the British Museum. The date of his birth is not known, but he was a member of the Parish of Allhallows Staining in London and he died in June, 1790.

To discuss adequately the literature of Arctic America and Hudson's Bay and glean from it a thorough survey of the bird observation that went on there over some three hundred years would necessitate a volume in itself. It therefore seems best merely to touch briefly on a few of the numerous voyages that have something to say on birds.

CAPTAIN GEORGE CARTWRIGHT

About the same time that the Cook voyages were penetrating North America from the Pacific Coast, many travellers were getting acquainted with the more accessible parts of the vast peninsula of Labrador. This is a portion of Canada that has lured ornithologists and other naturalists for hundreds of years; and Audubon himself explored this forbidding coast at the height of his career in 1833. Before him several others sought the gannets and puffins, the auks and murres of these rocky headlands, among whom was the faithful recorder and keen observer, Captain George Cartwright. George Cartwright was the brother of the better known Major John Cartwright (1740–1824), who was made Governor of Newfoundland in 1766. Though military by profession and capable of eminence in the field of soldiering, George Cartwright preferred adventure close to nature and gives us the story of the best part of his life in his book, *A Journal of Transactions and Events during a Residence of nearly Sixteen Years on the Coast of Labrador* (1792).

He was beloved by the Indians and taught them much about trapping; and in agriculture, too, he had many helpful ideas.

Bird notes are to be found throughout the three volumes. Cartwright mentions between sixty and seventy species, mostly water-birds but, also, several species of land-birds, as the snow bunting, pine grosbeak, swallow, horned lark, cross-beak linnet and shrike, as well as several birds of prey. The great auk and Labrador duck were common in Cartwright's day and were mentioned often, while the various gulls, murres, auks, puffins, shore-birds, and ducks are continually noted. Some of the local names of these birds are quaint and interesting, and they still persist among the natives:

Aunt Sary—Greater Yellow-legs
Bull—Dovekie
Brass-wing—White-winged Scoter
Bottle nose diver—Surf Scoter
Hound—Old Squaw
Lords and Ladies—male and female Harlequin ducks
Saddleback—Great Black-backed Gull
Shell duck—Merganser
Tucker—Razor-billed Auk

In many instances Cartwright showed the methods and instincts of the true ornithologist, as, for instance, when he described the moults of the ptarmigan and the eider. Of the latter he says (p. 267–268):

Upon examining the down of these ducks, which is so valuable, warm, elastic, and light, I found that it grows out of the body in the manner of a feather; whose whole length, both of quill and shaft, is extremely fine, and does not exceed one tenth of an inch in length. On this grows a bunch of feathery substances, resembling the harle [barb] on the sides of a peacock's tail-feather, which are from eight tenths of an inch to an inch and two tenths in length. I counted the number of harles on two of these stems, and found one to have ninety-six, the other fifty-two; but not having a microscope, I could not tell if either of them was entire or not.

Another bit of careful technique was his weighing of birds' eggs. On June 30, 1779 Cartwright took weights of eggs as follows:

Saddle back (Black-back
   gull) egg   4 ounces fifteen pennyweights
Eider-duck's egg   from 3 ounces six pennyweights to 4
   ounces
Pigeon egg   2 ounces five pennyweights
Also eider-down—37 little tufts weighed 1 grain

As one reads Cartwright's journal, it becomes obvious that this bleak Labrador country was the land he loved. Even in adversity, when he lost an entire shipload of furs and whalebone without one penny of insurance, he had no thought to go elsewhere but to clear all his debts by his own labor amongst Labrador's rich bounty. This was at the end of his fifth and next to last voyage to Labrador, and he was by this time an old man, the victim of the most painful sciatica. While waiting for his affairs to straighten out, it was necesasry for him to remain at home, in England, and he amused himself by transcribing his journal into verse, a whimsical twist for an eminently practical man, but the result is pleasing throughout. I quote a few of the more ornithological lines:

The Winter o'er, the Birds their voices tune,
To welcome in the genial month of June.
Love crouds with feather'd tribes each little Isle,
And all around kind Nature seems to smile.
Now Geese and Ducks and nameless numbers more,
In social flocks, are found on every shore.
Their eggs to seek, we rove from Isle to Isle,
Eager to find, and bear away the spoil:
These in abundance, every hand picks up,
And when our toil is o'er, on these we sup.

Cartwright's names for the islands and harbors of the Labrador coast still remain; and the location of his own residence there, known as Caribou Castle, perpetuates his name as the Hudson's Bay Company's Post of Cartwright. Although George Cartwright was buried in the ancestral ground of Nottinghamshire, his niece, Frances Dorothy Cartwright, caused a stone to be carved and erected to him and his brother, John, in the little cemetery at Cartwright. The case of George Cartwright calls to mind the long hard labors of Nicolas Denys,[15] a keen bird observer and, also, a practical business man, who became the Governor of Acadia, to the south of Labrador, some sixty or seventy years earlier.

---

[15] See this work, p. 432.

SAMUEL HEARNE

In conclusion of the arctic travels, it seems fitting, because of their superior bird observation, to discuss the remarkable expeditions of Samuel Hearne (1745–1792). These took place in the years between 1769 and 1772. Hearne made four trials before completing his long trek across arctic deserts to the Copper Mine River. But at last he was able to accomplish it. Starting July 15, 1771, he covered 1,300 miles on foot, going north and west by Lake Athabasca and the Great Slave Lake, and back to his headquarters at Prince of Wales Fort on the Churchill River by June 30, 1772.

The quality of Hearne's report concerning this region is different from all I have examined. Although he was only a young man in his early twenties when he undertook this expedition, and despite the fact that his formal education was short and interrupted, he had the stamina of an experienced explorer combined with the scientific integrity of a modern investigator.

His account of his years in Canada is embodied in his book, *A Journey from Prince of Wales Fort in Hudson's Bay to the Northern Ocean* (1795). The expedition was undertaken for the discovery of copper mines and the perennial quest for the northwest passage. To natural history the author devotes fifty pages of Chapter 10 and discusses quadrupeds, fish, frogs (including grubs and insects), birds, and lastly, vegetable productions.

The birds are described under forty-seven heads, with several kinds under such groups as owls, grouse, geese, ducks and gulls. Hearne's first list is as follows, augmented by sundry others later in the text: Eagles, hawks of various sizes; white or snowy owl; grey or mottled owl; cabodee cooch (screech owl?); ravens; cinereous crow (Canada jay?); wood-pecker; grouse: ruffed grouse, sharp-tailed grouse; wood partridge; willow partridge (ptarmigan); rock partridge (ptarmigan); red-breasted thrushes; grosbeaks; snow-bunting; white-crowned bunting; Lapland finch; larks; swallows; martens; hooping crane; brown crane; bitterns; curlews; jack snipe; red godwait; spotted godwait; hebridal sandpipers; plovers; black guillemots; northern divers; black-throated divers; red-throated divers; white gulls; grey gulls; black gulls; black heads (Bonaparte's gulls); pelicans; goosanders (mergansers); swans; common grey goose; Canada goose; white or snow goose; blue goose; horned wavey (small [lesser] snow goose); laughing goose; barren goose (believed not to breed because of smallness of gonads); brent geese; dunter goose (eider duck); bean goose; ducks: widgeon; teal; total 53 kinds.

Elliott Coues speaks of him as "honest old Hearne," as if, indeed, he had been an old man in the arctic, and commends the reliability of his accounts of birds, saying that they could still be used with profit. Such was Coues' opinion in 1878 and today after still another six decades the modern ornithologist may yet learn the difficult details of behavior and plumage of many American species from Hearne's, *Journey to the Northern Ocean*. On page 170 we read of the birds observed when he had achieved his goal at the mouth of Copper Mine River:

at the seaside (at the mouth of the Copper River) besides seeing many seals on the ice, I observed several flocks of sea fowl flying about the shores; such as gulls, black-heads [scaups], loons, old-wives [old-squaws], ha-ha-wies, dunter geese [eider ducks] and arctic gulls, and willichs [murres]. In the adjacent ponds also were some swans and geese in a moulting state and in the marshes some curlews and plover; plenty of hawk eyes (i.e. green plovers) (or spotted sandpipers) and some yellow-legs; also several other small birds that visit these northern parts in the Spring to breed and moult, and which doubtless return southward as the fall advances. My reason for this conjecture is founded on a certain knowledge that all those birds migrate in Hudson's Bay; and it is but reasonable to think that they are less capable of withstanding the rigours of such a long and cold winter as they must experience in a country which is so many degrees within the Arctic Circle as that is where I now saw them.

Few have made such careful observation of the moult of birds, for even today only the trained ornithologist recognizes the details of changing plumage. Yet Hearne most meticulously notes the change of plumage in the ptarmigan pointing out the fourteen black tail feathers tipped with white while the rest of the plumage is changed for a delicate white coat. He mentions also the aftershaft of the ptarmigan's contour feathers, calling it "additional clothing," but this is characteristic of all gallinaceous birds whether arctic in distribution or not. Hearne describes also the sharp-tailed grouse (*Pedioecetes phasianelus*), the wood partridge (*Canachites canadensis*), and the ruffed grouse (*Bonasa umbellus*), which last one he considers the most beautiful species of all. The amount of detail in the life habits of the various grouse and, indeed, of many other birds and mammals of the Hudson Bay fauna, makes his account read like a modern book. Of the ruffed grouse drumming, Hearne says, "There is something very remarkable in those birds and I believe peculiar to themselves, which is that of clapping their wings with such force that at half a mile distance it resembles thunder." Hearne likewise speaks of the grouse's lack of amenability to captivity and the many efforts at the Fort to raise grouse chicks with hens as mothers.

Hearne's comments on the passerine birds, though not so complete as those on grouse and water fowl, also, are good, and they indicate close observation of some dozen or more species of larks, sparrows, buntings, and thrushes. He made many observations on food habits, coloration, song, nests and eggs, all of which require almost daily conscious effort. Of the American larks (Alaudidae) Hearne says:

At their first arrival, and till the young can fly, the male is in full song; and, like the sky-lark, soars to a great height, and generally descends in a perpendicular direction near their nest. Their note is loud and agreeable, but consists of little variety, and as soon as the young can fly they become silent and retire to the Southward early in the Fall. They

are impatient of confinement, never sing in that state and seldom live long.

Besides good observation of plumage and habit, Hearne was mindful of bird anatomy. Considering his youth at this time, and the many years that he had been at sea, it is surprising that he had found time and occasion to acquaint himself with the writings of ornithologists. Yet throughout his journal there are scattering comments which indicate his familiarity with Pennant's writings and with Captain Cook's first voyages and the natural history observations of his artists and draughtsmen. In some cases he did not agree with the views already published. For example, take his opinion of the windpipe of the whistling swan:

Mr. Pennant, in treating of the Whistling Swan, takes notice of the formation of the windpipe, but on examination of the windpipe of both species i. e. the whistling swan and the trumpeter swan which frequent Hudson's Bay are found to be exactly alike, though their note is quite different. The breastbone of this bird is different from any other I have seen; for instead of being sharp and solid like that of the goose, it is broad and hollow. Into this cavity the windpipe passes from the valve, and reaching quite down into the abdomen, returns to the chest, and joins the lungs. Neither of the species of swan that frequent Hudson's Bay is mute; but the note of the larger is much louder than that of the smaller.

Little of Samuel Hearne's early life is known but he came of a good family in Somersetshire. Apparently he did not like his school and for this reason was put into the navy under Admiral Lord Hood (1724–1816). His first attachment to the Hudson's Bay Company was as mate on the whaling sloop *Churchill* in 1766, and in 1769 he was transferred to the brigantine *Charlotte*. But this did not satisfy his ambition, and he applied to the government for more creative work. The Company was prompt in giving him an opportunity to prove his ability and after orders to take possession of such arctic rivers as he might discover, Hearne became one of the Company's best furtraders and an explorer of note.

Great credit for perseverance is due him, for at the outset of his arctic undertaking he was handicapped by the treachery of the Indians who stole his guns and instruments with evil intent; yet he held to his task with the fortitude of a seasoned explorer, and learned to understand the Indian and the Eskimo as few others have done.

His account of his years in the arctic, as set forth in his *Journey to the Northern Ocean,* is packed with new information, topographical, geological, zoological, and botanical. Yet even this proof of his ability did not reach the world until three years after his death. Knowing the keen interest felt in England in arctic explorations at this time, we are constrained to wonder why Hearne's report was not promptly published. This finds explanation in the light of certain historical happenings of 1782.

The *Gentleman's Magazine* for September 1782 in its section Historical Chronicle, p. 501 and 546, related

FIG. 42. Samuel Hearne's name chiselled by himself in the rock face at Sloop's Cove, Churchill, Manitoba. Courtesy of Bureau of Northwest Territories and Yukon Affairs.

from the supplement to the *Paris Gazette* as its source, the news of the capture of Fort Prince of Wales by a French squadron under Captain de la Perouse (1741–1788?). Samuel Hearne, the Governor, was taken prisoner, the supplies of ammunition and merchandise were taken, and the rest was set on fire. It should be said for Captain de la Perouse that in going over the fort he found Hearne's Journal and stipulated in the conditions of surrender, when the fort could no longer hold out, that the Hudson's Bay Company should publish it. This was eventually complied with, but not until 1795. This matter is further elucidated in John Russell Bartlett's *Bibliotheca Americana,* Part III, Vol. 2, p. 379, where we read that Albert Gallatin (1761–1849) (naturalized American statesman and diplomat) was at Machias Maine when a French frigate of seventy-four guns, commanded by the celebrated navigator La Perouse, came into port. La Perouse told Gallatin that when he was at Hudson's Bay in 1781, he captured certain forts, among them Fort Albany, and he found here Hearne's Journal, where it had remained for ten years. The fort surrendered and La Perouse stipulated as part of the conditions of surrender that the Hudson's Bay Company publish the Journal. This was told to John Russell Bartlett, author of the *Bibliotheca,* by Albert Gallatin, who had it directly from the French navigator, La Perouse, and it is to him (Gallatin) that we are indebted for the final publication of Samuel Hearne's Journal. Samuel Hearne returned to England in 1787. He had carried with him a four-pound lump of copper, which he had found on his expedition to the mouth of the Copper Mine River. For many years this was on exhibition at Hudson's Bay House, London, but finally

was presented to the British Museum, where it can still be seen.

The only reward that accrued to him from his faithful service in the Hudson's Bay Company, since his Journal was published posthumously, was an expression of thanks and a "handsome gratuity" [17] presented after his survey of the Copper Mine River. His expedition finally blasted the last stubborn beliefs that the northwest passage lay through Hudson Bay. On his geographical discoveries alone, he is entitled to much honor and the naturalist who plans to study in the frozen north would be spurred to achievement by Samuel Hearne's example of thoroughness. His Journal is a fitting climax to the long series of arctic explorations, which began with the superficial and desultory comments of Captain Luke Fox, and closes with the fine account of the bird and animal life of the Hudson Bay region as rendered by this unusual writer.

It is interesting to know that the name of Samuel Hearne is carved on a large rock face in Sloop Cove one mile from Fort Prince of Wales on Hudson Bay.

XII. BIRD LISTS OF THE LATTER EIGHTEENTH CENTURY

The "faunal list" as ornithologists know it today is too formal a term to apply to the early lists of birds such as we have been discussing, and many bird students may well deem the comparative study of these lists as but a bit of antiquarian curiosity scarcely worth while. The fact remains, however, that these "germs" of modern descriptive ornithology are the nucleus around which better and more definitive writing has clustered. Indeed it would be possible to take each of these early regional accounts and trace the chronology of later writers and the development of more and more scientific descriptions of the birds of a given locality, thus providing ornithologists investigating each region with a veritable mine of inspiration as well as quantities of background information to enrich their bird studies.

It is obviously impossible to enter upon such an exhaustive historical treatment and we must content ourselves, at the risk of superficiality, with telling of American bird-lore as written first by the untutored scribes of three hundred years ago, again by colonial officers, missionaries, soldiers, or mere adventurers, and these accounts, as we have already seen, emanate from north, south, east, and west, from coastal colonies, from Mexican and Canadian borders, and occasionally from the far outposts of western migration.

Some of these scattered lists, both worthy and mediocre, have already found a place in this survey, and several others now to be described, and written by a varied assortment of observers, will bring us to the beginning of the nineteenth century. We shall then take up the American work of Louis Jean Pierre Vieillot, a French

[17] 200 pounds. MacKay, 1938: 102.

writer of whom little is known but who stands out as an intensive observer of American birds, more deeply interested and more scientifically equipped than any of his predecessors.

From the late eighteenth-century group, let us consider first Francisco Saverio Clavigero (1718–1793), whose *History of Mexico,* published first in Italian in 1780–1781 and rendered into English by Dr. Charles Cullen in 1787, contains an important treatment of Mexican birds in which many species common to both the United States and Mexico may be found. Clavigero[1] is another example of a Jesuit friar who like Charlevoix had a keen sense of history, a love of research and an appraising eye for detail. He lived for nearly thirty years in Mexico, having been born there in Vera Cruz in 1731, but when the Jesuits were expelled from Spanish territory in 1767 Clavigero retired to Bologna to write. Here he was busy with his *History of Mexico* and later with his *Storia della California* which was published in Venice in 1789.

Clavigero devotes fifteen pages of his *History of Mexico* to a description of the bird-life mostly by ancient Mexican names, and says that as Africa is the "land of beasts," so Mexico is the "land of birds," and, referring to Hernandez' estimate of two hundred species of birds, he says that many more deserve mention. He dwells with special interest upon the huitzitzilin (hummingbird) and the centzontli (the mockingbird, so named for its many songs). The quality of Clavigero's observation is very good but he was entirely duped by the beliefs of others concerning the hibernation of hummingbirds and swallows.

Referring to this subject, he says:

That sleep, or rather that state of immobility occasioned by the numbness of torpor of its limbs has often been required to be proved in legal form, in order to convince some incredulous Europeans, and incredulity arising from ignorance alone as the same kind of torpor takes place in many parts of Europe, in dormice, hedge-hogs, swallows, bats, and other animals whose blood is of the same temperature, although perhaps it does not continue so long in any of them as in the Huitzitzilin which in some countries remains from October to April.

A very astute and enlightened man otherwise, it is strange that he gave credence to this popular fable concerning birds.

Francisco Hernandez[2] was an earlier writer on the birds of Mexico who brought to our attention the fact that many birds of the United States pass the winters in Mexico, Central America, and other southern regions of the Western Hemisphere. These many migrants are also mentioned by Clavigero by their Mexican names, the recognition of which in their polysyllabic unpronounceability is a study in itself. The descriptions of these birds are of fine quality, embodying a great deal

of life history matter as well as accurate color descriptions but the bristling orthography of old Mexican nomenclature cannot but forbid the enjoyment of Clavigero by the modern reader. Therefore, on this count as well as the fact that we are concerned mostly with the east, we must turn again to the Atlantic States, and a few of the more important travels in the middle West which will be discussed before the State histories.

SOME INLAND TRAVELS

In the last quarter of the eighteenth century a group of three observers, who published works on the interior parts of the country, seems worthy of mention. These travellers, all army officers, were Captain Jonathan Carver (1732–1780), Captain Thomas Anburey, and Captain Gilbert Imlay. The first officer was well known for his good works with the Sioux Indians in Minnesota, the latter two were rather obscure and receive no mention in Elliott Coues' classical bibliography of ornithology.

JONATHAN CARVER

Captain Jonathan Carver was born probably in the town of Canterbury, Connecticut, in 1732. He had a long military service, first in Canada with Colonel Phineas Lyman (1716–1775) in the campaign of 1755; then with General James Wolfe (1727–1759) in the taking of Quebec; and lastly he was in the capture of Montreal and the conquest of Canada under General Jeffrey Amherst (1717–1797).

After the peace of Versailles in 1763 Carver retired from the army and began to consider a plan of travelling into the northwest by which he hoped to help his country to benefit from the vast territory recently acquired by the British from the French. He felt that the country should be mapped and studied. He dreamed also of finding the northwest passage as did many Britishers on the other side, and he gave himself wholly to the enterprise of penetrating far west, perhaps as far as the Pacific Ocean. His plan was to make friends with the Indians and write a narrative as he went. In this he was very successful, even to the extent that two Indian chiefs of the Nandowissie tribe granted him a large tract of land on the north side of Lake Pepin in appreciation of Carver's many gifts and teachings. At a council meeting held annually in May, it was customary for the Indians to come together in order to lay plans for the following year and to bury their dead which they brought with them wrapped in buffalo hides. At the meeting of 1767 Carver was invited to their council at which he made a speech and the grant was tendered.

This grant was later contested, however, because of the lack of witnesses to the original contract although the Indian chiefs each made his signet, one with the shape of a mud turtle, and the other a snake, upon the document.

Carver's travels were begun in Boston in 1766, and took him through the territory of New York, Ohio,

---

[1] A portrait of Clavigero may be seen in the Cumplido edition of Prescott, Wm. H., *History of Mexico,* **3**: 1846.

[2] See Chapter VII, p. 454.

Wisconsin, and Minnesota. It is interesting to know that on May 1, 1867 the Minnesota Historical Society at the site of the Great Cave in Saint Paul where the Indian chiefs presented the grant held a centenary for Carver to commemorate his service to the middle West, and his treaty which brought peace to the Nandowissies (Sioux) and the Ojibways. Soon after his return to Boston, he went to England but unfortunately he had already sold his manuscript to a bookseller. The government then ordered him to relinquish all journals, documents, and maps to the Plantation Office and it was ten years before the *Travels* could be published. Although the book was well received and translated into several foreign languages, Carver never realized any financial returns from it.

The first edition of the work *Travels through the Interior Parts of North America* came out in 1778, before the Revolution was well over. The book presents a true picture of the north central territory of the young nation and full accounts of the Indians with whom the author had dealings.

The natural history is not very complete but Carver mentions forty-one kinds of birds in an initial paragraph and eighteen species are described at some length, varying from a few lines to a page and a half. Under such general names as duck, partridge, blackbird, the author superficially touches on two or three kinds. The blue jay is perhaps the most carefully described, the account calling attention to the crest, the varied pattern of the wings, the soft blue of the back and the general manner and notes. Carver is one of the several authors who mentions the Wakon-bird—a bird that has puzzled ornithologists for more than a century. He describes it almost minutely yet fails to convey a picture of any living bird of this country. It appears that the Indians held it in superstitious veneration, but it must have been only a folk belief bird used for religious ceremonies. On the whole Carver's descriptions of birds are very incomplete and do not compare favorably with his accounts of snakes, fish, trees, and shrubs. It is disappointing also to see that his list of mammals is headed by the tiger, an animal which as far back as Francis Higginson in 1630 was given no credence as a native species of America.

Carver, despite long years of service to his country, despite his great vision to build a city (St. Paul) that should be a center of intercourse between the east and the west, which indeed it has become, despite also his envisaging in those western waterways the modern Erie Canal, seems to have failed of great honor. It may be that the "Grant," [3] which has been questioned as a possible hoax, has tended to make his public withhold praise. This, together with the stigmatizing fact [4] that he married in England, when he already had a wife and five children in America, seems to obscure his merits.

Nevertheless he was otherwise able, agreeable, beloved by the Indians, and his name lives in Carver Cave, Carver County, and the Carver River in Minnesota.

His writing, always picturesque and vigorous, had real literary merit especially when he transcribed the mystic yet simple emotions of the Indians. His descriptions of the dead Indian brave seated motionless at his hut surrounded by his family and friends, and the lamentations of these mourners set down in slow rhythmic cadences tuned to the Indian's reverent nature, were the inspiration of Schiller's (1759–1805) *Song of a Nandowissie Chief.*

Another factor that may have conspired to dissipate such honor as was due him was the publication of a large folio volume entitled *The New Universal Traveller* (London, 1779). [5] It is thought that Carver being in dire financial straits sold his name to the publisher of this propagandist compilation. At any rate his widow denied this to be the work of her husband.

THOMAS ANBUREY [6] AND GILBERT IMLAY [7]

Both of these writers are the authors of letters containing considerable bird description written in the late eighteenth century and sent from America to friends in England. Thomas Anburey served in the British Army in the American Revolution, under General Burgoyne, while Gilbert Imlay was American-born, a native of New Jersey, and served as first lieutenant [8] in Forman's additional Regiment, under Captain Burrows.

Anburey's letters, entitled *Travels throughout the Interior Parts of North America,* in two volumes published in 1789, were written at various points in the Colonies from Lake Champlain, Mystic in Connecticut, Sherwood's Ferry on the Delaware, and Charlottesville, Virginia. They contain rather careful notes on several species, showing that he spent a good deal of time in field observation.

Many subjects of general interest are discussed in the letters with birds of the following species claiming attention: the partridge, passenger pigeon, fire-bird (probably the scarlet tanager), the hanging bird [oriole], blue-bird, humming-bird, whipper-will or musquito hawk, mocking-bird and turkey bustard [*sic*]. Apparently he was engaged in making a collection of stuffed birds prepared by himself for his friend in England, and in collecting hummingbirds he devised a way of shooting them with a charge of sand in order better to preserve their delicate plumage. He collected also a

---

[3] For a documented discussion of the Carver grant, see *Wis. Hist. Coll.,* **6**: 220–270, 1869–1872.

[4] According to *Dictionary of Nat. Biog.,* 1921.

[5] Appleton's *Cycl. Amer. Biog.,* 1856; also *North Amer. Rev.,* **50**: 75–82, 1840.

[6] Friedmann, 1934: 200–206.

[7] "Gilbert" appears to be this writer's correct name, but in the copy of his letters, *A topographical description of Western Territory of North America,* which I am using, his name is given as George Imlay, a captain in the American army during the war and commissioner for laying out lands in the back settlements.

[8] Said also by one editor, Elizabeth Robins Pennell, to have held the rank of Captain.

nest of this species containing eggs, of which he wrote with careful accuracy as follows:

Upon an examination of the nest, I was not surprised at my discerning it with difficulty from the other moss that grew on the tree, for the outside has a coating of green moss, such as is commonly on old pales, enclosures, and old trees; the nest, as well as the bird, is the least of all others; that which I have taken is round, and the inside is of a brown and quite soft down, which seems to have been collected from the stems of the sumach, which are covered with a soft wool of this color, and the plant grows in great abundance here; the inner diameter of the nest is hardly a geometrical inch at the top, and the depth scarcely half an inch. I have taken peculiar care of it, as well as the nest of the Hanging-bird, and shall send them by the first opportunity, and am sure you will join with me in the adoration of that Being, who has endowed these creatures with such natural instinct, to guard against the wiles of man and other enemies: but what creature is there either offensive, or inoffensive, but some of its species has fallen a victim to the rapacious hand of man.

Concerning the turkey vulture, he tells the medicinal use made of their feet by dissolving them in an oil for the cure of sciatica and other severe pain. This remedy we recall was mentioned also by John Lawson in his *Natural History of Carolina,* in 1714. Another bit of folk belief is Anburey's statement that the mockingbird, rather than permit her young to be raised in captivity, would feed them poisonous berries in order to save them from a life of confinement.

Captain Anburey's work, printed first without his name, was indifferently noticed in the *Monthly Review* for July 1789 and from Sabin[9] we glean that it was to some extent considered a plagiarism upon General John Burgoyne's (1722–1792) narrative. It was said to have been written to remove some of the opprobrium of Burgoyne's unsuccessful campaign against the colonists. The fact that in its first edition it was published without the author's name seems to indicate that Anburey was not wholly satisfied with it, and the nature of his many remarks on the Indians and the Americans does not indicate particularly good literary taste. Be this as it may, his interest in collecting birds was quite commendable considering the difficulties under which an untrained pair of hands attempts to save bird specimens, and his account of the tame oriole in his room is certainly an engaging story.

According to Bartlett's catalogue of the John Carter Brown Library, Anburey's account has the reputation of containing the most graphic description of Burgoyne's campaign, surrender, and the subsequent captivity of his troops. It is therefore surprising that Anburey's bird notes, even though not of much importance, should have escaped the notice of ornithologists for so long a time.

In Gilbert Imlay (1754–1828) we meet one of the most romantic figures of the Revolution and post-Revolutionary days, a man deeply involved in business, intrigues, and a regrettable liaison with one of England's most famous women.

His connection with ornithology lies in his authorship of a *Topographical Description of the Western Territory of North America* (1793), in which he lists 111 kinds of birds by their popular names and, also, the scientific designation, either that of Linnaeus or Catesby. Some of the groups, such as the hawks, the ducks, and the woodpeckers, are fairly well covered, for Imlay lists twelve birds of prey, nine ducks, and eight woodpeckers, including in the last group the "white-bill," or ivory-billed woodpecker. The other groups are rather heterogeneous, finches, thrushes, flycatchers, and swallows being mingled together, showing that the author had no understanding of their relationships.

In another paragraph Imlay refers to the ivory-billed woodcock, saying it is "of a whitish colour, with a white plume. . . ." "It is asserted," says Imlay, "that the bill of this bird is of pure ivory a circumstance very singular in the plumy tribe." Here it seems the author has relied upon some native story, for the "Ivory-billed woodcock" could not be applied to any authentic species of American bird. It is suggested by one of Imlay's comentators[10] that he did not actually write these letters in America but wrote them from memory to a friend in England or Ireland after he had left Kentucky on some of his various business ventures.

The whole subject of Imlay's career offers many problems which, although they have been investigated by several students of history and literature, appear to remain unsolved to the present time. We are interested in him primarily for his studies in natural history, especially birds, which tell of wide observation combined with independence of thought and a love of nature. Imlay must have been indeed a versatile and romantic figure, with an appreciation of the newly-forming American character that seemed to him wholesome and refreshing. In speaking of the post-war emigrations into Kentucky, he says: "The country soon began to be chequered after that era with genteel men. . . . A taste for the decorum and elegance of the table was soon cultivated, the pleasures of gardening were considered not only as useful but amusing"; and the maple sugar business he regarded as an important industry and "a rational pleasure to meliorate the soul." He speaks as follows on this:

The season of sugar-making occupies the women, whose mornings are cheered by the modulated buffoonery of the Mocking bird, the tuneful song of the thrush and the gaudy plumage of the parroquet.

Many passages similar to this bespeak the author's love of the outdoor world at the same time that he was a keen business man, involved at least for a period in machinations directed to give New Orleans back to France, and in a love affair with Mary Wollstonecraft

[9] Sabin, Joseph, *Dictionary of books relating to America from its discovery to the present time,* N. Y., Author, 1868.

[10] Rusk, 1923: **57**.

(1759–1797), author of one of the earliest feministic books, *Vindication of the Rights of Women* (1792).

Unfortunately, it is difficult to throw much light on Imlay's reputed disloyalty to his country in conniving at the recapture of New Orleans. Mary Wollstonecraft's letters to him are available, but they are so cut with deletions and expurgations that it is impossible to piece together historical events and her many causes for worry with any accuracy. It is clear, however, that she bore him a beautiful and unselfish love which, when she discovered Imlay's faithlessness to her, drove her twice to attempt suicide. The child of their union was born in Le Havre in 1793, and the mother's letters to Imlay, written in despair and poverty, offer intimate personal glimpses into a nobility of character not often vouchsafed to the student of the by-gone makers of science. This child, Fanny by name, in later life committed suicide, because of the stigma of her illegitimacy. This tragedy likewise is believed to have induced Mary Wollstonecraft to go through the marriage form in her subsequent alliance with the agnostic philosopher, William Godwin (1756–1836), who was her literary friend and counsellor. Through Samuel Johnson (1709–1784), famous publisher and lexicographer, she obtained her first literary opportunities as reader and translator, and from this she progressed inevitably to self expression, proving herself a leader and thinker on the subject of women, first with her slender pamphlet, *Thoughts on the Education of Daughters* (1787) and later with her book, *Vindication of the Rights of Women* (1792), for which her name is still famous. After the Imlay friendship and the loss of her daughter, though at first broken in health and spirit, Mary Wollstonecraft regained her usual zest for life and entered upon her marriage with Godwin. Her happiness was to be brief, however, for she died shortly following the birth of her second daughter, Mary Godwin (1797–1851), who became famous as the second wife of Shelley (1792–1822), and, also, in her own right as a literary artist.

Her mother, during her friendship with Gilbert Imlay, lived with him for some time in Paris and they moved in a circle of great literary, artistic, and political figures, including such distinguished minds as LaFayette (1757–1834), Mirabeau (1749–1791), Bernadin de St. Pierre (1737–1814), author of *Paul and Virginia,* Jean and Marie Roland (1734–1793 and 1754–1793), General Dumouriez (1729–1823), and Thomas Paine (1737–1809), author of the *Rights of Man.* I find mention, also, of Georg Forster, the naturalist, Professor at Cassel and Librarian at Mainz, whom we recall as the artist of two unpublished drawings of American birds, which he made on Cook's second voyage.

Imlay is remembered and frequently cited as the first American novelist of the West, since he wrote a sort of autobiographical narrative called *The Emigrants* (1793). It is of slight literary merit, but serves to throw considerable light on his own career, although the characters have fictitious names. Gilbert Imlay was born in upper Freehold, Monmouth County, New Jersey, in 1754, and died on the Island of Jersey on November 20, 1828.

BIRD LISTS OF SOME EARLY STATE HISTORIES

It has been interesting to look through the early state histories for notes on the birds of the various commonwealths. Only a few were published in the late eighteenth century and of these I should like to draw attention to Samuel Peters' *General History of Connecticut* (1782), Jeremy Belknap's *History of New Hampshire* (1784), Samuel Williams' *History of Vermont* (1794), and John Drayton's *View of South Carolina* (1802).

The first of these, the *History of Connecticut,* devotes about three pages to the "feathered tribe" mentioning the following birds with running comments: turkeys, geese, ducks, barn-door poultry, pigeons, hawks, owls, ravens, crows, partridges, quails, heath-hens, blackbirds snipes, larks, humilities (any of various shore birds), whipperwills, dewminks, robins, rens, swallows, bluebird, hummingbird.

Omissions are numerous but the list is interesting for some of its quaint names as "humilities," which was a term used by William Wood in 1639, and dewmink a term not found in any other early description of birds. One possible equivalent is the "chewink" of "the size of an English robin and the flesh is delicious," and the notes "chee-wink" may be easily construed to say "Dewmink."

This author has evidently confused the whip-poorwill and the nighthawk both of which are crepuscular but it is the nighthawk which descends from on high with the great booming sound erroneously thought to come from the throat and described by Peters as "Pope Pope." This note, he says, alarms young people and fanatics very much for "it is a bird of ill omen, apparently a spy from some foreign court singing of whipping and the pope which portends a change of religion." The whip-her-I-will, he says, is reserved for the night. The hummingbird, according to this author, might wantonly be styled the "empress of honey-bees partaking with them of the pink, tulip, rose, daisy and other aromatiques" but it is doubtful that he could have observed the hummingbirds feeding at these particular species of flowers unless for small insects.

It should be noted that Peters' *History of Connecticut* has been attacked as a fabric of lies with special vehemence directed toward his migration of frogs story, his description of the Connecticut River, and his account of the old New England custom of "bundling." An edition of 1877 by S. McCormick, as well as the one of 1829, has undertaken to verify many of his disputed statements and it is reasonable to think that Peters' alignment with the Tory Party may account for some of the vituperation against him.

The naturalist reading Peter's *History* expects to discount some of the descriptions as exaggerated, and he realizes also that Peters had but a superficial knowledge of the birds and other groups. On the other hand there is a vigorous candor about many of the old clergyman's criticisms that is rather engaging to the modern reader.

Samuel Peters who refrained from using his name on the title page of the work, calling himself a "Gentleman of the Province," was born in the town of Hebron, Connecticut, in 1735; he graduated from Yale in 1759 and obtained the pastorate of the Baptist church in his home town in 1762. When the war came on he was out of sympathy with the colonists and became known and consequently persecuted for his royalist leanings. This forced him to seek refuge in England for some years but he returned and died in New York in 1826. It is said that his body was removed for burial to the village of Hebron.

So infrequent are the smiles drawn forth by those early earnest scribes in America that the reader cannot but welcome the mock sobriety of some of Peters' passages and after all, allowing for rhetorical hyperbole, his account of the migration of frogs and the army of caterpillars followed by the thousands of passenger pigeons which came to feed on them, is not beyond reason. It reminds us of the devastating hordes of lemmings that come periodically in the north, and the swarms of black crickets in the pioneer days of Utah that were annihilated by an influx of California gulls. We can see not only humor but truth in Peters' description of night sounds: "The tree frogs, whipperwills, and hooping owls serenade the inhabitants every night with music far excelling the harmony of the trumpet, drum, and jews-harp."

JEREMY BELKNAP

Two years after the stormy launching of Peters' *History of Connecticut,* came Jeremy Belknap's *History of New Hampshire,* a well-conceived and carefully written document fully authenticated and labored upon for a period of several years. The work is in three volumes; the first of which was published at Philadelphia in 1784 while the latter two appeared in Boston in 1791 and 1792.

The bird matter occupies part of Chapter X, following Belknap's discussion of quadrupeds and before his discussions of reptiles, fish, and insects.

The list is remarkably good, considering the fact that he was not a naturalist, and he endeavored to make all parts of the book as complete as possible. One hundred sixteen species of birds are mentioned exclusive of several group designations, and most of the birds receive some sort of scientific appellation which, however, in most cases does not hold today. There are also many indefinite popular names such as spring bird, winter sparrow, chipping bird, grape bird, hedge bird, skouk, quindar, the last of which has not been noted before, but Dr. John Zimmer suggests that it connotes the old-squaw (*Clangula*). "Skouk" is an onomatopœic word, evidently a species of heron, while the others are various members of the confusing fringillid group. Other

quaint names are the wooly woodpecker for the downy woodpecker, bird hawk for the shrike, Lord and Lady, also met with in the arctic travels, signifying harlequin duck; Tee-arr for the least tern, ox-eye for various shore birds also met with in the much earlier bird lists of the mid-seventeenth century. Grape bird must refer to some species that is destructive to grapes and swallow woodpecker probably means the sapsucker.

As to the annotations, these do not show any close observation on the part of the author but they bring to light several early notes of interest:

In winter, turkeys [says Belknap] frequent the seashore for the sake of picking small fishes, and marine insects which the tide leaves on the flats.

In the southern and middle states the quail is called a partridge and the partridge a pheasant. The true pheasant is not a native of our wilderness. The late Governor Wentworth (1696–1770) [of New Hampshire] brought several pairs of pheasants from England and let them fly in his woods at Wolfborough: but they have not since been seen.

This appears to be the earliest record of an introduction of birds into the United States.

Of the crossbill Belknap says, "The upper and lower parts of its beak cross each other like a pair of shears by which means it cuts off the wheat and rye, and then lays the side of its head to the ground to pick the kernels."

Lastly, Belknap's capitulation to the persistent stories of swallows hibernating is a little disappointing. Of the swallow he says, "It was formerly supposed to migrate, but the evidences of its retiring to the water or marshy ground, and there remaining torpid during the winter are so many that this opinion is now generally received."

Concerning Belknap's approach to the subject of the natural history of New Hampshire, we should quote his own words:

Few writers of this country have studied natural history as a science, and of those who have a taste for inquiries of this kind, none have had leisure to pursue them to the extent which is desirable. In the description of an American state it would be unpardonable not to take notice of its natural productions. With much diffidence I enter on this part of my work, sensible that my knowledge of the subject is imperfect yet desirous of contributing something to promote a branch of science, now in its infancy; but for which there is an ample field of inquiry.

This passage reveals the man's earnestness. He was earnest not alone in religious convictions which were his profession, but earnest and devoted in research which, as it touched other fields than his work as a clergyman, might be called his avocation. Jeremy Belknap was the founder of the Massachusetts Historical Society, having always had a taste for the antiquarian side of history, and a true sense of the importance of all historical documents and records. From his study in the old South Church steeple where Prince of Boston had started an historical collection, Jeremy Belknap radiated the true zeal of a scholar.

One of Governor Belknap's last and most important contributions to our early history was a journey to Cuttyhunk in 1797 to ascertain the exact location of Bartholomew Gosnold's (d. 1607) landing when he arrived here in 1602. It will be recalled that he is credited with the discovery of Cape Cod and adjacent islands as well as the founding of Jamestown in 1606. Belknap by his expedition discovered the cellar of Gosnold's store house and so plenished the data of Gosnold's expedition that it was necessary to rewrite the description incorporating all new information. His trip to the Indians at Oneida and New Stockbridge in 1796 was not so successful, leaving him discouraged with their lazy habits and their wish to spend their time hunting.

Belknap, a good husbandman, said in his report on this expediton, "They must lay aside the character of hunters for their game is gone and its haunts are rendered infinitely more valuable by cultivation." But this the Indian would not do and his race has all but vanished from the land that he once was master of.

For an entire year Governor Belknap realized his approaching end and worked the more diligently that he might finish his writing. He died on the twentieth of June, 1798.

SAMUEL WILLIAMS' LIST OF BIRDS

A somewhat briefer account than Belknap's description of birds is that given by Samuel Williams in the second edition of his *Natural and Civil History of Vermont* published in 1809. Here we find birds grouped into several categories as Birds That Endure Severe Winters, Birds of Passage, Singing Birds, and Water Fowl. The total list is between fifty and sixty, a small number, but an interesting detail of the list is the addition of arrival and departure dates for the Birds of Passage. This is given for only a few species, with times of arrival and departure as follows:

Snowbird, Nov. 20—April 1
Wild Goose, March 15—Nov. 20
Wild Pigeon, March 20—Oct. 10
House Swallow ⎫
Barn Swallow   ⎬ April 20—Sept. 20
Ground Swallow ⎭
Blue Martin

While it is interesting to find this bit of bird recording in such a general book as the *Natural and Civil History of Vermont,* it is by no means the first of its kind, for we shall see that William Bartram kept accurate migration data every season for a number of years as reported on in his *Travels through North and South Carolina* (1791). Likewise, Benjamin Smith Barton whom we shall soon discuss kept charts showing how the advance of spring affected not only birds but also plants and other forms. In England too where the great ornithologist John Latham held sway over the naturalists' world in the late eighteenth and early nineteenth centuries, there were records of this kind being kept. Indeed in the fourth volume of the *Transactions of the Linnean*

Society of London, the same number in which Latham's epoch-making drawings of the syringes of birds were published, there is a complete chart of the appearance and disappearance of Sussex birds for the decade 1784–1794 by William Markwick, Esq., F.L.S.

Thus we see that some of the methods of bird study so dear to the bird-lover of today had their origin a hundred and more years ago and were practiced by that small and esoteric fraternity known as ornithologists.

Another interesting feature of Williams' account is his description of the passenger pigeons which roosted in a certain forest in such prodigious numbers that the trees were killed and the undergrowth buried with their dung. Swallows also are described at some length. These are the house swallow, with forked tail and a red spot upon its forehead, the barn swallow, the ground (bank) swallow, and the black (purple) martin. The tree swallow (*Iridoprocne bicolor*) seems to be regularly absent from early lists of American birds, probably because it has little to distinguish it. Here may be read some of the most amazing testimony on the hibernation of swallows given with every mark of authenticity. The author even quotes from his own experience:

I saw an instance, which puts the possibility of the fact beyond all room for doubt. About the year 1760, two men were digging in the salt marsh at Cambridge, in Massachusetts: On the bank of Charles' river about two feet below the surface of the ground, they dug up a swallow, wholly surrounded and covered with mud. The swallow was in a torpid state, but being held in their hands, it revived in about half an hour. The place where this swallow was dug up, was every day covered with salt water; which at every high tide, was four or five feet deep. The time when this swallow was found, was the latter part of the month of February:

Small wonder it is that the belief in the hibernation of swallows has so long endured, when persons of education and acumen would affix their names to such tales. Jeremy Belknap also, Governor of New Hampshire and a very scholarly man, succumbed to the persistent stories of subaqueous hibernating swallows and said: ". . . this opinion is now generally received." In England too where Gilbert White of Selborne founded a new cult of nature observation, the myth prevailed and although our own William Bartram reasoned against it in the late eighteenth century, the wandering roots of the story grew and flowered again in the extensive bibliography on the subject by the eminent ornithologist and classical scholar, Elliott Coues (1842–1899).

It has been asserted that the chimney swift (called by Williams and other early bird observers chimney swallow) also hibernates although not under water. Williams tells of a hollow tree in Middlebury, Vermont, where the "swallows" were thought to tarry through the winter. Persons from all over the countryside would assemble to watch the exodus of the birds that went up in a huge perpendicular column until it reached above the adjacent trees and then dispersed in circular formation. In Bridgeport there was another "Swallow Tree" where thousands of swifts congregated at night and whence they came out in the morning. They were first noticed coming out in the spring, when the leaves begin to clothe the trees, and this is why a belief in their hibernation developed. The fact also that the exact winter home of the swifts of the United States had until 1944 not been discovered, has helped to keep alive a belief in their hibernation. Recent observations place the winter home of our swifts at least in part, in northern Peru.[11]

As a commentary on the appreciation of bird song by the layman of this period we may cite Williams' list of singing birds: robin, skylark, thrush, thrasher or mockbird, bobolincoln, wren, red-winged blackbird, catbird, golden robin or goldfinch, springbird [?], hangbird. Only thirteen species of birds to Williams seemed to merit the appellation of singing birds but stranger than his small estimate is his interpretation of bird song. Says Williams:

The only natural music, is that of birds. In the incultivated state, and parts of the country, this delightful sound is not to be heard. Either disgusted with so gloomy a scene, or disliking the food in the uncultivated lands, the musical birds do not deign to dwell in such places; or to put forth their melody to the rocks, and to the trees. But no sooner has man discharged his duty, cut down the trees, and opened the fields to the enlivening influence of the air and sun, than the birds of harmony repair to the spot and give it new charms by the animating accents of their music.

Of course there is no correlation between agriculture and bird song but the birds that live in the open country or that have adapted themselves to live about man's habitations are the ones that become known to the average person.

All the birds of Williams' list are of the "inhabited" open country group and the shortness of Williams' list of singing birds indicates the very elementary knowledge of birds that he possessed. His list of waterfowl numbers nine while his unclassifiable group which do not fall into his birds of passage, his singing birds, or his waterfowl are as follows: the eagle (two species), hawk (four), owl (three), woodpecker (seven or eight), kingbird, crow blackbird, cuckow, kingfisher, woodcock, woodsnipe, quail, curlew (two), plover (two), wild turkey, whip-poor-will, nighthawk, hedgebird, crossbill, hummingbird. Williams' list seems considerably inferior to Belknap's and below what might be expected of one who had achieved distinction as evidenced by his membership in several learned societies. Many other lists of earlier date such as John Clayton's in 1688 and John Lawson's in 1709 are better than Williams' list of 1809.

JOHN DRAYTON

A fourth list of birds culled from State histories is that by John Drayton, author of the *View of South*

---

[11] Lincoln, 1944.

Carolina which was published in Charleston in 1802. Eighty-six birds are mentioned, mostly without comment, but there are a few unusual popular names: Carolina bullfinch, crested bittern, chatterer, black-cap flycatcher, bull-neck duck. It is probable that the Carolina bullfinch connotes the cardinal, the crested bittern one of the night herons, the chatterer the waxwing, and the black-cap flycatcher the chickadee. "Maybird" might signify a variety of species while bull-neck is probably the golden-eye (*Glaucionetta*).

No discussion of the birds accompanies the list other than a brief statement that a few are migratory some coming from northern and others from southern latitudes. The bird matter is in sharp contrast to the botanical catalogue of twenty-seven pages which is replete with original observation and other indications of the author's real interest.

John Drayton was a district judge and later became governor of South Carolina. He published also a memoir of the American Revolution from materials collected during a tour of the northern and eastern states of America (1794).

GEORGE HENRY LOSKIEL

We are indebted through all our early history to the faithful missionaries of various orders for their descriptions of the country and events which, but for their conscientious offices, would have passed into oblivion.

We have already seen many accounts that have been preserved for us by the Jesuits in northern United States and Canada; others have come from the Moravians on the Labrador Coast; and in Greenland, where the good man, Hans Egede, with wife, children, and forty settlers, braved those icy winters entirely out of love of his religion and the wish to bring the Greenlanders a better way of life, we have a memorable lesson in human service.

Likewise the missionaries of the German sect known as the United Brethren worked for over a century among the North American Indians. The first contingent of these workers to go out from Germany, having been expelled by Schwenkfeld, the leader and Elector of Saxony, settled on the Danish Island of St. Thomas in the West Indies in 1732. Later some came to Georgia, others to Pennsylvania, and their teachings were so successful that in many cases they were able to induce the Indians to settle their disputes without bloodshed.

A good history of this religious work is set forth in the *History of the Mission of the United Brethren Among the Indians of North America,* (1794) by George Henry Loskiel. The materials for the volume which was written first in German and translated by Christian Ignatius La Trobe in 1794 were collected by Gottlieb Sprangenberg and David Zeisberger. Both of these men served as missionaries among the Indians known as the Delawares, the Nantikokes, and the Shawanese tribes of Pennsylvania and New York, for over forty years.

It is simply and directly written and in Chapter VII on Hunting and Fishing the author takes up quadrupeds, serpents, birds, and fish, making a loose use of scientific names many of which he seems to have coined himself as for instance Wild Geese (*Anas anser ferus*).

The list runs along as follows: common eagle (*Falco leucocephalus*); crane (*Ardea grus*); wild swans (*Anas cygnus*); pelican (*Pelicanus onocrotalus*); wild geese (*Anas anser ferus*); wild turkeys (*Meleagris gallopavo*); owls: white owl (*Strix nyctea*), little owl (*Strix passerine*); fishinghawk or osprey (*Falco haliaetus*); heron (*Ardea americana*); night-hawk or goat-sucker (*Caprimulgus europaeus*); hoopoe, raven, crow and pigeon-hawk; pheasants (*Phasianus colchicus*); wild duck (*Anas ferus*); loon (*Colybus*); partridges (*Tetras perdix*); parrots (*Psittacus*); gulls (*Larus*); wild pigeon (*Columba migratorius*); turtle doves; mockingbird; wipperwill; blue-bird; bird of the Great Spirit; snipes—woodpeckers, thrushes, swallows, starlings, catbirds, finches, tom-tits, and wrens; colibri (*Trochilus mellifugus*). From the accounts in this imperfect list, it is possible to select a few remarks of interest, for example, what Loskiel has to say of the eagle, its plumage, its nest, and its manner of hunting. He is apparently the first author who speaks of eagles attempting to take large fish, and being unable to disengage their talons from them with the result that they are drawn under water by the fish and drowned. His remarks on the fishing hawk also contain a belief not previously met with, namely that fish hawks possess an oily substance in the body (which they cast upon the water) and which lures the fish to the surface. The wild turkeys mentioned by Loskiel that become light brown, spotted with white, must be explained as domestic turkeys.

There is little of permanent value in Loskiel's account of birds but it is an interesting example of early effort in the field of bird observation with a little pseudo-scientific diction to give it dignity. A description of the mythical Wakon-bird clothed in new and different grandeur, reminds us that folk beliefs are hard to dispel. However, Loskiel has given us occasional accurate field observations.

From this obscure observer in the person of a German missionary among the Indians, we pass now to two distinguished students of bird life—one a governor of Virginia and future President of the United States, Thomas Jefferson (1743–1826), and the other a noted physician, botanist and antiquarian, Benjamin Smith Barton (1766–1815).

With the work of these two observers, we see that two other states, Virginia and Pennsylvania, in addition to Connecticut, Vermont, New Hampshire, and South Carolina, have state lists of birds dating back to the last years of the eighteenth century.

THOMAS JEFFERSON

Chronologically, Virginia's list compiled by Thomas Jefferson and published in his famous *Notes on the State of Virginia*, came first, having been written in Virginia in 1781, corrected and enlarged in 1782 and printed in Paris at the request of the Marquis Barbé-Marbois of the French Legation for private distribution. One or possibly two French versions appeared in 1785 and 1786. This first printing was brought out without the sanction of the author who inscribed a note in a copy now belonging to the John Carter Brown Library as follows:

Th. Jefferson having had a few of these notes printed to offer to some of his friends and to some other estimable characters, begs Dr. Bancroft's acceptance of a copy. Unwilling to expose to the public eye, he asks the favor of Dr. Bancroft to put them into the hands of no person on whose care and fidelity he cannot rely to guard them against publication.

Despite Jefferson's reluctance to publish these notes, they were at once popular and have remained one of his most enjoyed books. The first proper publication date is London 1787 and we find on pages 113 to 118 a list of seventy-seven species of birds under Linnaean, Catesbyan, and popular names with references by number to Buffon's *Histoire Naturelle des Oiseaux*.

The birds are arranged in columns across five pages with half a page of additional names of birds at the end. In the listing of the birds, the hawks, woodpeckers, the ducks, and other waterbirds, are grouped together, but in the large passerine group there is obvious confusion as to their relationships. For instance, the first bird on the list is the tyrant or field martin (probably kingbird) while the crested flycatcher is number 74, and the blackcap, little brown and red-eyed flycatchers are 79, 80, and 81. Of course the black-cap is probably the chickadee but the "little brown" might be any of the obscure small flycatchers, or some vireo or female warbler. The red-eyed flycatcher is of course the red-eyed vireo.

Among the sparrow or finch group this author is more at home for he mentions six species as follows: redbird, blue grosbeak, sparrow, towhee bird, American goldfinch, purple finch; ricebird and cowpen bird also are numbered with the sparrows probably because of their heavy bills, thus apparently indicating their affinity in the author's mind with the Fringillidae. Of the thrushes, Jefferson mentions only the fox-colored thrush (probably the wood thrush) and the little thrush (veery) while members of the blackbird family are scattered through the latter part of the list. Some unusual names, probably used by the country folk away from towns and villages, may be of interest: Royston crow, wet hawk, ball coot, sprigtail, mowbird (possibly a curlew), water pheasant, water wagtail, finch and creeper.

As to the water birds, there are seven ducks as follows: Buffel's duck, little brown duck, whiteface teal, summer duck, blue-wing shoveller, round-crested duck, blue-wing teal. To these may be added from the supplementary list at the end, the sheldrach or canvasback, sprigtail, and spoon-billed duck. These last three names show that Jefferson was not familiar with the ducks as "sheldrach" always connotes the mergansers and spoon-bill duck is another name for the shoveller already mentioned. "Sprig-tail," it seems, is the pintail.

In the heron list there are six species mentioned, perhaps a fair number, but there is one blighting error, that the crane and blue heron are given as synonymous. This is a common error today as well, but the cranes and herons belong not only to different families but to different orders, the Gruiformes and the Ciconiiformes and resemble each other only superficially in being large, long-necked, and long-legged.

Jefferson was a man of a great many interests, and some critics have been inclined to extol his knowledge of birds as something remarkable for his period. While it is true that he had a tolerable familiarity with some sixty or seventy birds, his knowledge of them was quite superficial and not to be compared with either William Bartram's or Benjamin Smith Barton's. He was scarcely an ornithologist even by avocation as have been many prominent men from many different professions; rather was he in the field of natural science an interesting dilettante exercising his versatile mind upon the creatures and phenomena of the great out-of-doors, deriving much pleasure therefrom, and enjoying a familiarity with both sides of many moot questions. This led him frequently into lengthy conversation and playful argument where he always displayed a scrupulousness of demeanor and an impeccability of speech so characteristic of the French whom he greatly admired. His memorable dispute with Buffon over certain bones of the moose skeleton is an example of his extravagant finesse for he ordered a special party organized for the purpose of procuring a moose and when secured he commanded that the skeleton be stripped of its musculature and shipped to Buffon in Paris at the expense of fifty pounds sterling.[12]

Jefferson's *Notes on the State of Virginia* is remarkable not alone for the information they contain but for the spirit in which they were written. During the period of 1781–1784 Jefferson was under great anxiety regarding his public life and also his private life. He had been criticized for mismanagement of the situation in Virginia when Arnold (1741–1801) entered Richmond; and the condition of his wife who had had to flee the scene of destruction and murder at Elkhill—these things plunged Governor Jefferson into a state of gloomy self-examination and made it impossible for him to do justice to his public life. He had been asked to serve as a plenipotentiary in Europe with Adams (1735–1826), Franklin (1706–1790), Jay (1745–1829), and Laurens (1724–1792), at the forthcoming peace congress in Vienna in 1781 but the question which had been raised regarding his own conduct, and the weakened condition of Mrs. Jefferson made it impossible for him to leave his post of duty.

About this time he was thrown from his horse so that he had to remain quiet for several weeks and it was during this confinement that he utilized his time to write the *Notes on Virginia*. Two persons, the secretary of the French Legation in Philadelphia, the Marquis of Barbé-Marbois, and his chief, de la Luzerne, were collecting information on the American States and it was in answer to the Marquis' many questions that Jefferson compiled his famous *Notes*. Jefferson seems to have been possessed of a tireless zeal to observe and learn; he had formed the habit of recording his discoveries and thus it was that such a mine of information on all phases of our natural resources, our geography, and our political and social organization could be so quickly assembled.

The book as prepared for the Marquis was not complete nor wholly accurate, and, when rendered into French, was so full of errors that Jefferson decided to revise and publish it in England in 1787 so that its readers would be able to see that the French rendition was not as he intended it to be. With regard once more to the bird matter contained in the *Notes*—Jefferson's list while failing of very good ornithology is one to stand ceditably among contemporary lists like Williams' and Belknap's but, as said before, it cannot be compared to Bartram's nor Barton's lists and we should enquire briefly into some explanation of why Jefferson has passed for an ornithologist.

It now seems probable that the eminence of the writer in other fields in which he worked has led critics to ascribe an ornithological learning to Jefferson in excess of what he really had. Furthermore the correspondence which Wilson and Bartram carried on with him were factors which tended to augment our opinion of his knowledge of birds and his interest in them, and lastly the erroneous story of Wilson's writing Jefferson to offer himself as collector for the Pike expedition, and Wilson's reported failure to receive a reply have built up a strong but unfounded confidence in Jefferson's ornithology.

Jefferson is too well known as a great statesman to need his biography sketched here, but it may be of interest to enquire whence came his great liking for the natural sciences. For it seems to be customary to think that that peculiar person who enjoys nature amid a world of sophistication and urbanity must be accounted for.

One critic, Frederick N. Luther, writing in the *Magazine of American History,* suggests that Jefferson inherited this liking, since he was the grandson of a great botanist Isham Randolf. The same writer points out the early influence of the Scottish tutor, Dr. Small, whom Jefferson had as a boy, and citing the diversified general culture meted out in the Scottish system of education he explains Jefferson's remarkable activity in several fields of science, on the grounds of good initial training in methods of study. These influences brought to bear on a brilliant mind would certainly have their effect and the close friendship of Jefferson with Erasmus Darwin (1731–1802), physician, physiologist, and

---

[12] According to Foley's *Jeffersonian Cyclopedia*, p. 607, the box containing these bones was lost and never received.

poet, over a period of several years when he resided in England, would tend to cultivate in him an educational balance between science and the humanities.

No doubt these factors contributed to Jefferson's wide interests and absorption in science but something more, born of an inherent love of study and a consuming ambition for knowledge, must have kept him open-minded and susceptible to the fascinations of nature after he had become deeply involved in politics. For he never relinquished his interest in natural science and even when he attended his inauguration as Vice-President of the United States, he carried with him to Philadelphia the bones of a strange edentate dug from a cave in Green Briar County, Virginia. These he had had sent to him at his house in Monticello thinking they would prove to be the bones of the mammoth which he always believed had lived in Virginia in prehistoric times. Through the studies of Dr. Caspar Wistar (1761–1818), however, these bones were identified as sloth bones of a more recent kind, and were presented to the American Philosophical Society where they were duly named after their discoverer, *Megalonyx jeffersonii*. Many other times can we find that Jefferson's love of scientific investigation went with him no matter what urgent matters of state were on his mind. Fossil bones were his particular delight but geology, zoology, and scientific agriculture also interested him.

Although Jefferson cannot be said to have contributed personally to our knowledge of bird life he was, however, fundamentally implicated in the progress of American ornithology through his organization of the famous Lewis and Clark expedition to the Rocky Mountains (1804–1806)—an expedition which added hundreds of new birds to our list. Jefferson is likewise unique among our presidents in having known more about birds than any other presidential candidate then or since, and he might well inspire other busy men of the government to seek nature as an occasional refuge from public life.

BENJAMIN SMITH BARTON

This brings us to the concluding figure of a somewhat disjointed and miscellaneous group of bird observers—those of the late eighteenth century. The person at the end of this period who published his *Fragments of the Natural History of Pennsylvania* in 1799 is Benjamin Smith Barton. Eminent botanist, physician, professor, and antiquarian, he was born at Lancaster, Pennsylvania on February 10, 1766, the son of an Episcopal clergyman, Thomas Barton, and Susan Rittenhouse. He was left an orphan at only fourteen and while still a student at the College of Philadelphia he went with his famous uncle, David Rittenhouse (1732–1796), on his expedition to survey the western boundary of Pennsylvania.

In 1786 young Barton went abroad to study medicine at Edinburgh and London, going later to Göttingen where he received the M.D. degree. After honors in Europe from the Royal Society of Edinburgh for his

FIG. 43. Benjamin Smith Barton (1766–1815), first naturalist to tabulate the migration of birds with relation to changes in the vegetation in his *Fragments of the Natural History of Pennsylvania* (1799).

distinguished studies, he returned to America in 1789 and was soon appointed to the Chair of Natural History and Botany at the College of Philadelphia, which was about to unite with the University of Pennsylvania. Dr. Barton next became Professor of Materia Medica on the resignation of Dr. Samuel Griffith from Pennsylvania University, and on the death of Benjamin Rush (1745–1813), he was appointed Professor of the Theory and Practice of Medicine at the University of Pennsylvania, but continued to hold his early title of Professor of Natural History and Botany. His biographer, William Barton, writing in the *Portfolio* for April 1816 intimates that it was Barton's intention to resign his teaching work in botany and natural history, believing that this should be the duty of a younger man still in the fire of youth. Barton disliked also the thought of having to substitute his usual field work with the indoor lectures of a "closet" teacher, which promised to become necessary before long because of his poor health. But he preserved his unremitting habits of study and writing despite frequent attacks of gout and haemorrhage. This stoicism may be explained by his love of research augmented by a consuming passion to succeed and by the laudable example of his predecessor, Dr. Rush, whom he greatly admired.

Although Barton's dates place him, from the point of view of modern ornithology, in an almost archaic period, and although his writing on birds is limited to a slim rare tract that never attained any appreciable circulation, he has given us a new idea. There is an almost modern perspicuity in this author's method of observation and his correlation of the annual bird calendar with the progress of vegetation and the sequence of activities in other forms of life.

Despite the great promise that Barton's studies of birds offered, this author never finished more than the first part of his *Pennsylvania Natural History*. It is well named therefore *Fragments of the Natural History of Pennsylvania* but the fact that it is only a part of a much larger contemplated project precludes its being accepted as a work of great importance in the literary history of ornithology.

Beside the fact that it is unfinished, its nomenclature, although binomial, is very indefinite and Dr. Elliott Coues found it necessary in his collation of the work to identify Barton's birds with the aid of William Bartram's list. Furthermore such descriptions as are given are too brief to be clear, or diagnostic. All these shortcomings leave Barton important mainly as the user of a new method which has become important in ecological study.

Doctor Coues declared Barton's tract the first paper devoted entirely to American birds—this it is, if we regard the botanical matter as merely furthering the author's observations on birdlife. The tract is prefaced by a long introduction on birds of some forty paragraphs in which the author explains the tables which follow and in which the reader gathers a rather stimulating impression of the author's general knowledge of birds and the literature and history of ornithology.

The main part of the work—the tables—is divided into sections. Section I lists between ninety and one hundred spring and summer birds of passage, with space for progress of vegetation and miscellaneous observations; section II deals similarly with thirty-two autumnal and winter birds of passage, while section III is an annotated list of Accipitres, Picae, grallinae, Gallinae and Passeres, totaling thirty-nine species followed by a few paragraphs on "accidental" and "occasional" visitants. The last part of the tract is an appendix containing further observations on the preceding lists, culled from the author's correspondents and friends as well as his own experiences.

The importance of this tract is not obvious on the face of it, for it mentions but a slim two hundred birds or less. But in estimating it fairly we should consider that it represents a great amount of systematic day-to-day observation carefully organized and collated with the seasonal advance of vegetation and other physical phenomena.

This kind of observation had not been done before and it is Barton's new approach to the subject that has lived, although it is probable that very few bird lovers who prize their bird journals ever heard of Benjamin Smith Barton.

It is gratifying to see that some of Barton's facile and expressive terms have survived and become common usage at least among ornithologists—such expressions are "resident species," "accidental," and "occasional visitants" which most of us met first probably in Chapman's *Handbook of the Birds of Eastern North America* (1928).

Likewise it is interesting to garner from a close perusal of Barton's *Fragments* a few additional bits of birdlore not previously met with—his remark that the flicker (*Picus auratus*) is known in Maryland as the "Dishwasher" and the fox sparrow in New York as the "Shepherd."

It is obvious from a study of Barton's many articles that he was a great admirer of Thomas Pennant so much so that he named one of his sons after him. He credits Pennant with being his inspiration, the example who stimulated him to the study of natural history. Barton is said to have been the first Professor of Natural History in America, a position, we recall, which was recognized in Europe in the mid-sixteenth century when a Chair of Natural History was established at the University of Bologna and given to Ulysses Aldovandus.

Benjamin Barton died in his fiftieth year, following a hasty trip to France which was intended to relieve his condition but which rather hastened his death on the nineteenth of December, 1815. As a concluding mark of his avid pursuit of study and accomplishment three days before he died he wrote a paper on a genus of plants named in his honor, asking his nephew and biographer William P. C. Barton to make a drawing of one of the specimens to accompany the paper. This was prepared for publication in the *Transactions* of the American Philosophical Society but it was never published and remains as a manuscript in the Library of the Society. The plant was to have been named *Bartonia superba*.[13]

We may perhaps judge by the obscurity of Barton in the ornithological field that, although he was a great student in several branches of science, he did not achieve much success nor recognition. The reason is not far to seek for we observe in his writing a diffuseness, and a lack of organization combined with too great diversity of interest.[14] His effort was too scattered and his ornithology, though it represented a great mass of observation and intelligent correlation of habit with environment, was sporadic, interrupted for long periods, and it represented only one of his many interests. It seems to be an unfailing rule that, in the field of ornithology especially, it is all-important to pursue that science intensively, to the exclusion of all other subjects unless these be definitely related to the study of birds.

---

[13] Consult *Bartonia,* **18**: 49–51, 1936; also Pennell, 1942.

[14] It is easy to understand the indefatigable Wilson's impatience with Barton's methods of work. In a letter (Grosart, A. B., *Life of Alexander Wilson,* 1: 232) to the French botanist, F. A. Michaux, dated June 6, 1812, Wilson says, "Dr. Barton has not yet published his *General Zoology,* which he has been announcing, from time to time, for so many years. It is much easier to say these things than to do them." According to George Ord, Barton's *Zoology,* intended to be entitled *Elements of Zoology* was ten years in press but at the time of the author's death contained only 56 pages and very little manuscript for its composition was left. Though Barton's learning qualified him for such a task, he failed to concentrate his efforts sufficiently to bring to completion any large piece of work outside his main field, which was botany.

We cannot do otherwise than admit that ornithology was a secondary matter with Barton but he was a distinguished botanist, author of the first flora of Philadelphia and vicinity, author of the first textbook [15] of botany in the United States, the *Flora Virginia* (1812), many scientific papers, also a *Prodromus of a Flora of the States of New York, New Jersey, Pennsylvania, Delaware, Maryland and Virginia*. William Bartram who had prepared the plates for his *Elements of Botany* again was his illustrator but, although there is proof that five hundred copies [16] of this work were printed, no copy has ever been found. It is thought that Barton was dissatisfied with the work after he learned the scientific and productive ability of his young German assistant, Frederick Pursh, who contributed many hundreds of new specimens to Barton's herbarium. Finding himself eclipsed by a student more skilled in systematics than himself, Barton, it is thought, deliberately destroyed the *Prodromus*. Only two fascicles of it remained and apparently were used in Barton's later publication *Flora Virginia*. If this be true it throws a penetrating light on his career which constantly seemed to open up to him and inspire him to undertake work that was beyond his power to execute. Had he been rugged physically instead of frail he would perhaps have brought to completion some of his ornithological dreams as well as more of his botanical ones.

A great deal of additional scientific and personal matter relative to Barton and not yet fully examined, was found in the attic of the Livingston estate on the Hudson River. Much of this was presented to the American Philosophical Society and, it is hoped, will in the course of time be presented as research reports to the public. The name of Barton is memorialized in the plant known as Muhlenburg's Bartonia (*Bartonia virginiana*) a member of the Gentian family. His hope that this name might be applied to another more beautiful species was frustrated by the rules of priority. To the ornithologist Benjamin Smith Barton is of particular interest on another count, namely that he had in his classes the English student, Thomas Nuttall (1786–1859), author of the first American handbook of birds, the *Manual of the Ornithology of the United States and Canada* 1832–1834 in two volumes.

XIII. BARTRAM, ABBOT, AND VIEILLOT

WILLIAM BARTRAM

Ornithologists for two generations have revered the sound learning that emanates from that exhaustive study, *Key to North American Birds*. Freighted with facts of the author's own finding, dignified with a solid

---

[15] Bartram, William, *Elements of botany,* illus. with 30 pl., 1803.

[16] The receipted bill for this number of the *Prodromus* was found in a box of Bartram and Barton papers in the attic of the house occupied by Mrs. Violetta Delafield. Consult Pennell, 1942.

grounding in the Classics, and humanized by touches of penetrating philosophy, this two-volume work still remains our most forthright text on American birds. It was the author of this book, that searching ornithological seer, Elliott Coues (1842–1899), who expressed his opinion of William Bartram (1739–1823) and his *Travels through North and South Carolina* as the starting point of "a distinctly American school of ornithology." For William Bartram is important to ornithology not alone for his own accomplishments in this field, but for the impress of his method and thought that is definitely marked upon his ardent follower, Alexander Wilson (1766–1813), and other devotees of the study of birds.

The Bartram family is famous in other branches of natural science as well, and a copious literature already surrounds it. John Bartram (1699–1777) the father of William was a successful farmer and worked at farming as a business, but from early youth, he had a passion for plants by which he acquired a good knowledge of botany and considerable practice in the doctor's craft among his neighbors. His meagre country school education, however, kept him from any serious aspirations toward medicine; however, he read many medical and botanical books and continually increased his store of learning by practical experience. In 1728 he purchased a tract of land on the west bank of the Schuylkill River, about five miles from the Philadelphia of his day, and there, with his own hands, laid out a modest garden and built an attractive stone house where his large family grew up.

His first wife Mary discouraged his pursuit of botany, but in 1729, two years after Mary's death, he married Ann Mendenhall of Concord Monthly Meeting, who seems to have had the wisdom and vision to let her husband follow his natural bent. When John could be spared from the farm he was off on horseback collecting and studying plants, bringing many roots and seeds home to his garden so that his family and friends could share in his modest explorations. Thus began the renowned Bartram garden and news of John Bartram's success in growing plants and his practical knowledge of them soon reached the learned botanists of Europe.

At this time in England and Holland especially, there were many famous and beautiful gardens. The great authorities on plants were avidly seeking for new species to naturalize in their flower beds and they were likewise interested in finding collectors who could procure for them the coveted prizes that grew in distant lands. John Bartram, because of his knowledge of plants, became an important agent to this enthusiastic group of plant lovers, and he was introduced through a Dr. Samuel Chew to Peter Collinson (1694–1768), who already was much interested in obtaining American species. Collinson some years previously had assisted Mark Catesby to carry on his collecting expedition, and Catesby no doubt brought back accounts of the great abundance of plant and animal life and the various men who were interested in this field of study. Some of the more active ones were John Mitchel (d. 1768) in Virginia, Jared Eliot in Connecticut, Alexander Garden (1730?–1791) in Carolina, and Lieutenant Governor Cadwallader Colden (1688–1766) in New York. Among the leading naturalists in Europe at this time were Sir Hans Sloane (1660–1753), President of the Royal Society, Dr. J. J. Dillenius (1687–1747), Professor of Botany at Oxford, and William Sherard (1659–1728), patron of botany. In Holland, where horticulture enjoyed superlative popularity, the famous physician and entomologist, Hermann Boerhaave, George Clifford, the President of the East India Company, Dr. Jan Frederick Gronovius, senator and botanist, were active in studying new species and adding them to their collections. In Sweden at this time the young student, Karl Linnaeus, also was gardening though on a small scale, and even so early in his career, he was formulating some of his botanical treatises which in a few years were destined to be published in Holland.

All these great names were friends or acquaintances by correspondence of the unassuming but skillful Quaker botanist, John Bartram.

Through Peter Collinson, Bartram was able to turn his interest in collecting and the cultivation of plants to account, for Peter, voicing the desire of several of his friends, invited him to ship boxes of plants, seeds, and roots over to England at five guineas a box and, for unusually good materials, at ten guineas.

Often other things such as turtles, frogs, snakes, shells, birds' nests, and eggs also were included. These things were eagerly viewed and discussed and some were exchanged for other items among Collinson and his friends.

Birds were not of primary concern to these men but there was certainly a growing interest in them and John Bartram frequently in his letters communicated valuable notes on their habits and occasionally also sent a few specimens. He seems to have been particularly interested in migration and in his letter of January 22, 1757 he made the following observations on this subject:

Many birds, in their migrations, are observed to go in flocks,—as the geese, brants, pigeons, and blackbirds; others flutter and hop about from tree to tree, or upon the ground, feeding backwards and forwards, interspersed so that their progressive movement is not commonly observed. Our blue, or rather ash-coloured, great herons, and the white ones, do not observe a direct progression, but follow the banks of rivers—sometimes flying from one side to the other, sometimes a little backwards, but generally northward, until all places be supplied sufficiently where there is conveniency of food; for when some arrive at a particular place, and find as many there before them as can readily find food, some of them move forward, and some stay behind. For all these wild creatures, of one species, generally seem of one community; and rather than quarrel, will move still a farther distance, where there is more plenty of food—like ABRAHAM and LOT; but most of our domestic animals are more like their masters; every one contends for his own dunghill, and is for driving all off that come to encroach upon them.

It is very probable that many kinds of birds, in their migrations, fly out of our sight, so high as to be unobserved,—as for instance, our Hooping Cranes, in their passage from Florida to Hudson's Bay. They fly in flocks of about half a score, so exceeding high as scarcely to be observed, but by the particular noise of their loud hooping. We then can but just see them, though so particularly directed where to look for them.

When his son William was a young boy, John began to ponder his education and future and when Billy was only fourteen he took the lad with him on a trip to the Catskills. Apparently Billy even at this age was rather a dreamer; he loved to draw and observe birds to such an extent that John feared he would not amount to much. He consulted Peter Collinson who in turn referred Bartram to Benjamin Franklin, at that time a successful printer. Billy's talent for drawing, it seemed, would combine well with the printer's trade, and engraving, which was on the increase, might offer an outlet for Billy's "favorite amusement" as his father was wont to speak of his artistic efforts.

Peter Collinson wrote in 1756 when William was seventeen:

I am glad . . . that Billy has a business offers, [sic] that may suit his genius. By all means don't delay it; for I think engraving a curious art,—and if he succeeds in it will not want [lack for] encouragement. We want one very much here, skilful in engraving birds, plants, etc. Edwards has in a manner, left off. We have engravers enough—I may call them scratchers; but a fine hand is much wanted.

This encouraged John to hope that William might become an artist-naturalist but being a canny Quaker he wanted to fortify his son with other experience for he realized from his own modest income that natural history offered no very sure livelihood. Therefore he apprenticed the boy to a merchant in Philadelphia and later established him as a trader at Cape Fear, North Carolina. These ventures came to naught, however, and John once again decided to have William accompany him on the major expedition of his life—his journey through the Carolinas, Georgia, and Florida.

John Bartram had long desired some professional recognition in England of his botanical labors and it was therefore a great satisfaction to him to be appointed through the efforts of Peter Collinson [1] and the Duke of Northumberland (1715–1786) as botanist to King George III (1738–1820) at an annual stipend of fifty pounds. The fact that John was without academic training caused some to look askance at the appointment but Bartram accomplished the task and filled the office well despite his lack of polish, as we may judge by his election to the Royal Societies both of London and of Stockholm.

In this atmosphere of ambitious study and exploration William grew up, but he seems to have been of a more

---

[1] According to William Bartram's biography of his father (*Phila. Med. & Phys. Jour.*, 1: 119, 1805) Joseph Brentnal, a merchant of Philadelphia conveyed collections and observations to Peter Collinson.

sedentary disposition than his father. At twenty-six he was still undecided as to his life work and was glad to join his father on his Florida journey. It seems likely that this trip laid the foundation of his literary and scientific work for in 1773, at the request of Dr. John Fothergill (1712–1780), his London friend who for years had watched his development, he set out on his own travels to explore Carolina, Georgia, and Florida.

1834) and William (1770–1850) and Dorothy Words-worth (1804–1847) with the *Travels* for traces of Bar-tram's influence. But while many passages apparently suggested by similar passages in the *Travels* can be found, this superficial imitation is of small consequence to English and American literature, in comparison with the solid standard of accuracy set by Bartram in all his statements.

FIG. 44.   William Bartram (1739–1823), first ornithologist born in America.   Portrait by
Charles Willson Peale in Old City Hall, Philadelphia.

The account of this journey *Travels Through North and South Carolina* (1791) has been read around the globe. It came at a time when the literary world was still unconvinced regarding the charm of nature learned at first hand, yet the "nature poets" albeit but slenderly versed in plant and animal life were led to imitate William Bartram in no small measure. Many critics have scanned and compared the writings of Coleridge (1772–

It is his intimate knowledge of living things combined with his poetic and sensitive diction that makes Bar-tram's *Travels* unique, and coming, as it did, in the same decade with Gilbert White's literary publications, it seems in close kinship with the Natural History of Sel-borne. More than a century and a half have passed since its publication yet it still holds a place in the early annals of American literature, and for the modern scientist, it is proof that scientific research and literature have common ground which scientists would do well to cultivate.

Bartram's principal contribution to ornithology lies in his Catalogue of Birds of North America of which he lists 215 species [2] with considerable observation on migration, song, nesting and other habits. Many of Catesby's and other writers' statements are challenged, and modern research has in many cases shown Bartram to be correct. We cannot agree with all of his statements, however. We wonder at his opinion of bird song when he says:

this harmony with the tender solicitude of the male alleviates the toils, cares, and distresses of the female, consoles her in solitary retirement whilst setting and animates her with affection and attachment to himself in preference to any other.

This anthropomorphic interpretation is a departure from his usually scientific attitude, but considering the status of life history study in his time it is not surprising that he failed of holding the modern view of song. This definitely postulates that song is used by the male as a challenge to other males and serves to warn them against entering the singer's territory. Whether the birds themselves have an appreciation of the beauty of their songs is doubtful but we do know that they recognize and respond to their mates' calls.

But it is not only Bartram's writings that have left their stamp on American ornithology. The Bartram home contented within, and surrounded by gardens of horticultural rarities which had been cherished by two generations of the family, dispensed an atmosphere that made it a Mecca for all travellers interested in nature. Peter Kalm, the Swedish naturalist, stopped there to collect; here Hector St. John de Crevecœur, author of the *Letters of an American Farmer,* although previously unknown to the Bartrams, was received with hospitality. Nearby at Gray's Ferry, Thomas Say (1787–1834), the distinguished entomologist, grew up, and, as a boy, was wont to carry his curious specimens to William Bartram, always the sympathetic friend of youth. And here Alexander Wilson, the father of American ornithology, a schoolmaster at Gray's Ferry, received inspiration and encouragement for his great work on birds.

A phase of bird study in which William Bartram was a pioneer was the difficult subject of migration. On the basis of this and his clear logical refutation of the various unschooled theories of previous writers, he merits the position of the first scientific American ornithologist. In speaking of the fauna of Carolina, Georgia, and Florida, he says:

there are few [birds] that have fallen under my observation but have been mentioned by the zoologists, and most of them very well figured in Catesby's or Edwards' work, but these authors have done very little toward illustrating the subject on the migration of birds.

It seems incredible that nearly a hundred years later than Bartram's time many reputable scientists still believed in the hibernation of swallows. But Bartram himself in his own mind was quite certain that this could not be.

Several pages of Bartram's *Travels* are given over to a discussion of migration with the names of the spring migrants from the south, which after raising their young return south again in the autumn; he gives also a list of those which in autumn arrive in Pennsylvania from the north and remain there for the winter returning north again the following spring. Again he distinguishes between the natures of the birds which continue the year round in Carolina and Florida and those that continue the year round in Pennsylvania.

It is interesting to know that frequent letters on the subject of birds passed between William Bartram and George Edwards who at the time of Bartram's greatest activity in the study of birds, was busy at his second ornithological work—the *Gleanings of Natural History.* These ornithologists never met but Bartram frequently sent specimens of birds to Edwards and from a letter [3] dated November 15, 1761 we gather that Edwards sent Bartram one of his volumes containing one hundred colored plates as a gift, but this unfortunately was not received. Said Edwards: "These books contain all the small birds you were so good to send me two or three years ago." Bartram was helpful likewise to Thomas Pennant in sending specimens to aid him for his book *Arctic Zoology.*

Despite Bartram's contribution to ornithology, he is remembered mostly for his botanical studies and we must regard his bird study as a secondary interest. Nevertheless it is memorable and even epoch-making since it transcends the time-honored practice of collecting specimens which formerly was the only method comprehended by the scientific world. In contrast to this school of thought Bartram is the apostle of the living bird as no one before him had been, and few since, and it is by reason of his close application to vital life history study that he may be called an American Gilbert White.

The taxonomy of American birds was destined to develop greatly during the explorations of the nineteenth and twentieth centuries, and it is well to have had the leavening influence of a Bartram writing from the point of view of the natural philosopher to teach an appreciation of bird life. Previous writers were keen to kill and possess these feathered creatures, to set up their dead effigies in some semblance of life and to add their names to a list of short dry descriptions of plumages. But Bartram, in quiet contemplation, preferred to ponder their daily lives in their native haunts, and that is why his literary and scientific *Travels* hold a fresh interest even for the overtaxed and exacting reader of today.

[2] Coues, 1875: 338–358.

[3] Darlington, 1849: 323.

In addition to his literary and scientific ability William Bartram had artistic talent. He began to draw natural history subjects when he was only a boy, but although he showed great promise he does not seem to have progressed beyond the amateur stage. Peter Collinson and Dr. Fothergill took a sort of paternal interest in his early efforts and the Duchess of Portland (*ca.* 1760), upon seeing some of his drawings, offered twenty guineas for additional ones.[4] Yet Bartram never acquired a professional attitude toward his art, much less any feeling of wanting to make his living by it. As late as 1772 we find Dr. Fothergill, when Bartram was no less than thirty-three, writing as follows:

I received thy obliging letter, and the drawings that accompanied it. They are very neatly executed;—If it was possible to be a little more exact in the parts of fructification, and where these are very diminutive, to have them drawn a little magnified, I should be pleased—. I should have wrote by the person who brought thy letter and the drawings over, but he went away before I was apprised of it. I shall desire Mr. Chalmers, of Charleston, to make thee a little present for the drawings; and I should be glad to contribute to thy assistance in collecting the plants of Florida, if thou would suggest what terms might be agreeable. I am not so far a systemmatic botanist as to wish to have in my garden all the grasses, or other less observable, humble plants that nature produces. The useful, the beautiful, the singular, or the fragrant, are to us the most material yet despise not the meanest. Mind thy studies in drawing. Thy hand is a good one; and by attention and care may become excellent.

But in the midst of all these attentions forget not the one thing needful. In studying nature forget not its Author. Study to be grateful to that Hand which has endowed thee with a capacity to distinguish thyself as an artist, avoid useless or improper company. Be much alone and learn to trust in the help and protection of Him who has formed us all and everything.

For thy father's sake I wish thee all good;————.

I am, and wish to be

Thy friend

J. Fothergill.

Dated London 23rd Oct. 1772

Had Bartram been a lad at this time "a little present for his pains" might have seemed in order. As one man to another, it keeps Bartram in the position of a protégé, not an artist in his own right.

At times William was neglectful of his orders, and Dr. Fothergill thus wrote to John Bartram when William was thirty-five:

I am sensible of the difficulty he is at in travelling through these inhospitable countries, but I think he should have sent me some few things as he went along. I have paid the bill he drew upon me; but must be greatly out of pocket if he does not take some opportunity of doing what I expressly directed, which was to send me seeds or roots of such plants, as either by their beauty, fragrance or other properties, might claim attention. However, I shall hope he will find some means of fulfilling my orders, better than he has done hitherto.

His father also was annoyed by his desultory attitude toward his work and on December 27, 1761, said:

4 Fox, 1919: 185.

And yet I have not received one single seed from my son, who glories so much in the knowledge of plants, and whom I have been at so much charge to instruct therein.

It seems that Bartram like Catesby had a great interest in zoology, as well as in botany; that he was a naturalist rather than a collector and probably spent a good deal of time in a study of all nature's forms, thus giving the impression of neglecting the main task for which he was engaged—the collection of plants.

Apparently John Bartram, the father, recognized in his son his love of living things, for from early childhood William, when not at school, was his father's constant companion. He planted and cultivated; he helped with the packing, labelling and shipping of plants to England. He accompanied his father on several exploring trips and altogether gave promise of carrying on his father's work with the additional advantage of knowing how to draw and also to express himself in writing. But not only toward his art but also toward professional life in general William Bartram remained indifferent. Under the mentorship of his self-taught Quaker father he acquired that uncompromising sense of values that dictates the simple life ungarnished by pomp or power.

When he returned from his southern travels he found his father had died and his brother John had taken over the old home. William continued there as John's partner in the place, but he never married. He continued to live his kindly and studious life close to the soil. Botanical studies and a heavy correspondence with the scientific world made him the most able and respected American botanist. It is therefore not surprising that he was offered the chair of botany at the University of Pennsylvania. This, however, he declined, perhaps sensible of his lack of formal academic training but pleading poor health as the reason.

Again President Jefferson, in 1786, tried to draw him into public service by offering him a post with the Lewis & Clark expedition, when it went west. Many of Bartram's friends, including Benjamin Smith Barton, urged him to go, but Bartram though only forty-seven, considered himself an old man and refused the opportunity. After many years he was elected to the Academy of Natural Sciences of Philadelphia, and, a little later, to the American Philosophical Society, the latter of which honors his father likewise had held.

Botany and drawing continued to be his delight, and, from the scientific center of the Bartram garden, the old gentleman radiated his benign influence to all visitors. Most of them were naturalists, but many other distinguished persons came there, including Thomas Jefferson, Benjamin Franklin, and Charles Brockton Brown (1771–1810), early American novelist.

A personal recollection of him is given by Malvina Lawson, eldest daughter of Alexander Lawson who was Alexander Wilson's engraver. She remembered William Bartram as a charming old gentleman who on one of her frequent visits to the Bartram garden gave her a "very double yellow rose," a great rarity at that time.

Fig. 45. Little Green Bittern (Heron). From an unpublished manuscript by William Bartram in the Department of Botany. Courtesy of the Trustees of the British Museum.

It is difficult to say how much ornithological work William Bartram did, his contribution to this science being so much a matter of method and influence. However, it is indicative of a deep interest in birds, early directed into useful channels, that in 1756 when he was only seventeen he was drawing birds and drying birds for George Edwards in England and, what is even more significant, he was shooting migratory birds and dissecting them in order to study the development of the gonads. From his observation of immature eggs in the females he concluded that these birds were birds of "quick passage" [5] and the assumption is that he understood from this that such individuals were transient visitants in Pennsylvania which were hurrying on to more northern nesting grounds.

In regard to his drawings, too, it is difficult to be specific. Undoubtedly he made many more than have ever been published and since he was in the habit of depicting birds, snakes, plants, and other forms all on the same drawing, it is not unlikely that drawings of birds so far not cited will come to light. It is known that some of

[5] Darlington, 1849: 207.

Bartram's drawings went to the Duchess of Portland [6] while Dr. Fothergill's series of drawings of rare plants (and possibly birds [7]) at Upton was purchased by the Empress of Russia.

We need not conjecture, however, regarding a series of bird drawings by William Bartram in the British Museum. These in due course found their way together with the manuscript volumes of Bartram's *Travels,* one on Georgia, and one on Florida, into the Natural History Museum, South Kensington, at the time of Fothergill's death.

The folio volume of Bartram's drawings and water colors contains a variety of flowers, fish, snakes, molluscs, and other forms, and in addition twenty-five drawings of birds which I believe have not been cited in their entirety before.

The following list of bird drawings was compiled by the present writer in 1936 from the drawings themselves.

LIST OF BIRD DRAWINGS

BY

WILLIAM BARTRAM

IN THE

BRITISH MUSEUM, DEPARTMENT OF BOTANY

1. The sandhill Crane, labeled by the artist, "Wattoola Great Savannah Crane"
2. Green winged Teal.
3. Great Mallard of Florida.
4. Little Green Bittern (Green Heron) [8]—half natural size, very accurately colored and posed.
5. A small Flycatcher of an olive colour, having the tips of first coverts white.
6. Little Brown Lark, and on the same sheet, the small olive Flycatcher.
7. The Little Brown Marsh Sparrow of Florida.
8. The Gray or Brant Goose.
9. A drawing of an unlabelled bird with a black crest—wedge-shaped tail.
10. Ortulan or Rice Bird on a spray of rice, a green frog, and little black and red speckled snake of Florida.
11. Crested Red Bird of Florida or Virginia Nightingale. This is a pencil sketch.
12. The Caron Crow of Florida. One half of the page is given to drawings of the head and foot "size of Life"; the other half shows the whole bird posed on a dead snag with the additional legend "6 first Quill feathers white or ash colored." The heads coloured pinkish might be taken for Turkey Buzzard but the legend "6 first Quill feathers white or ash coloured" suggest the Black Buzzard.[9]

[6] For catalogue of this collection, see Rev. John Lightfoot, author of *Flora Soctia,* 1778.

[7] George Edwards frequently speaks of going to Upton to observe some of Dr. Fothergill's rare birds.

[8] A drawing of a heron by Bartram is reproduced in an article by A. W. Exell, *Nat. Hist. Mag.,* 2 (9) : 55, 1929. This heron is said to be not specifically identifiable. It must therefore be a different drawing from the one called by Bartram "Little Green Bittern."

[9] This drawing with the caption, Fig. 3. "Turkey Buzzard, *Cathartes aura* Wied." (William Bartram's Drawings, p. 46) is reproduced in an article by A. W. Exell, *Nat. Hist. Mag.,* 2 (9) : 50–58, 1929, "Two Eighteenth-Century American natural-

13. A small unlabelled drawing of the Sandhill Crane similar to No. I. This occupies the lower left corner of a large drawing of the round leafed Nymphia.
14. An unlabelled drawing of a short legged long billed bird painted green and showing a red throat. Posed on a snag. The whole picture showing various vegetation and animal life including a snake devouring a frog, snails, a dragonfly, and the tail of a lizard.
15. Little Brown Hedge Sparrow. On the back of the drawing above Bartram's initials "of North Carolina" appears. It is posed on the ground about to snatch an insect from the stalk of low spring sweet Iris.
16. Yellow Rump Flycatcher [Myrtle Warbler]. This shows a large drawing of what is apparently intended for the male bird posed on a snag and the female is on the wing about to snatch an insect from mid-air. Above Bartram's initials appears "from North Carolina," and below the date "1769."
17. An unlabelled drawing of a sparrow-like bird with a heavy bill and heavy black area at corner of beak and a white throat.
18. The little Brown Sparrow of Florida or Savannah bird.
19. The Largest Wren. This shows merely the head and part of the back at the base of the perch on which is posed the little Brown Sparrow mentioned above.
    On the back of this drawing appears the following note. "Of the little Brown Sparrow of Florida or Savannah bird—sings most sweetly during the summer season. He is of a pale reddish-brown colour. They habit the pine groves near the grassy savannahs."
    Of the largest wren; the following notes appear: "The largest Wren of a redish brown colour beautifully marked with transverse lines. Throat breast and belly cream colour."
20. The Red Sparrow or Red Bird. This drawing is not so pleasing as No. 11 of the same species. The bird itself is depicted with the crest half raised and the eye thus somewhat out of place. The composition of the whole drawing is rather grotesque in that it shows a large fish approaching the bird apparently through mid-air with its eye directed toward the cardinal which in fright has averted its head and raised its crest.
21. An unlabelled drawing of a bird, probably intended for the Simpkin (*Aramus scolopacea pictus*). On the back of the drawing appear these notes in Bartram's careful handwriting: "This bird seems to be of a nature partaking both of the water hen and bittern, shot on the sea shore. He's about the size of a curlew, Bill two inches long, brown colour and yellow, Near the base, the whole body was of an ash colour or dirty dove colour, upper side darkest throat whitish to a white line from above the eye to the bill and a white spot under the eye. The belly mark't with transverse lines of deep slate colour the wings having mixture of a redish brick color legs and feet of an olive colour." W. B. It will be noted that colour is spelled with the *u* and without it but it is impossible to tell from the manuscript whether he left out the *u* sometimes or whether the script has become somewhat obliterated by time.
22. "Musicapa." On the reverse side Bartram has written as follows: "This small bird is of the kind called by naturalists Flycatcher it is here figured of its natural

size all its upper parts are of a deep olive colour darkest a top of the head back wings and upper side of the tail, breast and belly lightest inclining to yellow. Throat and sides of the head yellow a black line begins at the root of the upper mendable and passes through the eyes and another begins at the cormers of the mouth and forms a semi-circle under each eye, there are longish dashes of black on the sides of the neck down to the breast. He appeared in N. Carolina beginning of April, they feed on small insects, are birds of Passage and go northward to breed."
    This is copied exactly from the manuscript as far as the words are concerned but some of the punctuation has been added to make the meaning clear. The bird seems more like a warbler than a flycatcher. Perhaps a female prairie warbler, according to Dr. John Zimmer.
23. The Humming Birds. From the sea coast, Cape Fear, No. Carolina.
24. Scarlet Crowned Finch. This bird is pictured on a stump on one side of which springs a purple flower called Anisium Stellatum—the bird a sparrow-like creature with red crown like a purple finch and a yellow breast and yellow bill is perched on the other side.
25. An unlabelled water colour of a yellow breasted bird with many black spots and a white band near base of tail. The drawing does not appear to be of a kind with the other Bartram drawings, being on paper of a different texture and size and is more stained. At the top appears in what is apparently John Bartram's handwriting: "not M. Catesby Pennsylvania"—and at the bottom in a different handwriting "Wl. Bartram." This bird is the last of the Bartram drawings and is probably intended for Magnolia Warbler.[10]

This series of bird drawings shows Bartram to have been a capable artist and an excellent observer of detail. He was not, however, scrupulous of proportions nor of composition. Thus many of his drawings became rather fantastic and heterogenous compilations of several separate efforts. Apparently they were composed without thought of their being used and were sent from time to time over a period of years to his friend and patron Dr. Fothergill. At last at his death they came with other of the famous physician's effects to the British Museum.[11] Mention of them in the Bartram literature is very infrequent; they are cited in Brett-James'

---

ists." I am indebted to my friend Dr. Francis Harper, for this reference. Apparently this drawing is misidentified in this article, because according to the Check-list of North American Birds the black vulture (*Coragyps atratus*) is based on the *Vultur atratus*, the black vulture or carrion crow of Bartram. See his *Travels*, p. 289.

[10] A few of these drawings are published in "Travels in Georgia and Flordia, 1773–74. A report to Dr. John Fothergill." by William Bartram. Annotated by Francis Harper. *Trans. Amer. Phil. Soc.*, 33 (2), 1943. A list follows:

No. 1 of Brit. Mus. List Fig. No. 22, Am. Phil. Soc. Print.
No. 3   Brit. Mus. List Fig. No. 38, Am. Phil. Soc. Print.
No. 5 & 6 Brit. Mus. List Fig. No. 10, Am. Phil. Soc. Print.
No. 7 & 8 Brit. Mus. List Fig. No. 16, Am. Phil. Soc. Print.
No. 10   Brit. Mus. List Fig. No. 36, Am. Phil. Soc. Print.
No. 12   Brit. Mus. List Fig. No. 37, Am. Phil. Soc. Print.
No. 21   Brit. Mus. List Fig. No. 23, Am. Phil. Soc. Print.

[11] British Museum of Natural History, Department of Botany, South Kensington, London. It should be mentioned that since 1936 this manuscript has been cut, mounted on cards, and rearranged so that the whole appearance was quite different when I examined the drawings again in 1949. Four pages describe the bird drawings which run only from Tab. I. through XVIII but V, XIII and XV are wanting. A blue sheet laid in indicates the whole of this book has been photographed. Reference 55/47.

biography of Peter Collinson; again in the article by A. W. Exell referred to above.

As we think back on William Bartram, the botanist and ornithologist, he seems to be a unique character among the pre-Audubonian bird observers—unique in that he had no peers in his time and only now are we beginning to develop this sensitive and poetic type of observer.

There was perforce a long formative period in American literature before objective knowledge of birds was sufficiently ingrained in the small reading public of those early years to be transmuted into a deeper more contemplative interest in birds. William Bartram was one of the first to achieve this combination of scientific knowledge and aesthetic appreciation which he could weld into that rare type of writing—literary prose of true scientific substance. Few attain this dual feeling for nature but it seems that as time goes on Bartram's *Travels* should be read anew because of the growing interest in the literary treatment of natural history. William Bartram lived quietly at his home until he was eighty-four years of age, a man, like his father, religious but liberal. He died peacefully, 1823, of a ruptured blood vessel, just as he had written a new plant description and was going to walk in the garden. His name is memorialized in that wild open country bird the Bartramian sandpiper or upland plover. It has the habit of giving its ringing, attenuated notes while flying, and, as it alights on some fence post, it raises its fully spread wings straight up above its body. This bird for many years was near extinction over a large part of its range, but now happily is coming back to its once deserted fields.

JOHN ABBOT OF GEORGIA

We should not omit from this survey of early American ornithology some account of the English naturalist, John Abbot. He was primarily an entomologist, who prepared specimens and drawings for distribution in Europe, and two volumes of his entomological work are extant: James E. Smith published *The Natural History of the Rarer Lepidopterous Insects collected from Observations by John Abbot,* London, 1797, in two volumes.

His work on birds, however, remains unpublished even today, but has been described by three ornithologists as follows: in 1896 Walter Faxon (see bibliography), Curator of Invertebrates at the Museum of Comparative Zoology at Cambridge, described a set of 181 Abbot drawings, which he said had recently come to light in the Boston Society of Natural History.

In 1918 Samuel N. Rhoads reported on a second set numbering 122,[12] which in 1906 was purchased for the Wymberley Jones de Renne Georgia Library, at that time housed in an old colonial mansion on the Isle of Hope, Savannah.

FIG. 46. John Abbot (1751–1840?), artist-naturalist of Georgia. A self-portrait from his unpublished manuscript on the Natural History of Insects. Courtesy of the Dept. of Entomology, Cornell University.

A third set[13] of Abbot Bird Drawings, numbering 246 figures in two volumes, known as Egerton Manuscript 1137 and 1138, is preserved in the British Museum, London. Other Abbot drawings of birds are in Manchester and at the Zoological Museum at Tring.

John Abbot was born in London the first of June, "Old Stile" in 1751, the son of an attorney who had a large and valuable collection of prints and many paintings by the best masters. As soon as John showed interest in drawing and natural history, his father provided drawing lessons and books that would be helpful. John early acquired Eleazar Albin's work on insects, George Edwards' volumes on birds, and Lady Honeywood gave him Catesby's *Natural History of Carolina, Florida and the Bahama Islands.*[14]

---

[12] Rhoads, 1918: 271–289. These drawings are now at the University of Georgia, at Athens.

[13] Allen, E. G., 1942: 563–571.

[14] These biographical notes are extracted from John Abbot's *Notes on my life,* Lepidopterists' News, Pub. by C. L. Remington, Mar., 1948.

Abbot met the leading collectors and was invited to study their cabinets. He became an ardent collector himself, and built a cabinet for his specimens, made many drawings and conducted experiments in keeping insects in captivity.

He cared nothing for the law profession, at which he served as clerk in his father's office, and in 1773 was determined to go to America.

Abbot sold his elegant mahogany cabinet, and his drawings and insect collection. Then he had three smaller wainscot cabinets built to take with him to America. He came to Virginia in September, 1773, and remained about two years in the neighborhood of Jamestown, but, becoming disappointed with collecting there, he moved with the Goodalls, the family with whom he lodged, down into Georgia. The trip was made by horses and cart, and required some two months, from early December to early February, when they arrived at a plantation thirty miles south of Augusta, and there put up a small house, in which they lived for some years.

Most of Abbot's life in America, however, was spent in Savannah and in Burke, Scriven, and Bullock Counties. He married Penelope Warren and had a son, John, born in 1779. Abbot served in the Revolution [15] under Lieutenant-Colonel James McIntosh, and when the war was over, he was assigned a tract of 575 acres of land in payment for his military service. He lived here as a planter some twenty years and apparently had a comfortable home, but suffered reverses thereafter.

Both Alexander Wilson and George Ord (1781–1866) were acquainted with him, and Wilson met him and went birding with him while on his southern travels. In a letter to Ord in March 1814 Abbot refers for the first time to a large collection of stuffed birds he had made for a gentleman in England. On this subject Abbot says:

At the commencement of the war I had undertaken to make a collection of Stuffed Birds for a Gentleman in England, but last fall in despair of seeing Peace restored, I retired into the country after having made about two hundred twenty drawings, and after having throwed away a large collection of stuffed skins, have entirely laid it aside and entered into another line of employment where I am in hopes the mad and destructive ambition of the rulers of the world can but little interfer.

Abbot was already sixty-three years old in 1814, when he made this change in occupation and residence. After 1820 he is referred to as John Abbot of Bullock County. Just what his occupation was is not clear, but we know he was a prolific worker in collecting, raising, and drawing insects, and he must have spent most of his time at this work.

Parts of his vast collections of insects went to London, Dublin, Paris, Zürich, and Berlin. The set of 181 bird drawings referred to above went to Boston as the gift of Horace Gray, 1800–1893, in 1837, six years after the

Boston Society of Natural History was incorporated. Abbot's drawings of insects in this museum, on the other hand, were the gift of Asa Gray, the eminent botanist who held the chair of Botany at Harvard for many years. Despite this seeming relationship between these two Grays, they were not of the same family, Asa Gray (1810–1888) having come from Oneida County in New York and Horace Gray, the son of Lieutenant Governor William Gray, a famous merchant and shipowner of Salem, from Boston. Horace Gray was much interested in horticulture and conceived the plan of the Boston Public Gardens.[16] He was also a generous donor to the Library of the Boston Society of Natural History. Where he obtained the set of Abbot drawings which he presented to the Boston Society of Natural History I have not been able as yet to learn, but they were accepted by the Society on January 18, 1837.[17] The early history of the other set of Abbot bird drawings in this country known as the Wymberley Jones de Renne set in Athens, is likewise unknown, until it was offered for sale by George S. Smith of New York in 1906.

Abbot was such a prolific worker in his art of delineating birds and insects that he was probably forced to engage assistants. Not only did he collect, preserve, and draw each specimen, but he expanded each one to its life size, even the most minute ones, and by careful study he was able to devise conditions so natural that the insects would breed and mature in captivity. All the various stages of the lepidoptera, the egg, larva, pupa, and adult were prepared, drawn, and shipped to his customers abroad. His regular price was sixpence per specimen, certainly not high considering their meticulous perfection. John Francillon, a silversmith in the Strand and owner of a large entomological collection, was the intermediary through whom Abbot's orders passed to the large museums of England and the Continent.

According to· William Swainson (1789–1855) who was a correspondent of Abbot, the inveterate collector employed one or two assistants to draw and paint, and Abbot was in the habit of retouching the work that they did. By so doing their plates often passed as Abbot's own work but, according to Swainson, the originals of the master are readily distinguished by the experienced eye. It may be that Abbot had some assistance with his ornithological work as well, although this could not have been so time-consuming as the care of hundreds of live insects each of which probably had to have its natural food in order to thrive. It seems, however, that the Boston set and the De Renne set as well as the one in London, to be discussed later, are all by the same hand since the same details of execution are visible in all three.

Rhoads points out that the De Renne set was made several years before the set formerly in the Boston Society of Natural History and now at Harvard. It is bound in three quarter red morocco; the sheets measure

---
[15] Bassett, 1938: 244–254.

[16] Barker, 1916: 156.

[17] *Jour. Boston Soc. Nat. Hist.,* 1: 498, Item 27. Original drawings of Abbot's birds. 1834-1837.

nine and one-half by thirteen inches and have not been altered since the artist worked on them. The paper, however, when I examined the set [18] in 1939, was very stained from age and dampness, and the imprint of the bird in many cases could be seen on the opposite page. Placed within the cover is a letter from W. C. Lane, of Harvard College Library, to Mr. L. L. MacKall, Librarian of the Wymberley Jones De Renne Georgia Library, on the Isle of Hope, in regard to the transfer of the drawings to the Isle of Hope. On the back of the binding, printed in gold, are the words "Birds of Georgia" and, at the bottom, "1797." All the drawings except the last one, the magnolia warbler, from which the legend is torn, bear a notation, consisting of the scientific name and the length of the bird, upon the back in red ink, probably by the artist himself.

By a comparison of this series of Abbot bird-drawings with that in Boston, Mr. Rhoads points out that Abbot described ninety-two species in the De Renne portfolio, twenty-seven of which are not present in the Boston set.

The arrangement of the De Renne series was probably done after it passed out of Abbot's hands, as there is no regard for relationship of the various species, but warblers and hawks, buntings and ducks are listed entirely at random. This series is much less carefully done.

The third set of Abbot Bird Drawings is preserved in the British Museum Department of Manuscripts. While engaged in a study of pre-Audubon naturalists who worked in America, I chanced upon this collection in 1934 and was struck by the beauty of these two volumes of exquisite work, both portraits and handwritten text, on American birds. The drawings are mounted on heavy paper with gilt edges and are bound in covers of gold-embossed green leather. By actual count at the Museum, the set contains 295 drawings, beside extra figures of the same species in some cases, but, according to the description in the catalogue of the British Museum, it contains "246 highly finished figures." They are described as "a most beautiful assemblage of the birds of Georgia in America, accompanied with descriptions and the Latin, English, and Georgian names in manuscript collected and painted from life by John Abbot of Savannah, splendidly bound by Lewis."

They are dated MDCCCIV; some sheets are water-marked Edmeads and Pine, 1802; others are water-marked J. Whatman, without date, and still others are plain cartridge paper. The first volume opens with a paragraph entitled "Remarks on the Migration of North American Birds," done in the most meticulous script, and the drawings, no less, present a pageant of skill in observation from life, as well as in execution by pencil and brush. As a rule the coloring is accurate and delicately done, although there are a few instances of too vivid coloration, as in the Blue Jay, which is bright sky-blue. All the yellows are particularly good. Abbot had

<hr>

[18] Re-examined and repaired by the writer in Apr. 1947.

Fig. 47. Red-headed Woodpecker by John Abbot. From an unpublished manuscript "Drawings and Natural History of the Birds of Georgia in America" (1804), Department of Manuscripts, Egerton MS. 1137. Courtesy of the Trustees of the British Museum.

the same difficulty in drawing the eyes that he had in the De Renne set, for here, too, the high-light is too large, and often placed forward, giving the bird an unnatural look. The Carolina paroquet (plate 26), however, is an exception and is well drawn, as is also the hairy woodpecker, showing the buffy, feathery tufts at the nostrils and the plain outer tail feathers. Occasional inaccuracies are to be found, as the skimmer (*Rynchops nigra nigra*) being represented without webbed toes and the water turkey or snakebird (*Anhinga anhinga*) with the hind toe not included in the web. This set is not a copy of the Boston set nor the De Renne set as the numbers of the Boston Society collection do not agree with those of the British Museum collection, number four (the red-shouldered hawk) in the Boston set being the fishing hawk in the British Museum collection; number ten, the snowy owl in the Boston set, being the goshawk (barred breasted buzzard) in the British Museum collection, and so on. These numbers in the De Renne set in Georgia are further different, number four being the "Loupet Titmouse," *Parus bicolor*, and number ten the "Cat Flycatcher," *Musicapa carolinensis*, now *Dumetella carolinensis*.

I had started a detailed study and comparison of this set of Abbot Drawings with those in the Harvard collection and those now owned by the University of Georgia when it became necessary to return to the United States, and two subsequent bookings for England to continue these pre-Audubon studies were cancelled with little expectation of being able to return to them for some years. Hence, only a cursory impression of the drawings was obtained, while my search for the source of these drawings and for information on John Abbot himself, before he left England, is temporarily interrupted. During the war the two volumes of Abbot Drawings were taken to two different parts of England for safety and have only recently been returned to the Museum. Through the kind cooperation of Mr. A. W. Aspital, I have a complete transcript of both volumes, which will, in time it is hoped, be published. In addition to this material I have been fortunate in having Mr. A.

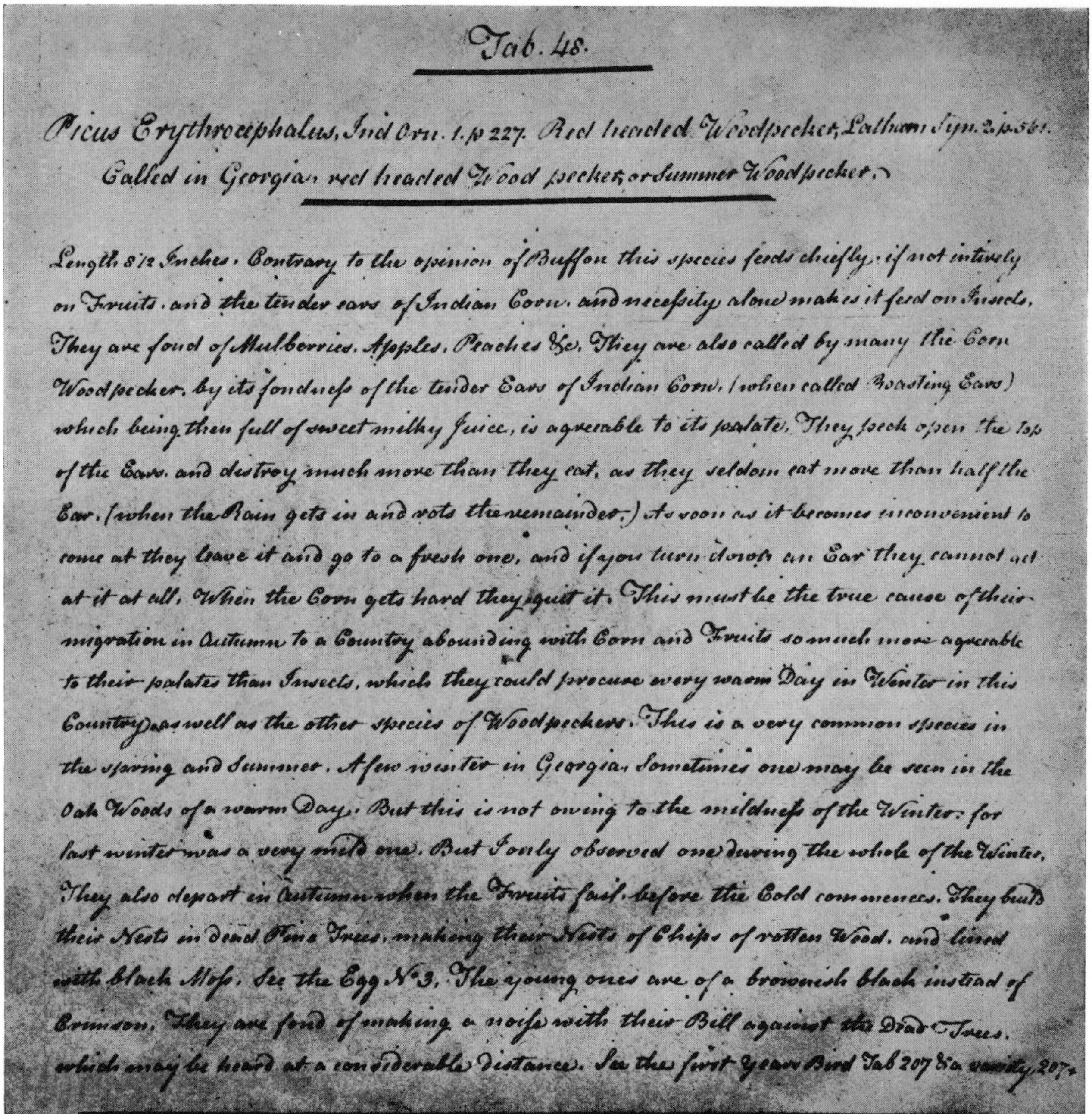
Tab. 48.

Picus Erythrocephalus, Ind Orn. 1. p 227. Red headed Woodpecker, Latham Syn. 2. p. 561.
Called in Georgia red headed Wood pecker, or Summer Woodpecker.

Length 8 1/2 Inches. Contrary to the opinion of Buffon this species feeds chiefly, if not intirely on Fruits, and the tender ears of Indian Corn, and necessity alone makes it feed on Insects. They are fond of Mulberries, Apples, Peaches &c. They are also called by many the Corn Woodpecker, by its fondness of the tender Ears of Indian Corn, (when called Roasting Ears) which being then full of sweet milky Juice, is agreeable to its palate. They peck open the top of the Ears, and destroy much more than they eat, as they seldom eat more than half the Ear, (when the Rain gets in and rots the remainder,) As soon as it becomes inconvenient to come at they leave it and go to a fresh one, and if you turn down an Ear they cannot get at it at all. When the Corn gets hard they quit it. This must be the true cause of their migration in Autumn to a Country abounding with Corn and Fruits so much more agreeable to their palates than Insects, which they could procure every warm Day in Winter in this Country, as well as the other species of Woodpeckers. This is a very common species in the spring and Summer. A few winter in Georgia, Sometimes one may be seen in the Oak Woods of a warm Day, But this is not owing to the mildness of the Winter, for last winter was a very mild one, But I only observed one during the whole of the Winter. They also depart in Autumn when the Fruits fail, before the Cold commences. They build their Nests in dead Pine Trees, making their Nests of Chips of rotten Wood, and lined with black Moss. See the Egg No 3. The young ones are of a brownish black instead of Crimson. They are fond of making a noise with their Bill against the Dead Trees, which may be heard at a considerable distance. See the first year Bird Tab 207 & a variety, 207.

FIG. 48. John Abbot's account of the Red-headed Woodpecker from Egerton Manuscript 1137. Courtesy of the Trustees of the British Museum.

J. Watson, of the Manuscript Department, look up several matters, and for many of the following notes I am indebted to him.

The few articles [19] on Abbot, including those in entomological journals and indices, emphasize Abbot's contributions to entomology and omit, or mention only cursorily, his work on birds. But, according to a letter [20] of Dr. A. A. Mumford, of the Grammar School in Manchester, to Sir L. Fletcher, of the Natural History Museum, London, dated as recently as March 23, 1917, it is stated that Abbot was employed by the Chetham Library of Manchester, between 1791 and 1802, to draw birds and spiders of Carolina and Georgia.

The only one with whom we know Abbot was closely associated is John Francillon—a name of considerable interest, for the combination of silversmith to royalty and entomologist is rather unusual. In one of the letters abstracted (folios 93–93ᵛ· dated London 25 March 1797) by Mr. Watson, John Francillon tells of meeting Mr. and Mrs. Blackburn [21] and showing them the jewels which he had prepared for the Prince of Wirtenburg. "He has appointed us his Jeweller," said Francillon, and he went on to say that "we set his picture about three months ago very richly ornamented with Diamonds, which was presented (by his desire) to the King for the Princess Royal, which she now wears on particular occasions." As an offset to these royal commissions, Francillon also took care of his large entomological cabinet, buying, selling, and exchanging specimens with scientists of England and the Continent.

It is difficult to learn anything about John Francillon. His sale catalogue, published in London in 1818, yields nothing biographical, and the London Directories, including the Trade Section, for the years 1792–1809, which Mr. Watson examined, made no reference to him. However, a group of letters by Francillon to John Leigh Philips (1761–1814) of Manchester (Additional MS 29533) makes frequent reference to these Bird Drawings. These manuscripts were presented to the British Museum by Dr. John Edward Gray (1800–1875), Assistant Zoological Keeper of the British Museum, and, in addition to the Francillon letters of present interest, they contain letters by other naturalists—Dr. Daniel Carl [22] Solander (1736–1782), John Ellis (1710?–1776), Bracy Clark (1760–1792), George Johnstone (1829–37), and others.

John Leigh Philips (1761–1814), of Manchester, was a wealthy merchant who helped many struggling naturalists from his private fortune. Hence there is some likelihood that Philips was one of John Abbot's sponsors, and that Abbot may have been an agent of the firm of J. Philips of Manchester after he settled down in America.

Be this as it may, we gather from Francillon's letters that Abbot made a set of 100 bird drawings, including eggs of many species, which, through the agency of a Mr. Bell, were sent to Mr. Philips of Manchester. They apparently went through Francillon's hands, too, for he showed them to the famous ornithologist, Dr. John Latham, then engaged in writing his *General Synopsis of Birds.* Dr. Latham pronounced the drawings so good that, as Francillon said when writing to Philips, "he [Latham] had wrote [*sic*] references to his own work on Birds opposite to each description which Mr. Abbot had wrote [*sic*] in his catalogue." The price was to be six shillings for each picture, but Francillon ventured to offer them for 5/6 each. This transaction was started in October 1792 and on November 21, 1792 Francillon wrote to Philips as follows:

I hope you will not take it amiss as I plead for a poor widow who is much in want at this time, to whom I am ordered by Mr. Abbot to pay the money too [*sic*] as soon as I could sell them. I suppose Mr. Radcliffe will not take it amiss if you mention the reason for asking him for the payment for the 100 Bird Drawings. But I shall leave it to your management whether to ask him or not.

We see from this that Abbot was helping some unfortunate, probably a relation, but whether here or in England is not clear.

Apparently Philips secured the payment promptly, for on the twenty-second of December, 1792 Francillon wrote to Philips:

I am infinitely obliged to you for your remittance of £27–10 for Mr. Abbot's 100 Drawings of Birds and the Woman whom I pay the money too [*sic*] is much obliged likewise to you and Mr. Radcliffe and the enclosed is my receipt for the same.

Mr. Francillon said also to Philips: "I have wrote to Mr. Abbot to continue to make all possible addition he can with the Eggs to them agreeable to your instruction and for the same price." This he apparently did, for the set contains 246 drawings, according to the British Museum Catalogue, and in reality there are 295 drawings in this two volume manuscript.

After the first 100 drawings had been sold to the Reverend John Radcliffe [23] they were bound at a cost of £8.

In August 1793 he sent to Francillon a collection of 1,021 sheets of Drawings of insects containing 1,664 different species or 1,833 figures with a manuscript description of the natural history of each insect. In the same letter he offered to add to the collection of 100 bird drawings "all in his power," suggesting that he would

---

[19] Kirby, 1888: 230; also Scudder, 1889: 651–654.

[20] This letter is in the Natural History Museum, South Kensington, London, and was shown to Mr. Watson in connection with this search for Abbot material.

[21] Probably the Blackburnes of Blackburne's Museum, and for whom the Blackburnian warbler was named. See *Gentleman's Mag.*, Jan.-June, 1787, and **44**: 80 of same magazine for brief accounts of John Blackburn and his sister Anne, and her Museum and Garden. Both spellings "Blackburne" and "Blackburn" are used.

[22] According to concise *Dictionary National Biography*, 1921, "Charles."

[23] A former librarian of the Chetham Library, Manchester and compiler of the two-volume work, *Bibliotheca Chethamensis.*

send a shipment in the spring of 1794. The next shipment definitely mentioned did not come until 1805. However, it apparently did not meet with approval, for on November 1, 1805, from his shop at 24 Norfolk Street, in the Strand, Francillon wrote to Mr. Philips as follows:

. . . I am sorry they are not approved of. I believe the Birds are as well drawn and colored to nature as those that have been sent to you before; the Plants, Stumps & Moss are not given as fine drawings, but only something for the Bird to stand or perch upon. If they had been good drawings of Plants &c &c it must have greatly enhanced the price, I suppose at least double. I should have liked them plain colored bare twigs, or stumps without leaves, of a brown color and very simple, which I think would have shown the Bird better and saved Him much trouble, but has [*sic*] he had began the drawings on this plan of color'd Plants, Stumps & Moss, He must now go on with it so, those who see them should only examin the Birds, and look upon the rest merely to carry or support the Bird. [folio 96 verso] I think it a great pity now (as the Gentlemen of the Library are so far advanced with them) not to have the whole as far as Mr. Abbot can find subjects to draw, which I think cannot be many more now, and it will render it complete being the drawings of one Man, and of one Country. As the Ship sailed sooner than I expected to Charleston, I ordered Him to proceed with them, not imagining there would be any alteration to the contrary, therefore if the Gent^n. of the Library should determine not to have any more, please to inform me as soon as you can after Christmas, and I write to Mr. Abbot by the first Ship that Sails. As there cannot now be a great number wanting to complete the Birds of that Country, I think it a great pity to discontinue this work, but this I must submit to your and the Gentlemens better Judgement. . . .

It is clear from subsequent letters that the "Gentlemen of the Library" for whom Philips was negotiating finally agreed to have Abbot complete the whole set of the birds of Georgia, for on January 13, 1806, Francillon wrote to Philips:

I am very much obliged to you for the pains you have taken in settling with the Gentlemen of the Library to continue to take the remainder of the Birds. I will write to Mr. Abbot by the first ships [*sic*] and request He will take more pains with the drawings in future.

On December 26, 1809 another group of forty-four more drawings of "Birds for the Manchester Library" were sent by Francillon to Philips with the bill and an urgent request that it be paid soon so that he might transfer the money to Abbot along with other sums and articles that were about to be posted.

So far it appears that these drawings were the property of the Manchester Library, but by various shifts of ownership they came at length to the Egerton Collection of the British Museum. This collection was founded in 1829 by Francis Henry Egerton VIII (1756–1829), Earl of Bridgewater. They belonged at one time to John Dent, were sold at auction in 1827, were bought again by Philip Hurd and, being sold at auction again by Evans of New Bond Street, July 30, 1845, were purchased by the British Museum for the Egerton Collection.

While these drawings and their wanderings do but little toward piecing out John Abbot's little-known biography, they are interesting as additional early ornithological work in America, and they are significant in that they offer suggestions for further lines of research. The vicissitudes through which an old manuscript passes may at any turn of the tortuous path reveal facts or leads in the author's life and work. There are, however, published remarks [24] on Abbot, which recent findings, especially his *Notes on My Life,* tend to invalidate, as for instance, that Abbot was already engaged to collect birds and spiders when he set out for America.

At that time he was only twenty-two, and apparently had no connections in America. However, contacts were soon made, and he obviously built a circle of friends and established professional connections with scientists in Europe after he emigrated. A series of Abbot letters in manuscript to William Swainson, preserved in the Linnean Society of London, gives many helpful details about Abbot after he was well established in America, but many more sources are necessary for the reconstruction of his very prolific career.

Another set of his drawings of birds has in recent years come to light in the zoological museum at Tring, which now is a part of the British Museum. It numbers 116 water color drawings of American birds and bears the date of 1827 on its handprinted and written title page.

This makes the fifth set of Abbot bird drawings that is known, three in England and two in the United States. It would seem that these must be duplicates of each other to a large extent, but I have examined them all, and only comparatively few appear to be exact copies. However, careful comparative study of all the sets may indicate further duplications. This study is now in progress.

Only one of the sets, that at the British Museum, Egerton MSS. 1137 and 1138, has a text to go with the drawings and from the study of these meticulous accounts, one can gather a clear idea of Abbot's general knowledge of birds their seasonal plumages and their life histories. Several of his records antedate those that are credited to later observers, the Swainson warbler, for example, which Abbot collected in Briar Creek Swamp, Georgia, twenty-eight years before the Reverend John Bachman got his specimen and received credit for the type. Other records by Abbot of birds now exceedingly rare or extinct in Georgia are the ivory-billed woodpecker, the scarlet ibis, the whooping crane, and the Carolina paroquet.

[24] Publisher of the *Natural history of the rarer lepidopterous insects,* collected from observations of John Abbot, 1797. Apparently Smith's published remarks about Abbot create discrepancies in Abbot's chronology. Compare Smith's statements with "Notes on My Life," published in *Lepidop. News,* March 1948. Effort has been made to verify Abbot's official connection with Chetham's Library as indicated (see p. 547) but so far unsuccessfully.

It should be pointed out in conclusion that Abbot did a prodigious amount of work on American insects including raising them in captivity and inflating the larvae.[25] Although our search is primarily in regard to his ornithological accomplishments, it is important that we become acquainted with the other aspects of his art and study.

The British Museum of Natural History has a seventeen-volume work in manuscript on American insects by Abbot. This was formerly the property of the Manuscript Department of the British Museum, but was transferred to the Natural History Museum February 21, 1883. The only published work by Abbot is the *Natural History of the Rarer Lepidopterous Insects,* collected from observations by John Abbot, published by James E. Smith (1797). It is the more important therefore that the search for Abbot material, and the careful collation thereof, go on so that the entire career of this giant of accomplishment may be known and serve as an inspiration to modern naturalists.

We have so long looked upon Audubon as the fountain-head of American ornithology, before whom little of interest or worth transpired, that it is difficult to make any readjustment of our ideas. It is true, however, that the older and more replete with earnest effort the study of birds in this country can be shown to be, the more interesting and significant it becomes. Let us, therefore, without detracting from Audubon's just fame, give fair recognition to his predecessors, especially Catesby, Abbot, and Wilson.

LOUIS JEAN PIERRE VIEILLOT, 1748–1831

In the seventeenth and eighteenth centuries when the collection and delineation of birds was a function of nearly every argosy that set sail, it was customary to write the descriptions of the specimens after the return of the expedition. Sometimes the shape and color of bill and feet were roughly indicated on field sketches, but finished drawings and accounts were seldom made while the expedition was out.

On return, the specimens were viewed by the leading authority on birds, and descriptions, aided by the study of the field sketches, were then written. Any drawings made by the artists and collectors who accompanied the trip were saved, and many such original and often unpublished drawings of birds can be seen in the British Museum and other repositories. In many cases such drawings may be the only record of the bird at the time, for skins and mounts of the early explorations were so perishable that they have long since been destroyed. When this has occurred the drawing of the bird becomes the "type" of the species.

Little attention was paid to the birds' life histories; indeed these remained practically unknown in the long

FIG. 49. Ivory-billed Woodpecker by Vieillot from *Histoire Naturelle des Oiseaux de l'Amérique septentrionale* (1807–1808). Courtesy of the Academy of Natural Sciences of Philadelphia.

epoch of descriptive ornithology, but a new approach to the study of birds through observation of their habits was intelligently worked out in elementary form by William Bartram. Since he was a home-loving naturalist, lacking the restless disposition of the explorer, he found complete satisfaction in the study of the living birds of his own garden. He it was who showed the interest and fascination to be derived from the bird in life although, of course, he often shot birds for purposes of study but not to amass a "collection."

Others who carried forward this new concept of ornithology were Louis Jean Pierre Vieillot, John Abbot, and Alexander Wilson. Under such exponents of ornithology, collections were accumulated with more thought and system. They became more comprehensive; accurate data on locality of every specimen were recorded and preservation methods were improved so that the skins and mounts could, in a measure, withstand the ravages of time. Observation of the living bird gradually came to be considered necessary in order that lifelike poses could be simulated and gradually too, it was acknowledged that familiarity with the bird's life habits would help the describer to a proper understanding of

---

[25] Jan Swannerdam (1637–1780), German entomologist, also practiced the inflation of insects by means of fine glass tubes filled with wax or other fluid.

the structure of the bird and its correct systematic position in the whole scheme of classification.

In the early days of collecting, likewise, little thought was given to the different plumages and it was not uncommon to put the male and female of the same species in different genera or even different families by mistake merely because of their dissimilar plumages.

Louis Jean Pierre Vieillot was one of the more discerning ornithologists who gave particular study to female, immature, and seasonal plumages. He was born at Yvetot, France on May 10, 1748; held a small clerical position in Paris during his young manhood, and at the same time devoted himself earnestly to the study of ornithology. But becoming dissatisfied with his slow progress in the scientific world he emigrated with his family, as did many Frenchmen of the time, to the French Colony on the West Indian island of Santo Domingo. Here he engaged in business pursuits but continued his interest in birds and collected material on West Indian species. But since he was on the proscribed list of Frenchmen wanted for military duty when the French Revolution was about to break out, he crossed over to the United States and apparently remained here for several years.

Vieillot had already done considerable taxonomic work on European birds and he identified also the plates of African birds by François Le Vaillant (1753–1824) from his expedition of 1783. Vieillot's particular skill lay in his ability to recognize generic similarities, but for some reason, his accomplishments were unappreciated and his name was always completely overshadowed by the striking social and scientific lion Georges Louis Leclerc, Comte de Buffon (1707–1788), and the equally famous Baron Cuvier (1769–1832).

Vieillot's collaborator in much of his ornithological work was Jean Baptiste Audebert (1759–1800), a French artist who had been employed by M. Gigot d'Orcy as a painter of his large zoological collection.

Vieillot and Audebert were at work on the costly book *"L'Histoire Naturelle des Colibris, Oiseaux-Mouches, Jacamares et Proméropes,"* when Audebert suddenly died in 1800, and Vieillot finished the text alone. They had intended to work together on the birds of America and make a well illustrated account, but Vieillot discontinued the project at the twenty-second livraison. The incomplete work came out in Paris under the title *Histoire Naturelle des oiseaux de l'Amérique septentrionale* in 1807–[1808]. It appeared first in two volumes with 131 plates and was reissued the following year with only 124 plates. It was published in three different formats, one with black and white plates, another with colored plates and a third on "Grand Papier Columbier Velin" of which only twelve copies were produced. Although the date of this work is given as Paris 1807–1808 there is considerable uncertainty regarding the actual publication time. According to

Charles W. Richmond [26] (1868–1932) only the first livraison came out December 1, 1807 and one may safely assume that the following twenty-one could not have come out the next year. More probably this took two or three years.

It was the practice of French publishers to issue the title page and table of contents with the first livraison thus antedating succeeding parts and causing confusion to the bibliographer and, in the case of descriptive zoology, to the worker in nomenclature.

The arrangement of Vieillot's birds also is loose, lacking systematic orderliness, not only in the absence of all water-loving birds but even in the confusion of higher groups where passerines and non-passerines are mingled.

The first volume opens with vultures, hawks, and owls, followed by the whip-poor-will and nighthawk; then passerine birds in the order of swallows, warblers, flycatchers, shrikes, vireos, blackbirds, todies, and waxwings. This concludes volume one, and it will be seen that scattering examples of the birds of Santo Domingo are introduced with the birds of North America, sometimes because they are migrants to that island, or merely because Vieillot was more familiar with the birds of the West Indies than with the birds of this large continent. Very few of the birds are mentioned by their vernacular names but such as are, are designated by the Creole appellations in modern use in Haiti.

The second volume of Vieillot treats mainly of thrushes, warblers, and woodpeckers but includes also a few wrens, the mockingbird and the thrasher, both members of the Mimidae, as well as the kinglets or Old World warblers. There are some misplacements as the water-thrush and ovenbird with the true thrushes while the bluebirds are confused with the warblers. Although these mistakes in classification occur, the individual descriptions of plumages are good, for the author states the color areas definitely and describes the various gradations of color quite accurately. Indeed he is the first of the older ornithologists to differentiate carefully between many dimorphic species having widely divergent male and female plumages. Before Vieillot, the females of many brightly colored birds such as the black-throated blue warbler were considered distinct species, but he, by careful study of the specimens collected, perceived that they were the same species. Likewise juvenal plumages interested him and he was, so far as I know, the first one to stress this phase of descriptive ornithology. His treatment of the bluebirds called by him "La fauvette bleue et rousse" male, female, and young, plates 101, 102, and 103, shows the difficult detail that he achieved not only in the drawing but also in the written descriptions. He was not familiar with the different types of scaling on the tarsi of birds and in the case of the thrushes represented them with scaled tarsi instead of the booted [28] type of tarsus which is characteristic of

---

[26] *Auk*, **16**: 327, 1899.

[28] "Booted" signifies covered with a single scale in front.

this entire family. Other minutiae, however, are well recognized as may be judged by careful descriptions of length and shape of wing and tail feathers, as in the woodpeckers, shapes of the bill, position of the nostrils and other details.

In very common birds such as the bluebird, Vieillot familiarized himself thoroughly with their habits, nests and eggs, and made a general estimate of their characteristics, but often his field observations did not compare favorably in quality with his plumage descriptions, for the reason that the former required constant field observation of the living bird while the latter was obtained by careful observation of the dead specimen. Colors and numbers of eggs are sometimes erroneously given and

scriptions which followed hard upon Vieillot. By this close juxtaposition of Vieillot to Wilson, the former ornithologist passed almost unrecognized for half a century, but it is certain that Vieillot made a substantial contribution to early American descriptive ornithology.

By an unknown series of wanderings, the copper plates of Vieillot's *Oiseaux de l'Amérique septentrionale* and of Audebert and Vieillot's *Oiseaux Dorés,* with books, objects, etc. of only incidental value, turned up in the Academy of Natural Sciences of Philadelphia probably in the 1860's. In the *Ibis* for 1865, p. 116, may be read an extract of a letter from John Cassin (1813–1869) to P. L. Sclater (1829–1913) concerning them, to the effect that Cassin was authorized to sell them at

Fig. 50. Bluebirds showing (*a*) male, (*b*) female, and (*c*) immature plumages by Louis Jean Pierre Vieillot (1748–1831) from his *Histoire Naturelle des Oiseaux de l'Amérique septentrionale* (1807–1808).

this author was obviously not familiar with any but the most common bird songs. Of the marsh wren he says: "L'endroit où elle place le berceau de sa progeniture est d'un accès si difficile que je n'ai pu y parvenir pour voir la couleur et le nombre des œufs." [29] Of the blackpoll warbler, one of the most incessant singers, he says: "Je ne puis rien dire du chant de cette espèce car elle se taît, ainsi que toutes celles qui font une courte apparition dans les Etats-Unis." [30]

Elliott Coues in his collation [31] of Vieillot set forth an appreciation of this author's contribution, for many of his species can be accepted as antedating Wilson's de-

the price of refuse or old copper. "My aversion" [to selling them], writes Cassin, "I cannot overcome and I write you in the hope a purchaser may be found. The plates are in colours, hence [there are] several plates for one bird in good condition."

In addition to Vieillot's American work, he began to publish in 1805 *Histoire naturelle des plus beaux oiseaux chanteurs de la zone torride,* in which gilding was employed in the plates. This was followed in 1816 by his *Analyse d'une nouvelle ornithologie élémentaire,* a useful and simplified classification that was widely adopted.

It is said that Vieillot's classification was communicated as early as 1813 to the Memorie della R. Academia di Torino but on investigation it was found not to have

[29] Vieillot, 1807: 56.
[30] *Ibid.,* 22.
[31] Coues, 1878–1880: 11: 596–597.

been published there. Rumor, however, indicated that it was hurried through the press in order that the publication might antedate certain papers by Cuvier (1773–1838). Vieillot's ideas of classification were used by him in his portion of the *Nouveau Dictionnaire d'Histoire Naturelle* (1816–1819) with some modifications so as to pass the criticisms of the *Analyse,* raised by another French ornithologist, C. J. Temminck (1778–1858). Another large project in which Vieillot was engaged was the continuation of J. P. Bonnaterre's [32] (1747– or 1752–1804) *Tableau encyclopédique et méthodique des Trois Règnes de la Nature, Ornithologie,* begun in 1790. Vieillot began work on this in 1820 and in 1821 undertook also the issue of the *Faune Français,* which was still unfinished in 1828. Lastly, he cooperated with P. L. Oudart (1796–?) in a work called *La Galerie des Oiseaux du Cabinet d'histoire naturelle du jardin du roi* (1820–1826).

Vieillot is the only one of the older ornithologists who may be called a prolific writer, and he stands out among all the other naturalists for his singleness of interest which, as ornithology has developed, seems to be an essential of the true ornithologist.

Vieillot had in mind first a work on the birds of Hispaniola and Santo Domingo, and during his sojourn there between 1790 and 1798 he prepared a series of bird notes, which on his return home he offered to Buffon, who was at work on his great *Histoire Naturelle des Oiseaux.* Buffon, however, had finished the part where Vieillot's contribution would have been used and he urged Vieillot to make a complete study of North American birds himself. According to Wetmore and Swales, Vieillot did not come again to America until some ten years later, but his mention of localities is so infrequent that we know little of his itinerary. He speaks often of seeing specimens in Peale's Museum, Philadelphia, and mentions also being in New York. His selection of birds for his plates indicates fairly wide travels in the southern states.

Our knowledge of Vieillot, beset as he was with misfortune, creates the feeling that he had a definitely tragic life without any success in business, and little in science. In Paris he was frustrated by jealous and successful opponents, and for this reason, emigrated to the Island of Santo Domingo. However, he must have attained a modicum of recognition, which induced some artist to cast the bust of the ornithologist now adorning the Division of Birds in the Paris Museum. A likeness of it also hung in Euxinograd Castle, Bulgaria, where Dr. Paul Leverkühn, Librarian, had assembled portraits of ornithologists from all parts of the world.

Unfortunately, Vieillot left no journals, and his biographical material is very limited. The best of these

accounts is by R. P. Lesson (1794–1849), who, in contrast to many hostile scientists, bore him a true friendship. His brief article and several other biographical notices are printed by Mr. Paul Oesher in his paper [33] on Vieillot written to commemorate the two hundredth anniversary of the ornithologist's birth.

Since his death ornithologists have come to a much greater appreciation of Vieillot's accomplishments in systematic work. No less than twenty-six generic names that he established are still in use, and thirty-two species show him to have been the original describer.

If we could work out his itinerary and collecting stations through the southern states, we would no doubt gain a better knowledge of him as a field ornithologist. His plates in the *Histoire naturelle des oiseaux de l'Amérique septentrionale* show definite understanding of seasonal and immature plumage, a point on which many ornithologists were weak.

Vieillot returned to France with his family aboard the ship *Adrastes,* leaving New Castle August 23, 1798. Ere he arrived at Bordeaux on September 28, he had lost his wife and three daughters from yellow fever.

He faced his return to Paris alone, where he bore with patience the hostility of the scientific world, yet nevertheless entered upon a long period of hard work and publication.

Vieillot's last years were spent in Rowen. His expensive writings had brought him close to real poverty but at last he finally received a small pension, so that he had at least the necessities of life. This help he enjoyed only a year before he succumbed, entirely blind, and died in June 1831.

With Vieillot we have stepped into the nineteenth century and thus approached close to the limits set for the present study. He marks the end of the French contributions before Audubon, and at the same time stands as a strong exponent of the new place finally achieved by ornithology as a science in its own right.

XIV. ALEXANDER WILSON, FATHER OF AMERICAN ORNITHOLOGY

So far in this account of American ornithology, we have traversed some two and a half centuries. Exact science had had a long, slow birth in the New World; and birds in their very nature, being so elusive and difficult to study, were the last department of natural history to receive serious attention. Only a few naturalists attempted a real survey of American bird life. Mark Catesby, the English botanical collector, produced a quaint work covering a hundred species, which he thought were "all" the birds of this vast country. Louis Jean Pierre Vieillot, a French naturalist, achieved a two-volume work on American birds with a hundred thirty-one plates. John Abbot, as we have just seen, was an

---

[32] L'Abbé Bonnaterre had first been associated with Maduyt de la Varenne, P. J. E., who discussed the birds of the *Encyclopédie méthodique.* Bonnaterre died while this second rewritten edition was in progress and L. P. Vieillot, proceeding from page 320, finished the ornithology.

[33] Oesher, *Auk* 65 (4) : 568–576, 1948.

F<small>IG</small>. 51. Portrait of Alexander Wilson in the Hall of the American Philosophical Society. Courtesy of the Frick Art Reference Library.

ornithologist of real ability, but his beautiful plates and accurate accounts live only in manuscript.

But before Catesby, and interspersed between him and Vieillot, there are many who have given us various kinds of commentaries on American birds, from the belabored verses of Jacob Steendam as *Of Birds there Is a Knavish Robbing Crew,* to the excellent summary of William Bartram, *Catalogue of Birds of North America,* in which he lists 215 species, with observations on migration, song and nesting.

With Alexander Wilson (1766–1813), however, a new era in American ornithology opens. He has given us 320 figures [1] of American birds, representing 262 species. Of these, 39 were new to science, and 23 others were sufficiently described to differentiate them from European species with which they had been confused.

How is it, then, that the name of Alexander Wilson is so unfamiliar? There are two principal reasons for this: *one,* his untimely death at forty-seven, before he had finished his proposed ten-volume work; and *two,* his close juxtaposition in point of time to the great bird artist, John James Audubon (1785–1851). The brilliance of the Audubon fame, with the inordinate com-

mercialization which it has undergone, has blinded us to the hard-working Scot who came to America in 1794 without a friend or a farthing to aid him. A man of meagre ability we are told, of unattractive personality his biographer says, with a quixotic scheme of writing and illustrating a great work on American birds; surely such a man, though a fund of genius lay hidden in his work, was no match for the talented Audubon.

It would be vain to attempt to remould the judgment of a century, but it should be pointed out that Wilson never took the position to which he was entitled both by priority and by certain scientific powers. Instead, Audubon, riding on the wave of bird interest that swept the late nineteenth century, has been lavished with praise, to the almost complete exclusion of a very able ornithologist.

Audubon's much vaunted position is due in part to a fortuitous combination of circumstances which will not concern us here; but it is necessary that Wilson be cleared of the unpleasant penumbra of inferiority from which his reputation has suffered for over a century.

It is true that his ambition was much greater than his ability to execute; but as a bird observer having the potential characteristics of a great ornithologist, he was preeminent at his time, exceeding all his predecessors, and even Audubon, in his ability to describe and interpret the living bird. There are many, no doubt, who will question this statement, but when Wilson and Audubon are compared as scientists and not as artists, Wilson's greater exactness, his patient method and his lucid and honest descriptions mark him unquestionably as the better ornithologist.

In this study the writer has been guided by Wilson's letters, his nine-volume *American Ornithology,* his poems and essays, more than by recent published biographical matter. The study has been greatly facilitated also by recent researches in Paisley, Wilson's home, in order to investigate his trial and the history of the Paisley memorials to him, together with contemporary comment on Wilson's career during his lifetime. From these sources it has been possible to glean not only factual knowledge of his life and work, but also an understanding of his background, his character, and his philosophy.

There has been a belief prevalent that Wilson came of an illiterate low-class family. This can be dismissed; for many letters of the elder Wilson indicate a man of fair education and a kindly personality. Alexander's mother was Mary McNab Wilson, a comely, devout woman of frail health. Alexander was the first son of this marriage; a sister Mary preceded him by several years. He was born July 6, 1766, in the village of Seedhills, Renfrewshire, now a section of modern industrial Paisley. In due time he attended the grammar school until his mother died in 1779. Then he was apprenticed to William Duncan, a weaver, who had married Alexander's older sister, Mary. The indenture, in manuscript, is now in the Paisley Museum, and indicates

---

[1] I am indebted to Mr. Gordon Wilson for this summary. From an unpublished dissertation, Alexander Wilson, Univ. of Indiana, 1931.

a three-year agreement. When this irksome period was over, the young Alexander gave thanks in the following lines:

> Be't kent to a' the warld in rhime
> That wi' right meikle wark and toil
> For three lang years I've ser't my time
> Whiles feasted wi' the hazel oil.

But unsuccessful and not equipped for other employment, he stooped over the wabs another four years, and then, not able to stand the confinement any longer, took to the road with a pack on his back and a few poems in his pocket, for he had begun writing verses as a boy at the loom, keeping his paper and pencil beside him, much to the annoyance of his employer.

During these last four years Alexander had matured a great deal and had begun to think about the downtrodden, underpaid workers. He grew bitter and very critical of the labor conditions, so that he was regarded by some as a person to be watched. Then again his simple verses seemed to belie that disturbing side of his nature.

He had a great desire to publish his poems, and many of them were accepted, some by the *Glasgow Advertiser* —others were privately printed, and most of them were harmless enough although there was an under-current of rebellion and satire in some of them.

In 1792 he published his best poem, called *Watty and Meg, or The Wife Reformed, a Tale,* which brought him a great deal of notoriety. It was rumored about that Robert Burns was the author. Wilson had brought it out anonymously as the characters in it were definitely persons of his acquaintance, but apparently no harm was done except to give Wilson a reading public, for several hundred thousand copies were sold. Perhaps this success gave him an inflated idea of his ability in verse, for he continued to carry samples of his writing on his journeyman trips, and would offer them to his customers with his wares. Soon after *Watty and Meg* he brought out another little book, *Poems Humorous, Satyrical and Serious.* Then having become interested in Scottish poetry, and deeming himself something of a critic, he entered a prize-winning debate in Edinburgh, on the merits of Allan Ramsay (1686–1758) and Robert Fergusson (1750–1774). His argument as to which poet had done more for Scotland's poetry took the form of a poem, *The Laurel Disputed,* delivered in the Pantheon at Edinburgh on April 14, 1791. He did not win the prize, but, according to the Scottish biographer, Alexander Grosart (1827–1899), he did "creditably."

Failure to win this prize and the obvious lack of interest in his poems among his customers caused him to reflect more sensibly on these literary ventures. He realized at last that the art of verse writing does not combine with the pedlar's life. As he expressed it in one of his letters, he was then at an age (twenty-two years) more abundant in sail than in ballast and he begged his readers to soften the rigor of their criticism.

Wilson was much more successful in writing humorous verse, sometimes sparkling with wit and again biting with its caustic racy rhyme. His friend, William M'Gavin, author of the *Protestant* (1833), remarks in his autobiography on Wilson's ability to write "clever and pungent" satire. The labor conditions, as we have said, burned in his mind, and once he had the temerity to attack a prominent manufacturer in a lampoon called the *Shark, or Lang Mills Detected.*

It is difficult to understand this indiscretion but the fact is that he sent a copy of it under assumed initials to the one against whom it was directed, with the amazing proposal that for five guineas he would suppress it. Wilson, failing to receive that amount, would find it beyond his power to stop its publication.

Justice was swift. Wilson's authorship of the piece was detected and he was imprisoned for libel. The outraged victim instituted proceedings which lasted some three months, in 1793, and although the *Shark* actually was published, Wilson in the end was shown clemency and the final sentence consisted merely in burning the offensive poem on the steps of the jail. According to M'Gavin again, the matter was not publicized and only a handful of passers-by witnessed the punishment.

This affair, combined with Wilson's general dissatisfaction with life, had a very deleterious effect on the young man. He became discouraged, despondent, and soured on his native town, and his health, never good, took a turn for the worse.

Fortunately he had many good friends to advise him, but none could dissuade him from going to America. Ruefully Wilson went back to the loom and saved every penny he could—it is said that he lived on a shilling a week while saving money for his long passage.

His young nephew, William Duncan, accompanied him, and when they arrived at Belfast to take ship they found all passenger space taken, but they secured permission to sleep on deck, and, after fifty-three days, they arrived at New Castle. Here they disembarked with their guns and luggage, and walked the rest of the way to Philadelphia, some thirty-five miles, although their ship was bound for that port. The first bird that crossed their path was a red-headed woodpecker. Wilson shot it and made a skin of it and he thought it the most beautiful bird he had ever seen.

WILSON'S EARLY YEARS IN AMERICA

A new world spread out before Wilson; strange birds, new trees and flowers stirred his love of nature, and life at once was full of promise. He scanned the landscape and settlements for possible employment, ruefully aware that weaving was the only trade he knew. Duncan got a job at the looms of James Robertson of Philadelphia; Wilson took one in a copper-plate print shop, abandoned it, and returned to weaving, in the service of Mr. Joshua Sullivan of Pennypack Creek, ten miles from Philadelphia. But the birds were on his mind; he could not forget the abundant whistling cardinals, and we see him again as a pedlar along the dusty roads, carrying a pack of silk and cotton materials. He reasoned that this way he could at least study birds. He set out for Virginia, settled for a few months at Sheppardstown, then at Bustletown, Pennsylvania, where he served as a country schoolteacher; and finally at Milestown, where he lived for several years.

Here Wilson began his self-education and worked at mathematics, surveying, German, drawing, and music. He became interested in American politics, and on the day of Jefferson's inauguration, March 4, 1801, he delivered his "Oration on Liberty," in which he displayed an amazing command of English.

Five days a week at his "pedagoging" job, studying at night to keep ahead of his pupils; surveying over week-ends to earn a little extra money; this was Wilson's schedule. Any time left he spent on drawing and studying birds, his ever-increasing delight. One vacation he seized the opportunity to take a walking trip to the Finger-Lakes region of central New York, there to visit his nephew in Ovid who by this time had been joined by his mother, Mary Duncan, and some of her other children.

The family had been considering buying a piece of land in the fertile strip of territory lying between Seneca and Cayuga lakes. Duncan made a trip there to study conditions, and on November 20, 1798, Wilson, in a letter to his father, stated that they had decided to purchase one hundred fifty acres there in the spring. The purchase was going to be in the names of Wilson and Duncan jointly, Wilson being aided by Mr. Joshua Sullivan, of Pennypack Creek, the weaver of Philadelphia who had employed him when he first came from Scotland. In a letter to Duncan, dated May 8, 1805, Wilson refers to the last hundred dollars he owed on the farm, apparently meaning his loan from Mr. Sullivan. He never lived on this farm, but gave it outright to the Duncans.

It was situated in the town of Ovid, about eighteen miles from Ithaca, and on his trip he lingered along Cayuga Lake, where hundreds of wild ducks were feeding. Of this he gives an account in his long poem, *The Foresters*. At times the farm [2] was a burden and yielded poorly, so that Duncan thought of engaging in the distilling business; he went so far as to enquire of Wilson about the prices of equipment and shipping. Again, to help out the family budget, he turned to betting, and once, at least, made money at a horse race. Apparently the farm increased in value, and in 1805 the owners were on the point of selling it, with the thought that Duncan should take up the teaching profession after Wilson had tutored him. The subsequent owners and

exact location of this farm at Ovid, New York, are being investigated.

From Milestown, Wilson went on a trip to New York, seeking employment, settling finally in Bloomfield, New Jersey. It was at this juncture of his life that he fell in love, apparently with a married woman.[3] It even seems that some unfortunate circumstances of Wilson's friendship with her were the cause of his leaving there, for on May 1, 1801, in a letter to his intimate friend, Charles Orr, a writing master of Philadelphia, he begs that Orr come to spend the week-end with him, saying:

I have matters to lay before you that have almost distracted me. Do come . . . your friendship and counsel may be of the utmost service to me. I shall not remain here long. It is impossible I can. I have now no friend but yourself, and *one* whose friendship has involved us both in ruin or threatens to do so. You will find me in the school house.

On July 12 Wilson exhorts Orr to call on a certain family, and

Get all the particulars you can, what is said of me and how Mrs. ——— is, and every other information, and write me fully . . . but mention nothing of me to anybody on any account. . . . I am very miserable on this unfortunate account.

On July 23, 1801, Wilson again refers to unhappy events in Milestown, as follows:

As to reports circulated in the neighborhood of Milestown, were I alone the subject of them, they would never disturb me, but she who loved me dearer than her own soul, whose image is ever with me, whose heart is broken for her friendship to me, she must bear all with not one friend to whom she dare unbosom her sorrows. Of all the events of my life nothing gives me such inexpressible misery as this. O my dear friend, if you can hear anything of her real situation, and whatever it is disguise nothing to me.

Without doubt in this hopeless friendship we find the explanation of Wilson's complete dissatisfaction with his teaching. He was forced to teach because he was reduced as he said to "three eleven-penny bits"; and he describes the village as "a settlement of canting, preaching, praying, sniveling ignorant Presbyterians." He calls attention to the large salary they paid their minister, and the wretched pittance they gave him, the village schoolmaster. Said Wilson, "I have no company and live unknowing and unknown. I have lost all relish for this country, and if Heaven spares me I shall soon see the shores of old Caledonia."

On August 7 of the same year, Wilson was still entreating his friend to get some intelligence for him, in these words:

I entreat you to keep me on the rack no longer. Can you not spare *one* day to oblige me so much? Collect every information you can, but drop not a hint that you know anything of me. If it were possible you could see *her*, or any one who *had*, it would be an unspeakable satisfaction to me.

---

[2] Through the kindness of Mr. J. G. Crisfield, County Clerk of Seneca County, New York, I learn that Liber A, p. 183, shows a deed executed by Andrew Dunlap to William Duncan, dated 1801, recorded February 9, 1805, conveying premises situated in the town of Ovid, containing 100 acres. The name of Alexander Wilson does not appear.

[3] According to Wilson's commentators, this woman was married, although there is not definite proof of this. Wilson refers in some letters to a "Mrs. ———," but we should not assume from this alone that this woman was the one in question.

My dear Orr, the world is lost forever to me and I to the world. No time nor distance can ever banish her image from my mind. It is for ever present with me, and my heart is broken with the most melancholy reflexions. Whatever you may think of me, my dear friend, do not refuse me this favour to know how she is.

Evidently Orr did not attend to Wilson's entreaties with the promptness that Wilson expected, and a near breach between the friends occurred; but finally, after another visit from Orr, Wilson withdrew his accusations and the wound was healed. Who the woman of Miles-town was it is not possible to determine from the letters at hand, but certain it is that she made a profound impression on Wilson during his Milestown residence, and caused him to turn more and more to poetry. He wrote occasional poems for the *Newark Centinel,* of which the *Dominie,* in imitation of Goldsmith's *Deserted Village,* is one. *My Land-Lady's Nose,* of rather uncouth stamp, reflects some of his bitter experience. He read a good deal from the Scottish pastoral poets and bards, and became fired with the idea of making himself famous and beloved for his own verses of the people, and Scotland's rugged landscape. He wrote to Orr on July 25, 1802:

My heart swells, my soul rises to an elevation I cannot express to think that I may yet produce some of these glowing wilds of rural scenery . . . that my name will be familiar in farms and cottages, in circles of taste and at scenes of merriment five hundred years hence, when the statutes of bloody ambition are mouldered and forgotten. By heavens! The idea is transporting and such a recompense is worth all the misfortunes, penury, and deprivations here that the most wretched sons of science have ever suffered.

We cannot mistake these vaunted words, which point to one of Wilson's greatest handicaps, a vain and consuming thirst for fame. He loved poetry and he loved nature, and attempted to combine these two interests to produce writings of lasting worth. But his poetic craftsmanship was too mediocre, and his psychological responses were simple and undeveloped. He was unequipped to be a poet, but if he could have realized this fact and directed his education toward natural history, a great zoologist probably would have evolved.

It was at Wilson's next post of duty that the general trend of his life took a turn for the better. After the stormy year in Bloomfield, he was employed at a school near Gray's Ferry, and, although, in his own words, he recommended "that painful profession with the same sullen resignation that a prisoner re-enters his dungeon or a malefactor mounts the scaffold," he was soon to be comparatively happy in a friendship with the famous naturalist, William Bartram. Here Wilson was free to study in the Bartram library, and he spent much time on the works of Mark Catesby and George Edwards, even then rather old and out of date. Already Wilson, from his long journeys on foot, had learned American birds well enough to detect numerous errors in these authors. All these findings he discussed with Bartram. He worked untiringly at drawing and painting, often by candle-light in his small room, and submitted specimens

Cedar Bird

Fig. 52. Cedar Waxwing by Alexander Wilson. His first colored drawing of an American bird. Courtesy of Mr. and Mrs. John A. Griswold. Note the inscription to Mrs. Lawson.

of his art to Bartram for criticism. Any available daylight hours were spent in the field obtaining specimens for his collection of birds, which he had been building up since the day he shot the red-headed woodpecker. Gradually he convinced himself that he would write a great work on American birds, and illustrate it with his own drawings.

He noted that George Edwards had engraved his plates, and taking heart from this, tried to learn how to draw and etch. Alexander Lawson (1772–1846), a fellow countryman, was his tutor, and Wilson soon acquired, as he said, an insatiable "itch" for drawing. Although keen in observation, he was not familiar with the names of the birds. On March 29, 1804, he said in a letter to Bartram,

I have now got my collection of native birds considerably enlarged; and shall endeavor, if possible, to obtain all the smaller ones this summer. Be pleased to mark on the drawings with a pencil the names of each bird, as, except three or four, I do not know them.

The only ornithological work Wilson owned was Thomas Bewick's (1753–1858) *British Birds.* Thomas Say (1787–1834) lent him William Turton's (1762–1835) *Linnaeus* (1806), and the Philadelphia library provided him with John Latham's *Synopsis of Birds* (1781–1785). Poverty alone was the reason for his meagre equipment, and we should banish from our minds all ready-made estimates of Wilson that present him as a persistent, but dull, student of birds. Although Wilson's schooling ceased at the green age of thirteen years, he continued his self-education to the end of his life, and his interests were not narrowed to birds alone. He had a wide interest in people; he studied the various sections of the United States with a critical and appraising eye, though never could he be called "worldly."

In a letter to Lawson, his tutor, Wilson said:

While in New York I had the curiosity to call on the celebrated author [4] of the *Rights of Man* [1791]. He lives in Greenwich, a short way from the city. In the only decent apartment of a small, indifferent-looking frame house I found this extraordinary man sitting wrapped in a night-gown, the table before him covered with newspapers, with pen and ink beside him. Paine's face would have excellently suited the character of Bardolph,[5] but the penetration and intelligence of his eye bespeak the man of genius and of the world.

Such are not the remarks of an uncultivated person.

These matters indicate a much more bookish and versatile man than Wilson is popularly conceived to be. He really had read widely, and knew the need for such a book as he wanted to write; and while he was pondering the Edwards and Catesby tomes, he noticed inaccuracies which, from his own field experience, he could correct. Wilson had no profession, only the trade of weaving, which he roundly hated. He felt almost the same antipathy toward the schoolmaster's job. He had become more and more a wandering naturalist, and he was seeking a definite field on which to concentrate and put to work his entire dynamic energy.

His friendship with Bartram was a stimulant to his studies and writing, while Alexander Lawson taught him the "bewitching art" of drawing, coloring, and engraving. Wilson with difficulty tore himself away from these new interests to pursue his poetry, which had slipped to second place in his affections; it was an even greater struggle to return each day to the irksome task of "pedagoging."

WILSON UNDER BARTRAM'S INFLUENCE

William Bartram (1739–1823) undoubtedly was a steadying influence in Wilson's life. Every conversation with this well-seasoned naturalist was fresh inspiration to him; Bartram provided him with many new specimens; also the Bartram home was a Mecca for visiting scientists and collectors from Europe. Wilson at last had the opportunity to mingle with the learned and the cultured.

He continued to teach in the Kingsessing School, which became successful and even crowded with pupils, so that all the daylight hours, and often the evening hours, were more than full. Thus Wilson's natural

history studies often had to be confined to the night, and many of his drawings were done by candle-light. On May 1, 1804, he sent another shipment of bird drawings to Bartram, and announced that these would be the last for some time, as he was still eager to write poetry. The *Solitary Tutor* and *The Rural Walk,* published in the *Literary Magazine,* belong to this period. However, the *American Ornithology* was taking form in his mind.

Birds from the St. Lawrence to the mouth of the Mississippi, and from the Atlantic to the interior of Louisiana, were his goal. To his engraver he said, "Don't throw cold water on my notion, quixotic as it may appear. I have so long been accustomed to the building of airy castles and brain windmills that it has become one of my earthly comforts, a sort of rough bone that amuses me when sated with the dull drudgery of life."

During 1804, starting out in October, Wilson made his second long journey on foot, a trip to Niagara Falls, taking with him his nephew, William Duncan, and a man whom he called Isaac, a faint-hearted traveller who needed constant encouragement. Wilson's endurance and determination far exceeded his companions'. They finally left him, but he went on, completing the journey of some twelve hundred miles in fifty-nine days, covering forty-seven miles the last day. *The Foresters* is the poetic account of this journey, but it is a drab, prosaic effort, of two thousand eighteen lines, all heroic couplets. The author's literary reputation was little enhanced by this tedious recital of hardship, but he garnered a vast amount of new material about birds, which was promptly built into his plan for an American ornithology. Two specimens of his bird drawings and a drawing of the Falls were sent to Thomas Jefferson, from whom he received a kindly letter of thanks. Jefferson displayed a fair knowledge of birds, and offered Wilson a further query regarding a bird [6] that had long evaded him. This spurred Wilson to redouble his efforts, that he might have some helpful notes to transmit to Jefferson, for he was always glad to assist, and eager to foster contacts that might further his own schemes of travel and study.

His next plan was to offer himself as a collector on the Zebulon Pike (1779–1813) Expedition to the Mississippi in 1806, and, on Bartram's advice, Wilson wrote to President Jefferson (1743–1826), giving a full account of his qualifications. Apparently this letter was never received, and Jefferson's failure to appoint Wilson to the Expedition has been elaborated by some commentators to intensify Wilson's supposedly unfortunate and unhappy state, and to impute to Jefferson a desire to discourage Wilson.

Wilson's letters at this time, however, do not appear at all despondent. His health was much better; he was exceedingly busy; he was associating with cultured people of kindred interests; and he was full of optimistic

---

[4] Thomas Paine (1737–1809) in reply to Burke's *Reflexions on the French Revolution* (1790).

[5] Falstaff's follower, the red-faced Bardolph in Shakespeare's Henry IV.

[6] This bird was probably the towhee, often called ground robin.

plans for his future career. He was disappointed, it is true, not to go on the Pike Expedition, but lost no time in making other plans to travel, although, with his usual prudence in money matters, he thought it best to wait until he could afford it.

Further success was now in store for him, for hard upon his failure to obtain the appointment by the President came an offer to become assistant editor of *Rees New Cyclopedia.*[7] This meant a great deal of writing and study, since he was to cover not only ornithology, but zoology, botany, geology, and in general to revise and render more full and interesting all articles on America. Wilson resigned his teaching position and, in April 1806, took up his residence in Philadelphia. This was difficult for him, immured as he was among books, with nothing to look at but walls and chimneys, and the constant noise of the city in his ears. Declared Wilson, "If I don't launch into the woods and fields oftener than I have done these twelve months, may I be transformed into a street musician." His flute and violin were often a comfort; or again he dashed out into the country early in the morning in pursuit of birds. Nothing was too strenuous for him, though, actually, his health was far from good.

In his letter to Jefferson he had declared that he had a constitution that waxed strong by its privations and fatigues; and of exercise he said, "Moderate, nay, even pretty severe exercise is the best medicine in the world for sedentary people."

He remained steadily at his new post of assistant editor for a year, but did not abate his efforts to accumulate a series of bird plates and a knowledge of the haunts and habits of the common species. In fact, when Wilson accepted the assistant editorship of *Rees New Cyclopedia* under Mr. Samuel E. Bradford, to whose two young sons he served as tutor, he saw in his move a possible outlet for his ornithology. This prospect, plus the substantial salary of $900 per annum, caused Wilson to tackle his new job with zeal and determination.

THE AMERICAN ORNITHOLOGY

From now on the book rapidly took form; Bradford agreed to publish it, and as early as 1807 a prospectus of the whole work was ready for distribution. Wilson sent a copy at once to Bartram for criticism, and received a letter of approval within three days. With the main format of the book well in mind, he began to think on other details, and nomenclature was one matter that disturbed him. Specific names, he contended, should be "expressive of some peculiarity in color, conformation or habit"; he also thought that "if it (a specific name) will equally well apply to two different species it is certainly an improper one." He questioned, therefore, that "migratorius" was a good name for the robin, since that specific name would fit any bird that migrates. Similar problems in other groups of birds occurred to him, and

he begged that Bartram would advise him whether he should hazard a new name or, by using a given name, sanction what he did not approve of.

He did not venture to make any radical changes in nomenclature, but it is noteworthy that he had such a good understanding of the principles of zoological nomenclature despite the fact that he had had no training in Latin nor in natural philosophy.

The first volume of *American Ornithology* was launched in September 1808. At the same time Wilson set out on his first soliciting trip through the state, a sample copy of his book in one arm and his faithful fowling-piece across his shoulder. Though sensitive to his difficult position in touring the country with his book, "like a beggar with his bantling," he preserved a friendly, dignified and sophisticated interest in all persons who examined it. Two weeks later found him in Boston, and in writing to a friend on October 10, he said that from thousands of persons who had examined the book, he had heard "nothing but expressions of the highest admiration and esteem." He cautioned himself against being too confident, but felt safe in saying, "If I have been mistaken in publishing a work too good for the country, it is a fault not likely to be soon repeated." Prophetic words!

Let us pause in this fast-moving period of Wilson's life to gain some understanding of the plan and execution of his *American Ornithology*.

Wilson first intended his long treatise on American birds to occupy ten volumes, six to be concerned with land birds and four with water birds. His introduction to Volume I sets forth his simple purpose: "To furnish instruction blended with amusement, to correct numerous errors by European writers, and to draw the attention of fellow citizens from the discordant jarrings of politics to a contemplation of the grandeur, harmony and wonder of Nature." Lastly, he appends a table of the orders and genera of birds, as worked out by the great English ornithologist, John Latham, which, in general, was the system that Wilson used.

Lucrative motive is not to be found in Wilson, but in its place there is a consuming desire to learn, combined with an equally strong desire to communicate his knowledge and interest to others, and thereby win recognition. Deploring the neglect or want of opportunity in many writers of observing the living bird in its unconfined state, he sounds the secret of his own success with the words, "personal intimacy." For, although Wilson was an inveterate collector of birds, he was no less a meticulous student of the plumage, haunts, habits and manners of every bird he saw.

The arrangement of the plates shows little regard for family relationships, in which, of course, Wilson was not well-versed. He chose for his first plate a trio of common but beautiful birds that everyone knew, the blue jay, the Baltimore oriole, and the goldfinch. These birds represent three widely different families, the crows, the blackbirds, and the sparrows, and, in addition to

---

[7] Formerly *Ephraim Chambers Cyclopedia.*

(Drawn from Nature by A. Wilson.)

Engraved by A. Lawson

1. Great Horned Owl. 2. Barn O. 3. Meadow Mouse. 4. Red Bat. 5. Small Headed Flycatcher. 6. Hawk Owl.

FIG. 53. A plate from Wilson's *American Ornithology* (1808–1814). Reduced 5/13.

these, in Volume I there are also birds representing the following families: wood warblers, thrushes, titmice, waxwings, shrikes, wrens, woodpeckers, larks, and fly-catchers.

The succeeding volumes are, likewise, heterogeneous in content, owing no doubt to the fact that Wilson made the plates of the birds in the order in which he obtained the specimens. Many of his birds went to Peale's Museum, of Philadelphia, which was founded by Charles Willson Peale (1741–1827), and his sons in 1784, and most of Wilson's accounts give the number of the specimen in the Peale Museum collection. In addition to this, references are given to Linnaeus's works in the synonymy which is at the head of each account.

We cannot commend Wilson for well-ordered, systematic arrangement of his subject matter, but we marvel at his separate accounts. Each one is a gem of literary prose, its flow of language graphic and interesting; and each is packed with a fund of reliable information that proves the author an excellent field observer. To enliven these essays the author frequently tells of birds he kept in capitivity; for instance, his ivory-billed woodpecker, which he wing-tipped and took home for a pet. Arriving at the inn, enveloped in his cloak whence issued baby-like cries, he asked for a room for himself and infant. At the appropriate moment, with proper tenderness, he drew out the great woodpecker from under his coat, to the loud consternation of the crowd.

He left the bird in his room while he went out hunting the next day, and returned to find that it had demolished the wall and a mahogany table and was about to escape. Wilson's experiences with his pet paroquet likewise furnish many delightful touches in his *Ornithology*.

By a study of the forgotten prefaces of these volumes, it is possible to learn more about the progress of the work; and the author's hopes, plans and difficulties in connection with its execution.

In Volume 2, for instance, with swiftly developing pride in things American, he tells of some beautiful ochres from the laboratory of Messrs. Peale and son, of the Museum above-mentioned, which he had substituted in place of certain French products with excellent soft results. Here also he solicits specimens and correspondence from interested parties, and gives directions for the care of birds in the flesh, for, as he said,

By such combined exertions and reciprocity of information we shall do honour to this branch of science and be enabled to escape in part that transatlantic and humiliating reproach of being obliged to apply to Europe for an account and description of the productions of our own country.

The following excerpt from Volume 2 shows a great advance in Wilson's method of preparing specimens over methods that obtained before. Note the author's regard for accuracy.

As soon as the bird is shot, let *memoranda* be taken of the length, the breadth (measuring from tip to tip of the expanded wings), color of the eyes, bills, legs and feet, and such particulars of its manner, etc., as may be known. Make

a longitudinal incision under the wing, sufficiently large to admit the body to be taken out; disjoint the wing close to the body under the skin, and endeavour with a pair of scissors or penknife to reach the neck, which cut off; pass the skin carefully over to the other wing, which also disjoint and separate from the body, then over the whole body and thighs, which last cut off close to the knees; lastly, separate the whole skin from the body at the roots of the tail feathers, which must not be injured. Return to the neck and carefully pass the skin to, and beyond, the eyes, which scoop out; cut off the neck close to the skull, penetrate this way with your knife into the brain, which scrape completely out; dissect all the fleshy parts from the head, wings, and skin; rub the whole inside with a solution of arsenic, sprinkle some of the same into the cavity of the brain, throat, etc.; stuff the vacuity of the brain and eyes with cotton to its proper size and form, sew up the longitudinal incision, and, having carefully arranged the whole plumage, sprinkle it outwardly with a little powdered arsenic; place it in a close box, into which some camphor has been put, and cover it with cotton or ground tobacco. In the whole operation, the greatest care must be taken not to soil the plumage with blood.

If arsenic cannot conveniently be had, common salt may be substituted.

Thus Wilson forged ahead, collecting, working on his engraving, doing his writing; and directing the coloring. And whenever he had a half hour to spare he slipped out to the woods and fields to observe or collect.

His first soliciting trip had taken him through New England and down through the coastal cities to the deep South. After three months he attained his goal of two hundred fifty subscribers, and felt encouraged by favorable comments on his book, in the Southern paper, *Republican*. The environs of Charleston, Savannah, and Georgetown, and the dark, mysterious waters of the Santee River all carried him back to his predecessor, Mark Catesby, separated from him by some four score years. He had been reading Catesby's great tomes, *The Natural History of Carolina, Florida and the Bahama Islands,* in Bartram's home and, as he traversed some of this country himself, he was struck by Catesby's knowledge of the rich flora of which he knew so little; but he felt that Catesby had missed many of the birds.

Down in Savannah he met another naturalist, John Abbot, painter of birds and insects, then resident there for three years. Abbot was affable and glad to assist him, and they exchanged some letters in regard to their bird collections. The people, however, were unsatisfying to Wilson with his Spartan outlook on life. Said he of the persons he wished to interview: "At nine they are in bed; at ten breakfasting—dressing at eleven—gone out at noon and not visible till ten the next morning." Indolence and dissipation among the wealthy characterized every community, while the slightest service, he said, was done by slovenly blacks. In Savannah a fever attacked the ornithologist, but since he intended to return to New York anyway by ship, he said, with a gibe at his indisposition, "I hope the sea air and sea-sickness will carry it off."

Soon after his return to Philadelphia Wilson, with justifiable pride, packed up a copy of his first volume and sent it by a friend, Mr. David Brown, to his venerable father in Paisley.

By autumn of the same year he was deep in plans for a long contemplated trip down the Ohio. The journey across Pennsylvania was to be made on foot, a dollar a day the maximum cost, this being ample for his simple needs, and walking being the most healthful mode of travel.

Many stops were made, at Lancaster, Hanover, Chambersburg, Shippensburg, Greenburg, and Pittsburgh. He spent four days in Pittsburgh and secured nineteen subscribers [8] among the city's most prominent residents. Here he purchased his small skiff, which he christened *The Ornithologist,* laid in a store of biscuit and cheese, tucked in a gift bottle of cordial, and a tin can for bailing the boat and drinking from the river. In high hopes, flouting all advice against going alone, the intrepid oarsman launched downstream for Cincinnati.

Steubenville, Charlestown, Wheeling, Marietta, were other places visited, with many side excursions after birds into the unknown wilderness. This trip extended from February 24 to March 17, 1810, when he moored his boat safely near the rapids of the Ohio at Bear Grass Creek after a total voyage of 720 miles. The town of Louisville could be dimly seen from the river. He groped his way across the marsh, and late that Saturday night entered the Indian Queen Tavern, carrying his satchel, gun, and paroquet, and asked for a room.

He had four letters of introduction to persons in Louisville, and spent five days there looking up these prospects and collecting birds. It is a singular coincidence that John James Audubon (1785–1851), who many years later became famous for his bird paintings, also was living at this tavern with his wife and year-old son; but it was not here that the two painters of birds met.

Monday morning, March 19, 1810, Wilson chanced to find Audubon in his frontier store. He and his friend, Ferdinand Rosier (1777–1864), had started out ambitiously in 1807 intending to have a high-class importing business. But the Embargo Act of President Jefferson, effective December 22, 1807, put a stop to all importations, and in 1810 the store was having but indifferent success.

Assuredly Wilson had no letter of introduction to this obscure shopkeeper, and likewise he had not the slightest knowledge that Audubon was anything but just another merchant. Carrying his two sample volumes of his work, Wilson, the itinerant ornithologist, came quickly to the purpose of his visit and opened his books upon the counter. He explained the scope of the work he was doing and asked whether Audubon would like to subscribe.

The latter had been turning the pages, and according to his story was "surprised and gratified at the sight of the volumes," and was about to sign his name when

[8] *The Cardinal,* 6–13, July 1925.

abruptly from the next room came his partner's voice in French:

"But my dear Audubon, what induces you to subscribe to this work? Your drawings are certainly far better, and again you must know as much of the habits of American birds as this gentleman."

The bottom fell out of Wilson's world at that moment. He was stunned. Two years before, in Boston, he had written to a friend (October 10, 1808), "If I have been mistaken in publishing a work too good for the country, it is a fault *not likely to be soon repeated.*" But he managed to ask whether Audubon had many drawings of birds. To this Audubon said,

I rose, took down a large portfolio, laid it on the table, and showed him, as I would you, kind reader or any other person fond of such subjects, the whole of the contents with the same patience that he had shewed me his own engravings.

But whether Mr. Wilson understood French or not, or if the suddenness with which I paused, disappointed him, I cannot tell, but I clearly perceived that he was not pleased. Vanity and the encomiums of my friend prevented me from subscribing.

Audubon, with pen poised to write his name to Wilsons' list, had reconsidered because his partner, with strange lack of courtesy, interrupted *in a foreign tongue,* to the detriment of an earnest naturalist under his roof. Wilson probably was not fluent in French, but it would take an obtuse listener indeed not to gather the meaning of Rosier's remarks; beside this Wilson had for years pored over Mark Catesby's *Natural History,* which was published in parallel columns of French and English; It is more than likely that he gathered the full meaning of Rosier's interpolation.

Many of Wilson's commentators, with the exception of George Ord, Wilson's friend and companion on his later travels, have displayed a rather cheap concern for Wilson's misfortunes. They have seized upon his poverty, his lack of education, his melancholic disposition, even his personal appearance, to construct their superficially conceived notion of him.

Take Audubon's first impression of him: "One fair morning I was surprised by the sudden entrance into our counting room (at Louisville) of Mr. Alexander Wilson, the celebrated author of the American Ornithology, of whose existence I had never until that moment been apprised." Poor Wilson! How could he have been called "celebrated?" And what does Audubon mean when he says "of whose existence I had never until that moment been apprised." Does he mean the *American Ornithology,* or the existence of the author? In all probability he means the author. But a man with a parrot staying at the same inn, playing Scottish airs on his flute, could not be entirely obscure.

Audubon continues his account of their meeting: "How well do I remember him as he then walked up to me. His long rather hooked nose, the keenness of his eyes, and his prominent cheek bones stamped his countenance with a peculiar character." Not content with drawing a word picture of a homely man, Audubon drew attention to his attire, which "was not of a kind usually seen in that part of the country." We wonder what the well-dressed man of Louisville wore in 1810; but Wilson was after birds, not frontier society.

After the two pioneer ornithologists had looked through Audubon's portfolio, Audubon continues his account of their meeting: "His surprise appeared great as he told me he never had the most distant idea that any other individual was engaged in forming such a collection."

Further along in his story he tells his readers, in the same precise language, that he presented Wilson to his wife and friends, and seeing that he (Wilson) was "all enthusiasm," Audubon says "I exerted myself as much as was in my power to procure for him the specimens which he wanted." According to Audubon they hunted together and obtained birds which Wilson had never before seen. "But reader," he says, "I did not subscribe to this work for even at that time my collection was greater than his."

We do not know the size of the collection Audubon showed Wilson, but it was probably impressive. He says that in 1805 and 1806, when he visited his childhood home at Couëron, France, he made drawings of about two hundred species of birds, all of which he brought to America and gave to his wife. We know also from his biographer, Francis Herrick (1858–1940), that he had some twenty dated pictures of American birds made between 1805 and 1810, and these also may have been shown to Wilson. Unfortunately we have no way of knowing exactly what Wilson wrote in his journal that night. His diary is not known except as fragmentary quotations used by George Ord in his biography of Wilson (1814), and the entries are very brief: [8a]

March 19 (the day Wilson called on Audubon)
Rambling round the town with my gun; examined Mr. ————'s drawings in crayons—very good. Saw two new birds he had, both Motacillae
March 20.
Set out this afternoon with the gun—killed nothing new. [People in taverns here devour their meals. Many shopkeepers board in taverns also boatmen, land speculators merchants &c.] *No naturalist to keep me company.*
March 21.
Went out shooting this afternoon with Mr. A. Saw a number of Sandhill Cranes. Pigeons numerous.
March 22.
March 23.
Packed up my things which I left in the care of a merchant here, to be sent on to Lexington; and having parted with great regret with my paroquet to the gentleman of the tavern, I bade adieu to Louisville, to which place I had four letters of recommendation and was taught to expect much of everything there, but neither received one act of civility from those to whom I was recommended, one subscriber, nor *one new bird;* though I delivered my letters, ransacked the woods repeatedly and visited all the characters likely

to subscribe. *Science or literature has not one friend in this place.*

Surely something is awry here; Wilson's account of his stay in Louisville does not tally with Audubon's; and it is impossible to get at the exact truth of this meeting of the two pioneers in ornithology unless we can find Wilson's journal. This has been given up as lost or destroyed.[9]

Continuing with Audubon's account of the meeting, he says that Wilson asked to borrow a few of his drawings during his stay in Louisville. Audubon further says that he offered to let Wilson publish the "results of his researches," merely on condition that what he [Audubon] had drawn or might afterwards draw and send to him, should be mentioned in his [Wilson's] work as coming "from my [Audubon's] pencil."

Audubon continues:

I offered to open a correspondence with him, which I thought might prove beneficial to us both. He made no reply to either proposal and before many days had elapsed, left Louisville, on his way to New Orleans, little knowing how much his talents were appreciated in our little town, at least by myself and my friends.

In regard to Audubon and his story, we should take into account that his meeting with Wilson took place nearly twenty years before he wrote it. This he did in Edinburgh far removed in time and space from the store in frontier Louisville. Audubon had come to Europe in April, 1830 to engage with Mrs. Audubon in a canvassing tour.

Everything augured well for him. As soon as he arrived in London he learned that he had been elected to the Royal Society on the eighteenth of March. The *Birds of America* was in process of being published, having started with Volume I, Parts 1–22, pl. i-cx, 1827–1830. With the most distinguished societies of England and America doing him homage, it is not surprising that Audubon remembered but imperfectly their encounter and in the glow of his new fame wrote his studied little fabric of conceits about Wilson.

Even at the time, and much more in retrospect, it was obvious that Audubon's drawings were much better than Wilson's. It is no doubt true that Audubon had no definite plans to publish them when he met Wilson, being then too busy with his mercantile interests; furthermore he was still young, only twenty-five, nineteen years the junior of Alexander. Whether Audubon in cool, considered sincerity offered to let Wilson publish his drawings seems unlikely, although it might have been so impossible a venture for Wilson that Audubon ran no risk of becoming involved.

It seems much more probable that Wilson, having divulged his scheme and laid it frankly on the counter there in Louisville, was the source of Audubon's first flutter of professional ego as an ornithologist.

[8a] Square brackets are from Charles Waterton who once stated that he had examined Wilson's Journal.

[9] Herrick, 1938: **1**: 224.

There he was not too well set up in business; he was not qualified for business, and never liked it. More and more he was letting Rosier serve behind the counter, while he tramped the country for birds.

But we must leave the Audubon story now and follow Wilson as he drearily left Louisville. He sold his boat in the town, and parted with his pet paroquet to the keeper of the inn. He then set forth on horseback southward into Tennessee, the memory of Audubon's drawings a gnawing dread in his heart.

Wilson's ultimate goal was New Orleans, 780 miles through the wilderness. Not one mention is made of his meeting with Audubon in the letters he wrote on this trip—one to Lawson from Lexington; another from Nashville on April 28, both giving fine accounts of his other adventures. On May 1, he wrote from Nashville to Miss Sarah Miller, a woman in Philadelphia whom, perhaps, he intended to marry.[9a] This letter describes the slovenly natives, their neglect of their starving animals, and the coarseness of the women, who flogged their negroes. His complete dissatisfaction with Kentucky is lightened with humorous touches about his traveling companions: a zealous Methodist, whom he overtook on the road, who tried to convert Wilson as they jogged along, singing hymns. If he became too vehement, says Wilson, all he had to do was to gallop down the first decline and by the time the preacher caught up with him, the thread of his discourse was broken.

Wilson left him in Nashville to post a parcel of drawings to Lawson, the result of every moment of leisure he could obtain. Many of these birds were entirely new, with full descriptions, but unfortunately this shipment was lost.

He then took up with a good Presbyterian and spent five days in his hospitable home, scouring the flat country around Bowling Green for new birds and earning his keep by giving drawing lessons to the daughters of the house. His host, he said, would have gladly kept him a month, but Wilson pressed on to Natchez, Mississippi Territory, and here sold twelve subscriptions to his book.

At Natchez, which he reached about May 18, he contemplated a western extension of his journey to Saint Louis. Heavy rains, however, and the fact that the migration was already far advanced persuaded him to head through the Chukkasaw and Chocktaw territory to New Orleans.

This was to be the supreme test of his endurance, and he prepared well for the dangers: a fine, new horse, a loaded pistol in each pocket, a loaded fowling piece across his shoulder, a pound of gunpowder in his flask, and five pounds of shot in his belt. Food seemed the least of his concern; biscuit and dried beef the only items mentioned.

[9a] There seems to be insufficient evidence for this statement.

Wilson returned from this southwestern trip September 2, 1810. A prodigious amount of work lay ahead of him for only two volumes of the proposed ten had been published. Such, however, was his determination that the next four volumes came out during 1811 and 1812, at the rate of two a year, and by April, 1813 the seventh was ready.

It was at this time that Wilson reduced the intended ten volumes to nine, dismissed the last of his colorists and planned to do more and more of the work himself. The most meticulous care went into his labor in order that his patrons would detect no diminution of the author's effort nor in the elegance of the work.

Letters of this period indicate a speeding up of travels, though in shorter trips, mostly to the seashore, after water birds, and close application to writing and drawing while at home.

Even in this harried time, as seen by his letter of June 6, 1812, to Mr. F. A. Michaux (1770–1855), Wilson did not forget that he had promised to help the French botanist to publish his great work on American forest trees. He had taken the matter up with Bradford and Inskeep, and had had one of his friends translate parts of it into English for Mr. Bartram's inspection, for Bartram was the most influential figure in the American botanical field. Michaux had collected many American birds and had even made some bird drawings, for which Wilson expressed admiration. In like manner, Wilson had shown genuine interest in John Abbot of Georgia and his promising ornithological studies. Wilson's complete silence on Audubon over a period of two years is, therefore, pregnant with meaning, and we are in no wise obligated to accept Audubon's prolix rationalization of his attitude toward Wilson when the two naturalists met under his roof in frontier Louisville.

We cannot but feel that Wilson, desperate with disappointment, sensed his condition, and took the only course left to him—bearing down more and more heavily upon himself ere he forever should abandon his pen and brush. It was a literal race with death.

We are not informed in any of Wilson's letters of the circumstances of his meeting with the learned philologist and scientist, George Ord (1781–1866), who became his most intimate friend. We gather from some of Ord's writings,[10] however, that the two naturalists went on several collecting trips during the last year or two of Wilson's life. One of these expeditions was to Great Egg Harbor, on the New Jersey coast, where they spent a month studying waterfowl and other aquatic species.

This material was incorporated in Volume 8 and contains Wilson's accounts of some twenty ducks, several of the herons and ibises, the sooty tern, the oystercatcher, and the whooping crane.

Though rapidly failing in strength, Wilson wrote the usual full accounts of the birds, whenever possible, but,

[10] Observations on the Cow Bunting of the United States, *Mag. Nat. Hist.,* 9: 57–71, 1836.

in the case of several ducks, the author was not familiar with their breeding habits, since many of them nest in central and northern Canada. To balance this lack he used interesting matter culled from European writers, or he described dissections of internal parts, such as the reproductive and excretory systems, or the syringes.

It seems remarkable that he was familiar with Sir Francis Willughby's dissections of the voice apparatus of certain ducks. To these he added his own views on the subject, but we do not know where he saw these volumes. Wilson showed himself to the last a capable ornithologist, well versed in the writings of others, skillful in dissection, keen in interpretation, proficient in expression, and unsurpassed in field observation.

Every day Wilson worked until far into the night. His friends would try to remonstrate with him and he would reply, with portent, "Life is short—nothing can be done without exertion." A rare bird that he chanced to see brought on his last relapse. He shot it down, but not without pursuing it across a river, and this caused complete exhaustion.

He was close to the completion of the eighth volume when on August 23, 1813, death stole upon him.

Looking back to 1794 when the frail young man of twenty-eight, already the victim of tuberculosis, came to America, we are struck with the boldness of the battle he waged for nineteen years, and so near was his goal that his collapse moves one with sorrow, not only for the frustrated hopes of so resolute a spirit but also for the arrested progress of the study and appreciation of birds.

Amid simple surroundings in the home of William Jones, with whom Wilson had lodged, the funeral service for the ornithologist was held on August 24, 1813 at nine o'clock in the morning. We may assume that a few of his close friends were present and that some, at least, stood by for the interment in the churchyard of Gloria Dei.

This is the Swedish Church of Southwark, which already in Wilson's day was over a hundred years old. It was the gift of Charles XI (1655–1697) and Queen Christina (1626–1689) of Sweden and was erected amid a grove of great beech trees at the corner of Christina and Swanson Streets. These trees, however, had been cut down and in Wilson's time the church stood above a busy wharf so that Wilson's wish that he might lie in a spot where birds would sing over his grave was not vouchsafed to him. Today, however, other large trees shade the churchyard and a maple tree, from which hangs a bird-feeding tray, spreads its ample boughs over the ornithologist's resting place. Sarah Miller, sister to the Honorable Daniel Miller, Congressman from the Upper Section of Philadelphia, is said to have provided a simple slab of marble over the grave. Today, however, a large stone casket stands there, carved with Wilson's name and the cause [11] of his death. These changes

---

[11] Dysentery.

were probably made by George Ord some time after the burial. [12]

GEORGE ORD

Although we cannot discover the beginnings of Ord's friendship with Wilson, let us acquaint ourselves with this new and valued associate, to whom Wilson entrusted the precious task of finishing the eighth volume and entirely writing the ninth and last.

George Ord was of Swedish descent on his mother's side, while his father, probably an American, was a sea captain who became a ship chandler and ropemaker on Willing's and Francis Wharf in Philadelphia in 1798. In 1800 the son became his father's partner in the business, and in 1806, when the elder Ord died, the son and his mother continued in it until 1829.

The Ords became a family of wealth and influence in Philadelphia. The son was a member of that interesting coterie of naturalists who founded the Academy of Natural Sciences of Philadelphia in 1812, and is described as a "wealthy gentleman of leisure." We gather from his references to European travel and book collecting and his gifts to the Academy and the American Philosophical Society that his contacts with these organizations were in the capacity of patron and adviser. He is known mostly for his editorship of Wilson's eighth volume and for the text of the ninth volume, to which he added a biographical account of his ornithologist friend. This, however, was hastily composed without the research necessary to make it a thoroughly authentic piece of work. Ord wrote several articles on birds, among which may be mentioned the following:

An Account of an American Species of the Genus Tantalus or Ibis. *Jour. Acad. Nat. Sci. of Phila.* 1: 53–57, 1817.
Observations on Two Species of the Genus Gracula, Latham. *Jour. Acad. Nat. Sci. of Phila.* 1: 253–261, 1817.
An Account of the Florida Jay, Bartram. *Jour. Acad. Nat. Sci. of Phila.* 1: 345–347, 1817.
Some Observations on the Moulting of Birds. *Amer. Phil. Soc. Trans.* 3: 292–300, 1830.
Observations on the Cow Bunting of the United States. *Mag. Nat. Hist.* 9: 57–71, 1836.

This last article is of particular interest in this study of the development of ornithological observation, for, in addition to its wealth of factual knowledge on the parasitism of the cowbird, it indicates George Ord's daily observations at the nests of several species of birds harboring young cowbirds, and his clear reasoning in re-

---

[12] I am indebted to my friend, Mrs. Francis S. Scheetz, for many kindnesses in connection with the investigation of Wilson's Philadelphia record. We went together to the Church of Gloria Dei on September 18, 1947, to see Wilson's grave, which is very close to the church. At a later date Mrs. Scheetz took photographs of it and also enquired of the Rector, the Reverend John Craig Roak, for the burial record. In Burials 1803–1816 it is recorded that Alexander Wilson was buried in the lot belonging to Mr. William Jones, of 233 Spruce Street, with whom for years he had lived.

futing the statements of other writers, especially Audubon and Nuttall.

The article was written in 1836, and, although Alexander Wilson had died over twenty years previously, Ord's ardent championship of his friend's statements and his uncompromising scorn for the slipshod observation of others who sought to calumniate the faithful Scot had not one whit abated. Ord had retired to a country place at Buckingham, Pennsylvania, when these investigations took place. He loved the seclusion of nature where the birds could have sanctuary; and in this study of the cowbird he tells us he literally lived in the woods, coming to the nests early in the morning and remaining all day. He observed nests of chewinks, song sparrows, wood thrushes, indigo buntings, and red-eyed flycatchers [vireos], all of which contained cowbirds' eggs.

At the time that Ord was most intimate with Wilson he was in his early thirties, fifteen years the junior of Wilson, a man of wide culture, wealth, and infinite educational advantages over his friend. Yet, despite these inequalities, there grew up between them a friendship of mutual confidence so that Wilson could ask Ord to continue his work should he be forced to lay it down.

Probably Ord's main work on Volume 8 was the proofreading for the printing had already started when Wilson died. The publication date was delayed until Ord could employ an artist, probably Alexander Rider, whom Wilson had had before. The book appeared January 19, 1819, five years after the demise of its original author.

THE NINTH VOLUME

This concluding volume of Wilson's *American Ornithology* contains four plates with thirteen species and accounts of sixteen species. It represents a great labor by George Ord, who, though he calls himself the editor, was actually the writer. He had Wilson's fragmentary journals to refer to, but on many of the species he could find no notes, so that he frequently shouldered his gun and went to the shores and marshes and woods in search of the birds for which he had the drawings. He also corresponded with other naturalists and artists, or he wrote for information to institutions in which Wilson had placed specimens.

One finds frequent reference in this volume to the field work which he and Wilson did together in 1812 and 1813, and from this we glean a little understanding of their friendship and the circumstances under which some of the specimens were secured. The accounts are likewise enriched by Ord's interesting knowledge of antiquities and ancient writers whose countries cherished many birds as pets because of their beauty and amiability, or as sacred propitiators of their gods. The brilliant purple gallinule, says Ord, was known by the ancients as the Porphyrion [13] because of its elegant red and pur-

Fig. 54. George Ord (1781–1866), friend and field companion of Alexander Wilson. He completed the ninth volume of Wilson's *American Ornithology*. Portrait by T. Henry Smith after John Nagle, in the Hall of the American Philosophical Society.

ple plumage; by Europeans, according to Buffon, as the sultana hen, because of its chicken-like habits and bright colors. · These glamorous epithets have become the simple "mud hen" of modern parlance.

Mr. Ord speaks of Wilson's search for the gray and red phalaropes. A single specimen of the former (*Lobipes lobatus*) was presented by Wilson to Trowbridge's Museum, at Albany. There being no account of the Wilson's plover, and no description of it among previous writers, Ord honored this unusual bird with Wilson's name, calling it *Charadrius wilsonia wilsonia* Ord. Three specimens, two males and a female, were collected by Ord and Wilson on their final trip together, May 13, 1813, on the shore of Cape Island, New Jersey. The ornithologists explored the shore-line of Cape May, enquiring of gunners respecting the Wilson plover's habits and whether it had been seen before. They could learn nothing from the natives and concluded it was a new species which, from the fact that the female's oviduct contained a partially developed egg, was interpreted to be a nesting species on the dry sandy shore of Cape May. By his admirable description [14] of both male and female birds we may judge of his ability as an ornithologist, although his natural bent was more toward history and literature.

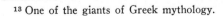

[13] One of the giants of Greek mythology.

[14] Wilson's *American ornithology,* **9**: 77, pl. 73, fig. 5, 1814.

Many honors came to George Ord during his long life. Elected a member of the Academy of Natural Sciences of Philadelphia in 1815, he was Curator of their collections until 1817, Vice-President from 1816 to 1834, and a member of their publications committee from 1817 to 1821, and again in 1832 and 1833. He finally was chosen President of the Academy in 1851 and served for seven years. While a member of the Academy he was active also in the American Philosophical Society, having been elected in 1817. His services there as librarian and benefactor have already been mentioned. In addition to his completion of Alexander Wilson's *Ornithology,* and his *Life of Wilson,* he wrote, also, a life of Thomas Say (1787–1834), the entomologist, another of C. A. Lesueur (1778–1846) the prominent French ichthyologist.[15] George Ord's work on general zoology is usually overlooked today, but we should bear in mind that he wrote the zoological sections of Gutherie's *Zoology,*[16] published in 1815, which is the first systematic work on American zoology and it is important in this study because of its several first descriptions of birds and mammals.

Ord, with his many scientific attainments, nevertheless, continued to have an abiding love for literature and history and achieved a knowledge of philology that enabled him to compile a large part of the data in the first edition of Webster's Dictionary. According to Samuel Rhoads [17] (b. 1862), Webster used Ord's material without acknowledgment to him. Ord, though a most modest research worker, objected to Webster's lapse of courtesy and refused to help him further unless he would make his later editions of the *Dictionary* conform to the Johnsonian spelling. This, Webster would not agree to do, but a later worker, Robert Gordon Latham (1812–1888), who revised *Johnson's Dictionary* in 1870, secured Ord's entire manuscript, representing forty years of work, and made acknowledgment to Ord's researches in every case where he used his manuscript. This Latham is no connection of John Latham, the ornithologist, but an ethnologist and philologist, Professor of English Language and Literature at University College, London.

When Ord hastily got together the materials for a biography of his friend Wilson in 1814, and published it as an appendix to the ninth volume of the *American Ornithology,* he was by no means through with his services to the ornithologist. In 1828 he enlarged and republished this biography, as a *Sketch of the Life of Alexander Wilson, Author, of the American Ornithology.* This was in the same year that Audubon was bringing out his engraved plates in England, and Ord probably timed his publication, hoping to detract from Audubon's reputation.

Audubon had visited Philadelphia in 1824, expecting to find encouragement for the publication of his drawings, but at that time he was indifferently received by most of the Philadelphia savants. Especially did Ord conceive a dislike for him, and for the rest of his life he strove to have justice done to Wilson at the expense of Audubon's growing fame.

"The Wilson-Audubon Controversy," it has been called, and many persons unfamiliar with the ornithological literature of the period have thought that Wilson and Audubon engaged in a quarrel in print. But this is wide of the truth, for Wilson never spoke nor wrote any derogatory word about Audubon. It was Ord who replied to Audubon's charges of plagiarism against Wilson, and made some accusations [18] of his own against Audubon. Space is lacking to recount this long argument, and as Wilson was long since laid to rest, let it suffice to say here that his reputation for honesty is fully proved. Simple and modest in personality, it seems fitting that he maintained complete silence on Audubon, his art and methods, although he recognized in him a dangerous rival.

As to Wilson's standing in the scientific world, it is clear that he was completely eclipsed by a better artist. Recognition of his contribution to ornithology has, therefore, been slow and scant. However, three basic and solid honors came to him just before he died.

In 1812 he was elected to the Columbian Society of Fine Arts.[19]

The following year Wilson was made a member of the American Philosophical Society, the honor he esteemed most, and shortly after he was elected to the Academy of Natural Sciences of Philadelphia, but did not live to sign the register.

IN WILSON'S MEMORY

When we consider the meticulous personal attention that went into all phases of Wilson's work, the drawing, the engraving, the coloring, and the writing, the price of $120.00 per set does not seem unreasonably expensive. It was, however, too high to draw a large public. Perhaps Wilson had contemplated cheaper editions. George Ord and Charles Bonaparte (1803–1857), both with this thought in mind, brought out three and four volume sets,[20] respectively, in 1828 and 1831, but it was then too late to capture more than a slight following for Wilson, for by this date Audubon was publishing his plates in England, and his public, both here and abroad, was enthusiastic.

[15] *Amer. Jour. of Sci. & Arts,* ser. 2, **8** (art. 15) : 189–216, 1849.

[16] Now a rare publication.

[17] Rhoads, Samuel, Goerge Ord, *Cassinia,* **12** : 1–8, 1908.

[18] *Proc. Amer. Philos. Soc.,* **1**: 272 et seq., 1840.

[19] According to *American Daily Advertiser* for August 24, 1813, the Columbian Society of Fine Arts resolved to wear crêpe on the left arm for thirty days in testimony of the high consideration in which the virtues and talents of the deceased (Wilson) were held by the Society.

[20] For a description of subsequent editions see Allibone, S. Austin, *Dictionary of authors,* **3**: 2765–2766, Phila., 1871; also Walter Faxon, *Auk,* **20** (2) : 236–241, 1903; **36** (4) : 623–626, 1919.

FIG. 55. Alexander Wilson (1766–1813), Father of American Ornithology. Statue in the Paisley Museum.

Wilson's recognition came slowly and modestly, and it took varied forms. The historian, Jared Sparks (1789–1866), considered Wilson to be held in high esteem abroad soon after his death. According to Alexander Lawson, numberless persons sought information from him about this eccentric, but gifted man; while Sir Joseph Banks (1743–1820) exhibited the *American Ornithology* when he was entertaining continental dignitaries in 1816, as the only natural history work at that date worthy of their special examination.

In 1833, twenty years after Wilson's death, a group of his friends and townsmen, presided over by Thomas Crichton, met to honor him, and "His memory was drank in solemn silence after a speech from the Chair." [21] Another tribute by his native country was the bronze marker placed on the house where he was born by Mr. David Anderson, of Perth, in 1841.

The installation of the tablet was a great occasion in Paisley. Flags, banners, flowers, music, and speeches marked the event. It inspired several of Wilson's admirers to meet to discuss a monument to his memory. This was in 1844.

A chapter of the Odd Fellows known as the Alexander Wilson Lodge pushed the project for several years, and by 1855 there was a fund of £200; in 1857 it had grown to £400.

It became a plan for the whole city to work on and Scotsmen resident in America contributed. George Ord especially was helpful in this. But interest sometimes languished. Then in 1865 a committee requested models from three well-known sculptors. Mr. Mossman of Glasgow received the commission but it was thirty years after the initial meeting that the memorial was realized. The monument set on a pedestal of Aberdeen Granite was at last unveiled October 8, 1874 and occupies a choice spot in the Abbey grounds.

The figure represents Alexander Wilson, a little more than life size, dressed for his work, his gun slung by a leather strap about his shoulder, a freshly killed bird lying in his hand; his sketch book and pet parrot at his feet. The face is thoughtful, and in his right hand he holds a drawing pencil. I am indebted to the late Dr. George S. Duncan, of Washington, D. C., for the accompanying illustration, a photograph made of the model of this statue that stands in the entrance hall of the Paisley Museum.

In this Museum may be seen, likewise, a few of Wilson's early manuscripts, the original indenture covering his apprenticeship as a weaver, and other memorabilia.

Many years passed by after the unveiling of the Paisley statue before any other memorial to Wilson was established.

Through the late Dr. Witmer Stone we learn that a statuette [22] of Wilson by Alexander Calder [23] (1846–1923) was exhibited at the Academy of Fine Arts in Philadelphia, some time during the seventies. This was at about the time of the unveiling of the monument in Paisley, and there was considerable interest expressed in having Calder's work cast in life-size bronze and placed in Fairmont Park. The plan was not carried out at that time, but in 1913 the City of Philadelphia again considered a statue of the ornithologist to be erected in front of the Academy of Natural Sciences. The Calder statue became the property of the Academy of Natural Sciences, and for many years stood in the Library. Like the one in Paisley, it shows Wilson in thoughtful mood, contemplating a bird that he has just shot, his drawing pencil in his right hand and his faithful fowling piece beside him. The gun,[24] we learn, after some peregrina-

[21] Dunlap, William, *History of design in the United States,* 19, Boston, 1918.

[22] This statuette was exhibited; it came to the Acad. of Nat. Sci. of Phila. as a gift from the Calder family around 1920.

[23] The wrtier has been informed by letter from the secretary, Mr. J. T. Fraser, that this was exhibited in plaster as item No. 384 in the 53d Ann. Exhib. at the Acad., Oct. 24, 1882 to Dec. 9, 1882.

[24] *Cassinia,* 17: 2, 1913. Wilson's gun passed through several hands. At his death it went to John Cassin, thence to William

tion became the property of a Mr. J. M. Wade, of Philadelphia, and the artist modelled the gun in the statue from Mr. Wade's trophy, while the face of the statue was modelled after a study of all extant engravings of the naturalist.

Mr. Stone, in the same article in *Cassinia,* reports on the fate of Wilson's trunk. This was left at the time of his death to Sarah Miller, whom Wilson intended to marry, and from her it apparently passed to a member of the Rittenhouse family, probably the one whom she later married. Thus it was probably Sarah Miller's son from whom William Redwood Wright, together with William P. Turnbull, purchased the trunk. The trunk with its contents was held for $100.00, but it was a chance whether it was worth it, for Wright and Turnbull did not know what it contained. It was agreed that they would buy it jointly and divide the spoils which, on inspection, proved to be mostly printed matter, a set of the letterpress and plates of Wilson's *American Ornithology,* a sketch of Wilson's schoolhouse, a colored drawing of the hermit thrush, a portrait of Michael Hernego, and the negative of Wilson's silhouette. Probably some few other items of interest were included. From Mr. Turnbull these Wilson relics passed to a Mr. Robert Gray, of Edinburgh, and upon his death were held by his widow, Elizabeth Gray. This transaction took place in 1866, and Mr. Turnbull, who purchased the trunk and divided its contents with William R. Wright, informs that he obtained it from Mrs. E. R. Rittenhouse, who was the widow of Sarah Miller Rittenhouse's son.

The original of the Wilson silhouette is in the National Portrait Gallery of Edinburgh, and it is believed that other Wilson memorabilia are housed there.

Certain it is that the influence of Alexander Wilson was felt in Scotland and particularly in Paisley and neighboring cities. His monument taught a lesson, his poems and other writings are still remembered, and his first success, *Watty and Meg,* achieved a record sale. This poem is said to have been composed during his three-day confinement for libel in the Paisley jail, but since it was publicly attributed to Robert Burns, it was sold by hawkers through the city. Burns is said to have called to the hawker, "That's a lee, Andrew, but I would make your pluck a bawbee [25] if it were mine."

As recently as 1923 another tribute was paid to him in the form of a memorial tablet, which was unveiled at the Academy of Natural Sciences of Philadelphia on May 17. It was presented by the St. Andrew's Society,[26] a charitable organization founded in 1749 for the aid of indigent immigrants from Scotland. There is no indication that Wilson ever received any financial assistance from this society, but, as a Scottish organization, it wished to pay tribute to a son of Scotland who had contributed so much of worth to the study of science in America.

The tablet was the gift of Dr. J. Lawson Cameron, of Paisley, and it was designed by R. Tait McKenzie, distinguished sculptor, anatomist and surgeon. It consists of a medallion of the head of the ornithologist with appropriate inscriptions. The unveiling took place in the presence of the members of St. Andrew's Society, the Delaware Valley Ornithological Club, and the Secretary and President of the American Ornithologists' Union. Mr. Samuel Scoville, Jr., delivered the address.

One other memorial,[27] unique in kind and appealing in its message of admiration and loyalty for the ornithologist, should be mentioned. Deep in a glade of Lawrence County, Indiana, stands a simple five-foot column of native stone graven with a crude likeness of Alexander Wilson upon its western face. It is surrounded by a circular fence of iron pickets four feet high. The tract of land in which it stands is known as Spring Mill State Park, near Mitchell, Indiana. This was formerly the 101 acres of land purchased by George Donaldson, of Paisley, Scotland, and called "Beautiful Shawnee," after the tribe of Indians of that territory.

The simple inscription consists only of "A. W." in tall scrolled letters underneath the quaint long-haired likeness of the naturalist, with the words "Died 1813" below. A painted sign, within the enclosure, bears the following words:

In Memory Of
Alexander Wilson
Father of American Ornithology

This Monument was Erected By
George Donaldson
His Fellow Townsman

The complete story of this rough-hewn memorial, its conception and execution, has never been told in detail so far as we know, but Donaldson lived there in his secluded woodland for several years, having purchased the tract in 1865 of James C. Lynn, and at once built a home where friends and relatives from far distant Scotland and other places were welcome to come and stay. Donaldson was only a child when Wilson died, in 1813, but, growing up on Wilson's native soil, he must have had an appreciation of Wilson's nature-loving way of life, and he sought to honor his memory by protecting and studying the bird and plant life about him. At any rate, he erected this monument in 1866, the centenary of Wilson's birth, and only a year after he had acquired his woodland retreat. He remained there until 1871, when he moved to Alabama. He finally returned to Ayrshire, in Scotland, where he died, in September 1898. He was buried in the Old Necropolis of Glasgow.

P. Turnbull, thence to Willis P. Hazard, and from him to Wade with a statement of its history, including how the powderhorn that belonged with it was lost by a boy who used it. See Coues, Elliott, *Bull. Nuttall Ornith. Club,* 14: 193–204, Oct. 1880.

[25] Bawbee—half-penny. This incident is recounted in Park, Allan, *Alexander Wilson,* p. 6, London (1863); it is said to have been told by Mrs. Burns, the poet's widow to Roberts Chambers, his biographer.

[26] Scharf, J. Thomas, and Thompson Westcott, *History of Philadelphia,* 2: 1464–1465.

[27] Perkins, S. E., III, *Wilson Bull.,* 1: 13–17, 1938.

This concludes all memorials up to the present time, but it seems that, as our knowledge of birds increases and birds become more familiar to all nature-loving people, the memory of Alexander Wilson and the vast work he accomplished will live peerless in the ornithological annals of this country.

To the modern student of ornithology, and perhaps also to those of his time, Wilson remains an enigma, a strange combination of impassioned interest in his subject irrevocably mated to a negative and mediocre ability in certain phases of the work he was called upon to do—particularly the various art techniques of his bird portraiture. But what he lacked in native talent for drawing and composition was compensated by an intense perseverance, combined with a sort of inspired interest that spells accomplishment in any difficult endeavor. Elliott Coues called it genius, and, in an article in the *Bulletin* of the Nuttall Ornithological Club, for October 1880, he formulated, from Wilson as his model, a definition of genius which all aspiring ornithologists would do well to ponder: "Genius is that union of Passion and Patience which bears fruit unknown to Passion alone, to Patience alone impossible."

How well this fits our ornithologist, who with long labor brought to fruition the cherished dream of his American career. But in his personal living he was always too engrossed in his work to undertake marriage, despite several friendships that gave promise to such an ending. Many commentators have tried to inject romance of the time-honored complexion into Wilson's life, first with a Scottish lass before he left Paisley, then with Ann Bartram, then with an anonymous woman of his school-teaching days, and lastly with Sarah Miller, to whom he was reportedly betrothed at the time of his death. But Cupid's darts were never loosed—all these affairs of the heart, like pale phantoms, lapsed into insignificance before the bright fire of his love of birds.

Wilson's nearest relatives in this country were his sister, Mrs. William Duncan, and her various children of Ovid, New York, the eldest of whom, William Duncan, accompanied Wilson to America in 1794. The next son, Alexander Duncan, after growing up on the fertile stretch of country between Cayuga and Seneca Lakes, moved, in his young manhood, to a farm near South Lyon, Oakland County, Michigan. He had two sons, Robert and James, and several daughters; the son James became prosperous enough to add to the old homestead in Michigan, improving the house and increasing the land to some eight hundred acres. One of the daughters moved to Ann Arbor, and in 1895 was still living there.

James Duncan,[28] the grandnephew of Alexander Wilson, continued, at least until 1895, to live on his farm on Silver Lake, Michigan, and every year, with his dogs and gun, he went into northern Michigan after deer, his favorite game. Though not much of an ornithologist, his love of the outdoor life, combined with a stern will, were strongly reminiscent of his distinguished uncle.

Most of Wilson's specimens went to Peale's Museum, later called the Philadelphia Museum, and a few went to Trowbridge's Museum, Albany, but, although great improvement had been wrought in taxidermy since the crude methods of Johann Reinhold Forster,[29] very few of Wilson's specimens are still in existence. Two skins —a Mississippi kite and a broad-winged hawk—are kept in the vault of the Academy of Natural Sciences of Philadelphia where is preserved a series of type specimens, and a few others are in the Museum of Comparative Zoology at Harvard. In 1880 four relics of Peale's Museum came to this museum by way of T. M. Brewer (1814–1880). They are eggs of the avocet, the turkey vulture, the eagle, and the horned owl, all collected by Alexander Wilson and obtained by Moses Kimball in 1850, when he, with P. T. Barnum (1810–1891), purchased the natural history collection of Peale's Museum.

When Dr. Elliott Coues described his visit [30] to the home of John M. Wade, in Rockville, Connecticut, in 1880, he mentioned seeing more than half of the originals of Wilson's plates for his *American Ornithology*. His general impression was that these drawings, made by Wilson himself, showed "decided superiority" over the published engravings by Alexander Lawson. He believed the great praise generally accorded Lawson's engravings had its origin in the outpouring of Wilson's gratitude to him for consenting to do the work at all, when such uncertain and meagre rewards could be paid by the author. It is true that the intrinsic merit of Wilson's work belongs to Wilson, and it is the more impressive because he was but slenderly equipped for scientific observation and literary expression, yet in both of these essential fields he came to true distinction and won the honor of being named the Father of American Ornithology.

[28] Purdy, James B., A relative of Alexander Wilson, *Auk,* 12: 396, 1895.
[29] See this work, p. 502.
[30] Coues, Elliott, Behind the veil, *Bull. Nuttall Ornith. Club,* 5: 193–204, 1880.

ABBOT, JOHN. n. d. MS. Catalogue to the 4 volumes of his bird drawings in Chetham's Library containing Abbot's notes on his drawings and John Latham's annotations with references to his Synopsis of birds, 1781–1785. Chetham's Library, Manchester, England.

—— n. d. MS. Drawings of birds in Chetham's Library, Manchester, England. 4 v.

—— n. d. MS. Index to John Abbot's American birds. Chetham library set.

—— 1797. The natural history of the rarer lepidopterous insects of Georgia . . . Coll. by Sir James E. Smith. London, Print. by T. Bensley for J. Edwards. See Smith, Sir James E.

—— 1804. MS. Drawings and natural history of the birds of Georgia in America. 2 v. London, Egerton MS. 1137–1138, British Museum. Dept. manuscripts.

—— 1810. MS. Drawings of the birds of Georgia. Cambridge, Harvard Univ. Library, Houghton Collection.

—— 1816–1820. MS. 8 letters from John Abbot to William Swainson, between dates 20 December 1816 and 15 January 1820. London, Linnean Soc.

—— 1827. Birds of Georgia, consisting of the most rare and beautiful birds, drawn and colored from nature. John Abbot MS. drawings. Tring natural history museum.

—— 1906. Letter from Abbot to George Ord, Mar., 1814. *Auk* 23: 365–368.

ABBOTT (*sic*), JOHN. 1797. Birds of Georgia, from the Wymberley Jones De Renne Georgia library. Athens, Ga., Univ. of Ga.

ACOSTA, JOSEPH DE. 1880. Natural and moral history of the Indies. 2 v. Hakluyt Soc. lx, lxi.

ADAMS, RANDOLF. 1935. An effort to identify John White. *Amer. Hist. Rev.* 41 (1) : 87–91.

ADELMANN, HOWARD B. 1933. The "De ovorum Gallinaceorum generationis primo exordio progressinque et pulli Gallinacei creationis ordine" of Volcher Coiter. *Annals of Med. Hist.* 5 (5) : 327–341; 444–457.

—— 1942. The embryological treatises of Hieronymus Fabricius of Aquependente. Ithaca, N. Y., Cornell Univ. Pr.

AIKEN, PAULINE. 1947. The animal history of Albertus Magnus and Thomas of Contimpré. *Speculum, Jour. Medieval Stud.* 22 (2) : 205–224.

ALBIN, ELEAZAR. 1736. Natural history of spiders. London.

—— 1738. Natural history of birds. 3 v. London.

ALDROVANDUS, ULYSSES. 1601. Ornithologia. 3 v. Bononiae.

ALEXANDER, W. B. 1936. Note about Alexander Wilson—portrait held by Rev. J. M. McWilliams of Glasgow. *Auk* 43: 130.

ALLEN, ARTHUR A. 1929. Ten years experiments in rearing the ruffed grouse in captivity. *Trans. Amer. Game Conf.* 16: 3–21.

—— 1934. Sex rhythm in the ruffed grouse. *Auk* 51 (2) : 180–199.

ALLEN, ELSA G. 1936. Some 16th century paintings of American birds. *Auk* 53 (1) : 17–21.

—— 1937. New light on Mark Catesby. *Auk* 54 (3) : 349–363.

—— 1938. Jaques LeMoyne, first zoological artist in America. *Auk* 55 (1) : 106–111.

—— 1939. Nicolas Denys, a forgotten observer of birds. *Auk* 56 (3) : 283–290.

—— 1942. A third set of John Abbot bird drawings. *Auk* 59 (4) : 563–571.

—— 1948. A resumé of John Abbot's "Notes on my life." *Oriole* 13 (4) : 31–32.

—— 1949. A Paisley hunt. *Paisley daily express,* May 20.

—— 1951. A sixteenth century classification of birds. *Proc. Tenth Internat. Ornithol. Cong.* 10. Sweden, Univ. of Upsala.

ALLEN, FRANCIS H. 1940. Nicolas Denys and the nighthawk. *Auk* 57: 417–418.

—— 1940. Nicolas Denys's birds. *Auk* 57 (1) : 75–84.

ALLEN, G. M. 1903. A list of the birds of New Hampshire. Manchester.

ALLEN, J. A. Jan. 1876. The availability of certain Bartramian names in ornithology. *Amer. Naturalist* 10: 21–29.

—— 1908. Linnaeus as a zoologist. *Ann. N. Y. Acad. of Sci.* 18: 9–19.

—— 1910. Collation of Brisson's genera of birds with those of Linnaeus. *Amer. Mus. Nat. Hist. Bull.* 28: 317–335.

—— 1908. Pennant's Indian zoology. *Bull. Amer. Mus. Nat. Hist.* 24: 111–116.

—— 1916. Autobiographical notes and a bibliography of the scientific publications of Joel Asaph Allen. N. Y., Amer. Mus. Nat. Hist.

—— 1917. Rev. of Wayne's A list of avian species for which the type locality is South Carolina. *Auk* 34 (3) : 346.

ALLEN, JAMES L. 1920. Alexander Wilson. (Rev. of Reprint of a chapter from Mr. Allen's book the Kentucky warbler) *Auk* 37 (1) : 174.

ALLIBONE, S. AUSTIN. 1871. Dictionary of authors 3: 2765–2766.

AMERICAN ORNITHOLOGISTS' UNION. 1910. Check-list of North American birds. 3d. ed. Lancaster, Pa.

—— 1931. Check-list of North American birds. 4th ed. Lancaster, Pa.

ANDERSON, EDGAR SHAMON. 1928. American botanical gardens and English poetry. *Bull. Mo. Botan. Garden* 16: 115–122.

ANDERSON, JOHANN. 1746. Histoire naturelle de l'islande du Groenland du Détroit de Davis. Paris.

ANKER, JEAN. 1938. Bird books and bird art. Copenhagen, Levin and Munksgaard.

Anon. 1770–1772. New and complete history of Essex, by a Gentleman. [Peter Muilman] Chelmsford.

—— 1848. William Sharp and Fiscal Alexander Wilson, 1792–3. *Scottish Jour.* 2: 228.

—— 1862. Vögel Deutschlands. (Review of Dr. Blasius and Baldamus's Continuation of Naumann's 'Vögel Deutschlands.') *Ibis* 4: 40–58.

—— 1894. Sale of an egg of great auk, Feb. 22, 1894 for 300 guineas. *Auk* 11: 191–192.

—— 1944. The bird and animal artist of 4000 years ago and the present day. *London Illus. News* 115 (3002A) : 31–34.

ARBER, AGNES. 1938. Herbals, their origin and evolution; a chapter in the history of botany 1470–1670. new ed. Cambridge, Univ. Press.

ARISTOTLE. 1863. Die thierarten des Aristotles von klassen der säugethiere, vögel, reptilien . . . Trans. from the Swedish by C. J. Sundeval. Stockholm.

—— History of animals. See Thompson, D'Arcy Wentworth.

ARNDT, WALTHER. 1925–1926. Die vögel in der heilkunde. *Jour für Ornithol.* 73 (1) : 46–65; (2) : 214–246.

AUDUBON, MARIA. 1898. Audubon and his journals, with zoological and other notes by Elliott Coues. 2 v. New York, John C. Nimmo.

AVERY, JOHN. 1903–1904. Essex worthies IV: George Edwards, the Stratford naturalist. *Essex Naturalist* 13: 343–348.

AYER, EDWARD E. Cat. of the Ornith. Libr., Field Mus. of Nat. Hist. See Zimmer, John Todd.

AYSCOUGH, SAMUEL. 1782. Catalogue of the MSS preserved in the British Museum, hitherto undescribed. London.

BACHMAN, JOHN. 1834–1837. Remarks in defense of the author of the Birds of America. *Jour. Boston Soc. Nat. Hist.* **1**: 15–31.

BACON, FRANCIS, VISC. ST. ALBANS. 1803. Novum organum. *Philos. Works* **8** (2). London Port.

BAILEY, ALFRED M. 1933. Along Audubon's Labrador trail. Bird study today and a century ago. *Nat. Hist. Mag.* **33** (6) : 638–646.

BAILEY, FLORENCE MERRIAM. 1928. Birds of New Mexico. Washington, U. S. Dept. of Agriculture.

BAILEY, G. W. n. d. Spalding gentlemen's society. Reprint. from the *Lincolnshire Mag.*

BAILEY, HARRY B. 1881. "Forest and stream" bird notes; an index and summary of all the ornithological matter contained in *Forest and Stream v. 1–12*. New York.

BALDNER, LEONARD. 1653. Addl. MSS. 6485 and 6486. London, Brit. Mus. Dept. Manuscripts.

BANKS, JOSEPH. 1766–1820. MS. Correspondence Mus. Nat. Hist. 21 v. London.

BANKS, SIR JOSEPH. 1896. Journal of the Right Honorable Sir Joseph Banks . . . during Capt. Cook's first voyage in H. M. S. Endeavor in 1768–71 to Terra del Fuego . . . New Zealand, Australia, the Dutch East Indies, etc., ed. by Sir Joseph D. Hooker. London and N. Y., Macmillan.

BARDSLEY, CHARLES MARIENG. 1901. English and Welsh surnames, 92. N. Y., H. Frowde.

BARTLETT, J. R. 1875. Catalogue of the John Carter Brown Library, 5. Providence.

BARTON, BENJAMIN SMITH. 1799. Fragments of the natural history of Pennsylvania. Phila.

—— 1805. Letter to M. Lacépède of Paris, on the natural history of North America. *Tilloch's Phil. Mag.* **22**: 204–211.

BARTRAM, J. 1764–1771. MS. Seven autograph letters to John Fothergill. British Museum Dept. Manuscripts. London.

BARTRAM, WILLIAM. 1791. MS. Folio volume of drawings and water colours containing flowers, fish, snakes, molluscs and 25 drawings of birds . . . London, Nat. Hist. Mus.

—— 1791. Travels through North and South Carolina, Georgia, East and West Florida. Phila. James & Johnson.

—— 1805. Biography of John Bartram. *Phila. Med. and Phys. Jour.* **1**: 119.

BARTRAM, JOHN and WILLIAM. n. d. Drawings and manuscript. London, Brit. Mus. Dept. Botany Ref. 55/47.

BASSETT, ANNA STOWELL. 1938. Some Georgia records of John Abbot, naturalist. *Auk* **55** (2) : 244–254.

BATCHELDER, CHARLES FOSTER. 1937. An account of the Nuttall Ornithological Club, 1873–1919. *Mem. Nuttall Ornithol. Club* **8**. Cambridge, Mass. Published by the Club.

BAY, J. CHRISTIAN. 1916. Conrad Gesner, the father of bibliography; an appreciation. *Papers, Bibliog. Soc. of Amer.* **10**: 53–86.

BEAMISH, N. L. 1841. Discovery of America by the Northmen. London, T. and W. Boone.

BECKER, F., see Thieme, Ulrich, and Felix Becker.

BELKNAP, JEREMY. 1784. History of New Hampshire **3**. Boston.

BELON, PIERRE. 1553. Les observations de plusieurs singularitez et choses memorables, en Grece, Asie, Indée et autres pays estranges. Paris.

—— 1555. Histoire de la natvre des Oyseavx. Paris.

BENSON, ADOLPH, ed. 1937. Peter Kalm's Travels in North America, Introd., p. XI. N. Y., Wilson Erickson.

BENT, ARTHUR CLEVELAND. 1932. Life histories of North American gallinaceous birds. *Bull. U. S. Nat. Mus.* **162**.

BERT, EDMUND. 1891. Bert's Treatise of hawks and hawking for the first time reprinted from the original of 1619. London, Quaritch.

BINYON, LAURENCE. 1898–1907. Catalogue of prints and drawings by British artists and artists of foreign origin working in British Museum in Department of Prints and Drawings. 4 v. London.

BISHOP, MORRIS. 1948. Champlain. The life of fortitude. N. Y., Alfred Knopf.

BLACK, R. DELAMERE. 1934. Charles Fothergill's notes on the natural history of Eastern Canada, 1817–1837. *Trans. R. Can. Inst.* **20** (1) : 141–168.

BLACKBURN(E), ANNA. 1794. Obituaries of considerable persons with biog. anecdotes. *Gentleman's Mag.* **64** (2) : 180.

BLANTON, WYNDHAM B. 1930. Medicine in Virginia in the 17th century. Richmond, Wm. Byrd Press.

BLOCK, MARCUS E. 1782–1784. Naturgeschichte der ausländischen fische. Berlin, Hr. Hesse.

—— 1788. Preface. *Ichthyologie* **6**: 5–6.

BODDAERT, PIETER. 1783. Daubenton's Planches enluminéez d'histoire naturelle. Utrecht.

BOMBARDIER. 1944. Chaucer: ornithologist. *Blackwood's Mag.* **256**: 120–125.

BONAPARTE, CHARLES LUCIEN J. L. 1825–1833. The American ornithology, or the natural history of birds inhabiting the U. S. not given by Wilson. 4 v. Phila., Carey, Lea & Carey.

—— 1845. Dissertations on the state of zoology in Europe. Printed for the Ray Soc. by H. E. Strickland. London.

BOND, FRANK. MS. Comprehensive index of bird artists of the world. Libr. Cong. Fine Arts Div.

BONNATERRE, JOS. P. 1788. Tableau encyclopédique et méthodique des trois règnes de la nature ornithologie.

BOSSU, JEAN BERNARD. 1771. Travels through that part of North America formerly called Louisiana. Trans. by Johann R. Forster. 2 v. London, Print. for T. Davies.

—— 1772. Letter of J. B. Bossu. *Monthly Review* **46**: 61.

BOUBIER, MAURICE. 1925. L'evolution de l'ornithologie. Nouvelle ed., 1932. Paris, Libr. Felix Alcan.

BOULGER, G. S. 1916. Unpublished material relating to John Ray. *Essex Review* **25–26**: 57–71.

BOURINOT, J. G. 1882. Cape Breton and its memorials. *Trans. Roy. Soc. of Can.* **9**: 11.

BOWLES, JOHN HOOPER. 1934. Ornithologists. *The Murrelet* **15** (2).

BRACEY, ROBERT. 1818. Eighteenth century studies. Oxford, B. Blackwell.

BRADBURY, J. 1817. Travels in the interior of America in 1809, 1810 and 1811 including a description of upper Louisiana. London, Sherwood, Neely and Jones.

BRANNON, PETER A. 1939. William Bartram's route across Alabama. *Montgomery Advertiser,* June 25.

BRASCH, FREDERICK E. 1931. The 'Royal Society of London and its influence upon scientific thought in the American Colonies. *Sci. Monthly* **33**: 336–355. Oct.

BREHAUT, E. 1912. An encyclopedist of the Dark Ages (Isidore of Seville) N. Y. Columbia Univ. Diss.

BRETT-JAMES, NORMAN G. 1925. Life of Peter Collinson, 120–121, London, Dunston & Co.

BREWSTER, WM. 1885. Swainson's warbler. *Auk* **2** (1) : 65–80.

BRICKELL, JOHN. 1737. Natural history of North Carolina. Dublin, James Carson.

BRISSON, MATHURIN JACQUES. 1723–1806. Ornithologie, ou méthode, contenant la division des oiseaux en ordres, sections, genres, espèces et leurs variétés. 6 v. Paris.

BRITTEN, JAMES. 1909. John Clayton. *Jour. Bot.* **47**: 297.

BRITTEN, JAMES, and GEORGE S. BOULGER. 1931. A biographical index of deceased British and Irish botanists. London, Taylor and Francis.

BRODHEAD, JOHN ROMEYN. 1866. Hennepin never in Albany. *Hist. Mag.* **10**: 268.

BROWN, REV. J. WOOD. 1897. An enquiry into the life and legend of Michael Scott. Edinburgh.

BROWN, THOMAS. 1901. Brown's illustrations of the American ornithology of Wilson and Bonaparte. (A Review) *Osprey* **5** (7) : 109.

BROWNE, SIR THOMAS. 1924. Religio medici. Cambridge, England.

BRUCE, ED. C. 1860. Loungings in footprints of the pioneers. *Harper's New Monthly Mag.* **20** : 721–736.

BRYANT, HAROLD C. 1934. The first recorded lists of birds in the United States. *Auk* **51** : 451–453.

BUFFON, GEORGES LOUIS, LECLERC, COMTE DE. 1778–1786. Histoire naturelle des oiseaux. 10 v. Paris.

BURNEY, CAPT. JAMES. 1819. A chronological history of north-eastern voyages of discovery. 202–234. London, Payne & Foss.

BURNS, FRANK L. 1908. Alexander Wilson; the Audubon controversy. *Wilson Bull.* **20** (1) : 3–18.

—— 1908. Alexander Wilson; the mystery of the small-headed fly-catcher. *Wilson Bull.* **20** (2) : 63–79.

—— 1908. Alexander Wilson III. The unsuccessful lover. *Wilson Bull.* **20** : 130–145.

—— 1915. A bibliography of scarce or out of print North American amateur and trade periodicals devoted more or less to ornithology. *Oologist*, Suppl. **32** (7). Albion, N. Y.

—— 1917. Miss Lawson's recollections of ornithologists. *Auk* **34** : 275–282.

—— 1917. The Schuylkill heronries; an historical account. *Bird-Lore* **19** (4) : 197–199.

—— 1929. The mechanical execution of Wilson's ornithology. *Wilson Bull.* **36** (n. s.) : 19–23.

—— 1932. Charles W. and Titian R. Peale and the ornithological section of the old Philadelphia Museum. *Wilson Bull.* **44** (1) : 23–35.

BUSHNELL, DAVID I., JR. 1928. Drawing by Jacques [sic] Le Moyne de Morgues of Satirioua, a Timucua chief in Florida 1564. *Smithsonian Misc. Coll.* **81** (4) : 1–9.

BYRD, WILLIAM. 1866. History of the dividing line. 2 v. Richmond, Va.

CAIUS, JOHN. 1570. De rariorum animalium atque stirpium. London.

CALL, ELLSWORTH. 1895. Life and writings of Rafinesque. *Louisville Filson Club Publ.* **10**.

CAREW, RICHARD. 1769. Survey of Cornwall and an epistle concerning the excellencies of the English tongue, with the life of the author by H. C. Esq. London.

CARPENTER, MATHILDE M. 1945. Bibliography of biographies of entomologists. *Amer. Midl. Nat.* **33** (1) : 1–116.

CARTWRIGHT, GEORGE. 1792. A journal of transactions and events during a residence of nearly 16 years on the coast of Labrador. 3 v. Newark.

CARUS, JULIUS VICTOR. 1823–1903. Bibliotheca zoologica. 2 v. Continuation of Englemann's Bibliotheca historico-naturalis 1700–1846; further continuation Taschenberg's Bibliotheca zoologica. 5 v. 1886–1907. London and Leipzig.

CARVER, JONOTHAN. 1779. The new universal traveller. London.

—— 1796. Three years travels through the interior parts of North America for more than five thousand miles. Phila., Key & Simpson.

CASEY, REV. HYACINTH. 1932. The scientific work of St. Albert the Great. *Irish Eccl. Record,* ser. 5, **39** : 476–488.

CASSIN, JOHN. 1865. Letter to P. L. Sclater concerning Vieillot's copper plates. *Ibis* **1** (n. s.) : 116.

Castle Hedingham. 1675. MS. Parish registers of the Norman church of Saint Nicholas.

CATESBY, ELIZABETH. 1753. Will of Elizabeth Catesby. London, Somerset House. Princ. Registry Dept. for Lit. Enquiry.

CATESBY, JOHN. 1684. MS. A document signed by John Catesby, mayor of Sudbury, and all aldermen petitioning Charles II for the restoration of their privileges. *Suffolk Archaeolog. Soc.* **13** (3).

—— 1705. Will of John Catesby. Gee, folio 4. London, Somerset House, Principal probate registry.

CATESBY, MARK. 1683. Baptismal record from Church of St. Nicholas. Castle Hedingham. MS. cop. by the Rev. R. W. Cozens.

—— 1731–1743. The natural history of Carolina, Florida and the Bahama Islands. 2 v. London.

—— 1735–1736. MS. A letter from Mark Catesby, author of Flora Carolina, to Dillenius. Oxford, Eng., Libr. Botanic Garden.

—— 1737. Hortus britanno-americanus. London, Christopher Gray.

—— 1745. Letter from Catesby to Linnaeus referring to Isaac Lawson. *Linnean correspondence.* Ed. by J. E. Smith, **2** : 440.

—— 1748. Birds of passage. *Gentleman's Mag. and Hist. Chron.* **18** : 445.

—— 1749. Death notice. *Gentleman's Mag.* **19** : 573.

—— 1750. MS. Record of death and burial at sea. Log of the Ship Portfield. London, Indian Off.

—— 1763. Hortus britanno-americanus, or a curious collection of trees and shrubs, the produce of the British Colonies in North America; adapted to the soil and climate of England. Printed by W. Richardson and S. Clark for J. Ryall.

—— 1767. Hortus Europae americanus; or a collection of 85 curious trees and shrubs, the produce of North America. London, Print. for J. Millan.

—— 1771. The natural history of Carolina, Florida and the Bahama Islands. 2 v. Ed. by G. Edwards. London, Print. for Benj. White.

—— 1783–1835. MS. Drawings of insects chiefly from Surinam and Guinea No. 5271. MS. Drawings of Plants and Trees No. 5283. MS. Drawings of birds, fish, shells, etc. No. 5269 all in Bibliotheca Sloanianum Index to Additions to Dept. of Manuscripts of the British Museum.

CHAMPLAIN, SAMUEL DE. 1859. Narrative of a voyage to the West Indies and Mexico in 1599–1602. Trans. by Alice Wilmere. *Hakluyt Soc. Publ.* **23**.

—— 1878–1882. The voyages of Sieur de Champlain. 3 v. Boston, Prince Soc.

—— 1880. Voyages of Sieur de Champlain. 2 v. Boston, Prince Soc.

CHAPMAN, FRANK M. 1894. The ornithology of Columbus' first voyage. *Auk* **11** : 89.

—— 1895. The ornithology of Columbus's first voyage. *Our Animal Friends,* 31–32.

—— 1896. World Congress on ornithology. Papers presented, 181. Chicago, Charles H. Sergel.

—— 1916. Travels of birds, 104–105. N. Y., Appleton.

—— 1917. Daniel Giraud Elliot [1835–1915]. *Auk* **34** (1) : 1–10.

—— 1937. Fuertes and Audubon. A comparison of the work and personalities of two of the world's greatest bird artists. *Nat. Hist.* **39** : 205–212.

CHARLEVOIX, F. X. DE. 1761. Journal of a voyage to North America. 2 v. London, R. and J. Dodsley.

CHASTELLUX, FRANÇOIS JEAN, MARQUIS DE. 1828. Travels in North America. 1780–1782 Trans. by J. Kent. 2 v. London.

CHATIN, M. AD. 1858. *Bulletin de la société botanique de France,* **5** : 580–582. Paris.

CHILDREY, JOSHUA. 1661. The natural rarities of England, Scotland and Wales. London.

CHRISTY, BAYARD H. 1925. Wilson's Ohio River journey. *Cardinal* **6**: 6–12.

—— 1925. Wilson's Pittsburgh subscribers. *Cardinal* **6**: 13–15.

—— 1926. Alexander Lawson's bird engravings. *Auk* **43** (1): 47–61.

—— 1927. The earliest list of Pennsylvania birds. *Cardinal* **11** (2): 30–33.

—— 1933. Topsell's fowles of heauen. *Auk* **50** (3): 275–283.

—— 1936. Kirtland marginalia. *Cardinal* **4** (4): 77–89.

—— 1937. John James Audubon. *Cardinal* **4** (5): 123–124.

—— 1938. A Wilson memorial. *Wilson Bull.* **49** (1): 17–21.

—— 1942. The bird itself. *Cardinal* **5** (8): 173–186.

CHRISTY, MILLER. 1922. Short notes; an early Hudson Bay collector. *Jour. Botany* **60**: 239; 336–337.

CHURCH, SIR ARTHUR. 1907. Classified papers of the Royal Society. MS. vol. London, Roy. Soc.

CLARK, AUSTIN H. 1934. Samuel Champlain's notes on West Indian birds. *Auk* **51**: 535.

CLARK, RICHARD. 1836. Reminiscences of Handel, the Duke of Chandos, Powells, the Harpers, the harmonious blacksmith and others. London.

CLAVIGERO, F. S. 1787. History of Mexico. *2* v. Trans. by Charles Cullen. London, Print. for G. G. J. and J. Robinson.

CLAYTON, REV. JOHN. 1671. A MS. on Virginia. London, Royal Society.

—— 1693. His letter to the Royal Society giving a further account of the soil and other observables of Virginia. *Phil. Trans.* **17**: 978–999.

COITER, (VOLCHER). 1573. Externarum et internarum principalium humani corporis partium tabulae atque anatomicae excercitationes observationesque variae. . . . Nurnberg.

—— 1575. De avium sceletes et praecipuis musculis. Caput II De differentiis avium. Trans. by Ethel Davis, 1947. Author's MS. Ithaca, N. Y.

—— 1575. Lectiones Gabrielis Fallopii. Nurnberg.

COLE, F. J. 1944. A history of comparative anatomy, from Aristotle to the eighteenth century. London, Macmillan.

COLENSO, W. 1877. On the day in which Capt. Cook took formal possession of New Zealand. *Trans. N. Z. Inst.* **10**: 99–108.

—— 1877. Manibus Parkinsonibus sacrum. A brief memoir of the first artist who visited New Zealand. *Trans. N. Z. Inst.* **10**: 108–134.

—— 1877. Notes chiefly historical on the ancient dog of the New Zealanders. *Trans. N. Z. Inst.* **10**: 135–155.

COLERIDGE, ERNEST HARTLEY. 1906–1909. Coleridge, Wordsworth and the American botanist William Bartram. *Trans. R. Soc. of Lit.* ser. 2, **27–28**: 69–92.

COLLINSON, PETER. 1758. Migration of swallows. *Trans. R. Soc. London* **51**: 459–464.

COOK, CAPT. JAMES. 1768–1770. MS. Drawings by several hands in Capt. Cook's 1st voyage. Bequeathed by Sir Joseph Banks in 1832. Brit. Mus. Dept. Manuscripts.

—— 1766. Eclipse of the sun. *Royal Soc., Phil. Trans.* **57**: 215–216.

—— 1768–1771. MS. Death entry Sydney Parkinson, Jan. 26, 1771. Logbook of the Endeavor, MSS. 8959–8960. Brit. Mus. Dept. Manuscripts.

COOKE, W. W. 1884. Bird nomenclature of the Chippewa Indians. *Auk*, o. s. **9**; n. s. **1**: 242–250.

COUES, ELLIOTT. 1875. Fasti ornithologiae redivivi. 1. Bartram's travels. *Proc. Acad. Nat. Sci., Phila.,* 338–358.

—— 1876. Note on the Labrador duck. *Amer. Naturalist* **10**: 303.

—— 1878. Birds of the Colorado Valley. *U. S. Geol. Survey. Misc. Pub.* **11** (1) Bibliographical appendix: 567–807.

—— 1878–1880. Bibliography of ornithology. 4 v. v. 1–3, American ornithological bibliography; 4. Faunal publications relating to British birds. Wash.

Part I. Faunal publications relating to North America. *Extract from Misc. Publ. U. S. Geol. Surv. Terr.* **11**: 567–748, 1878. Indexes.

Part II. Faunal publications relating to rest of America. Extract from Bull. U. S. Geol. and Geogr. Survey Terr. **5**: 239–330, 1879.

Part III. Systematic publications relating to American species, arranged according to families. From the Bull. U. S. Geol. and Geogr. Survey of the Terr. **5**: 521–1072.

Part IV. Faunal publications relating to British birds. From Proc. U. S. Nat. Museum **2**: 359–477, 1880.

—— 1880. Behind the veil. *Bull. Nuttall Ornithol. Club* **5** (4): 193–204.

—— 1882. Check-list of North American birds. **121**: 37. Boston.

—— 1884. Structure of birds' ears or a hearing of birds ears. *Science 2* (34, 38, 39): 422–424, 552–554, 586–589. Review: *Auk* **1** (2): 182.

—— 1896. Presidential address at World's Congress on ornithology, 29. Chicago.

—— 1898. William Swainson to John James Audubon [a letter]. *Auk* **15**: 11.

—— 1899. The finishing stroke to Bartram. *Auk* **16**: 83–84.

—— 1903. Key to North American birds. 2 v. Boston, The Page Co.

COX, JOHN. 1910. The Parish registers of England. London, Methuen & Co.

CRANTZ, DAVID. 1767. History of Greenland. 2 v. London, Print. for the Brethren's Soc. for Furtherance of the Gospel among the Heathen.

CREVECŒUR, MICHEL GUILLAUME JEAN DE. 1783. Letters from an American farmer conveying some idea of the interior circumstances of the British Colonies in America. London.

CRICHTON, THOMAS. 1819. Biographical sketches of the late Alexander Wilson, author of poems and American ornithology . . . *The Weavers' Mag. & Lit. Compan.* **2**. Paisley.

CRIÉ, L. 1882. Pierre Belon du Mans et l'anatomie compareé. *Rev. Sci.* **4**. Paris.

CUBE, JOHANN VON. 1497. Hortus (ortus) sanitatis. Herbal with zoological references and illustrations. Strassburg, Johann Prüss.

CURTIS, ELIZABETH, and ROBERT C. MILLER. 1938. The sclerotic ring in North American birds. *Auk* **55** (2): 225.

CUVIER, GEORGES. 1841–1845. Histoire des sciences naturelles. Paris, Fortin et Masson et Cᶦᵉ.

DE COSTA, B. F. 1883. Ingram's journey through North America in 1567–1569. *Mag. Amer. Hist.* **9**: 168–176.

DE COSTA, MENDEZ. 1812. Notices and anecdotes of literati collectors, etc. Coll. between 1747 and 1788. *Gentleman's Mag. & Hist. Chron.* **82** (1): 206.

DALE, SAMUEL. n. d. Manuscript letters in Sherard MSS. **2**: 206, 211–212, 220, 226–227, 231. R. Soc. of London.

DAMPIER-WHETHAM, WILLIAM CECIL. 1930. A history of science and its relations with philosophy and religion. London, Macmillan.

DARLINGTON, WILLIAM. 1849. Memorials of John Bartram and Humphrey Marshall. Phila.

DAVIS, ETHEL. 1948. MS. Translation of Volcher Coiter's De differentiis avium. Author's MS. Ithaca, N. Y.

DAWSON, WARREN R. 1925. The bee-eater (Merops apeaster) from the earliest times and a further note on the Hoopoe. *Ibis* ser. 12, **67** (3): 590–594.

Deane Collection of portraits of ornithologists. See Palmer, T. S.

DE BRAHM, JOHN GERAR WM. 1849. History of the province of Georgia, 1–55. Wormsloe, Ga.

DE BRY, THEODORE. 1591. Peregrinations. 1st part Hariot's Virginia with John White's drawings. 2d part LeMoyne, Florida with LeMoyne's drawings. Frankfurt am Main.

—— 1591. Brevis narratorio. America part 2. Frankfurt am Main.

—— 1904. Catalogue of the DeBry collection of voyages, narrative of LeMoyne 2. *N. Y. Pub. Libr. Bull.* **8**: 232.

DELAUNAY, DR. P. 1922–1925. L'aventureuse existence de Pierre Belon du Mans. *Rev. du seizième siècle* **9** : 251–268; **10**: 1–34; 125–147; **11**: 30–48; 222–232; **12**: 78–97; 256–282.

—— 1922. La jeunesse de Pierre Belon. *Rev. du seizième siècle,* 451.

—— 1935. La vie medicale aux XVI, XVII et XVIII siècles: 247. Paris.

DE LIUT, DR. J. G. 1934. De tentoonstelling en het portret van Volcher Coiter te Leiden Nederlandsche Tijdschrift voor Geneeskunde **78**: 2486–2487.

DENNY, MARGARET. 1948. Linnaeus and his disciple in Carolina: Alexander Garden. *Isis* **38** (3–4, nos. 113–114) : 161–174.

DENYS, NICOLAS. 1908. The description and natural history of the coasts of North America. Tr. & ed. by Wm. F. Ganoung. Toronto, Champlain Soc.

DERHAM, W. 1718. Philosophical letters of John Ray. London. Print by W. & J. Innys.

—— 1798. Physico-theology **1**: fig. 9–11, pl. H: viii. London.

—— 1846. Select remains and life of Ray. Ed. Lankester, Memorials of John Ray. London, Ray Soc.

DÉRY, D. A. 1933. First mention and original descriptions of certain birds of the Province of Quebec. *Alauda* **3** (3).

—— 1933. First notes and original descriptions of certain birds of the Province of Quebec, by explorers, missionaries, colonizers, privateers and adventurers of New France from 1534 to 1730. *Auk* **50**: 14.

DICKSON, JOHN BATHHURST. 1856. Life, labors and genius of Alexander Wilson. Paisley.

Dictionary of national biography. 1885. London, Oxford Univ. Pr.

Dictionary of national biography (concise). 1921. London, Oxford Univ. Pr.

DIOGENES LAERTIUS. 1853. The lives and opinions of eminent philosophers. London.

DIOSCORIDES. See Gunther, Robt. T.

Dow, R. P. 1914. John Abbot of Georgia. *Jour. N. Y. Ent. Soc.* **22**: 65–72.

—— 1913. Matters of coleopterous species. *Bull. Brooklyn Ent. Soc.* **8**: 37.

DRAYTON, JOHN. 1802. A view of South Carolina as respects her natural and civil concerns, p. 629. Charleston, S. C.

DRIESEN, LUDWIG. 1846. Leben des Fursten Johann Moretz von Nassau-Siegen, x, 101–112. Berlin.

DUNLAP, WILLIAM. 1918. History of the rise and progress of the arts of design in the United States, Boston.

DU PRATZ, LE P. 1763. History of Louisiana or of the western parts of Virginia and Carolina. 2 v. London, Print. for T. Becket & P. A. De Hondt.

DURRIE, D. S. 1869–1872. Capt. Jonothan Carver and Carver's grant. *Wis. Hist. Coll.* **6**: 220–270.

EARNEST, ERNEST. 1940. John and William Bartram. Phila., Univ. of Penna. Press.

EDEN, RICHARD. 1885. The first three English books on America (1511–1555). Ed. by Edward Arber. Birmingham.

EDWARDS, BRYAN. 1797. Historical survey of the French colony at Santo Domingo, London.

EDWARDS, EDWARD. 1870. Lives of the founders of the British Museum, with notices of its chief augmentors and other benefactors. London.

EDWARDS, GEORGE. 1743–1751. A natural history of birds. Most of which have not been figur'd or describ'd. 4 v. London.

—— 1764. Gleanings of natural history. London.

—— 1771. The natural history of Carolina, Florida and the Bahama Islands, by M. Catesby. Revised by Mr. Edwards. London. See Catesby, M.

—— 1780. The emigration of British birds. 4th ed. Salisbury.

EGEDE, HANS. 1745. Description of Greenland showing the natural history, situation, boundaries, and face of the country. London, Print. for C. Hitch.

EGGLESTON, EDWARD. 1882. The beginning of a nation. *The Century* **25** (n. s. 3) : 61–83.

EILSWORTH, R. 1895. Life and writings of Rafinesque. Louisville. *Wilson Club Publ.* **10**.

ELLIS, HENRY. 1748. A voyage to Hudson's Bay by the Dobbs Galley and California, in the years 1746 and 1747 for discovering a northwest passage. London, Print. for H. Whitridge.

ELLIS, W. 1782. A narrative of a voyage performed by Captains Cook and Clerke. 2 v. London.

ELLIS, W. W. 1776–1780. MS. 115 original water colour sketches of animals, birds, fish, etc., made by W. W. Ellis on Cook's third voyage, 1776–1780. Brit. Mus. of Nat. Hist. Banksian MS. No. 33.

Encyclopedia Britannica. 1926. A dictionary of arts, sciences, literature and general information. 13th ed. London and New York. Encycl. Brit. Co.

ENGLEMANN, WILHELM. 1846. Bibliotheca historico-naturalis. Verzeichniss der bücher über naturgeschichte welche . . . in den jahren 1700–1846. Leipzig.

ESSIG, E. O. 1931. History of entomology. N. Y., Macmillan.

EWEN, L'ESTRANGE C. 1938. The north-west passage, light on the murder of Henry Hudson, 2 and 3. [London?], printed for the author.

EWEN, CECIL HENRY L'ESTRANGE. 1931. A history of surnames of the British Isles. London, K. Paul, Trench, Trubner & Co.

EXELL, A. W. 1929–1930. Two eighteenth century American naturalists (John and William Bartram). *Nat. Hist. Mag. Brit. Mus.* **2**: 50–58.

FAIRCHILD, THOMAS. 1722. The city gardener. London.

FARADAY, F. J. 1890. Selections from corr. of John Leigh Philips. *Mem. & Proc. Manchester Lit. and Phil. Soc.* 4th ser. **3**: 13–54.

FAULKNER, THOMAS. 1829. Historical and topographical description of Chelsea. London.

FAXON, WALTER. 1896. John Abbot's drawings of the birds of Georgia. *Auk* **13**: 204–215.

—— 1901. Early editions of Wilson's ornithology. *Auk* **18**: 216–218.

—— 1903. A rare work on American ornithology. *Auk* **20** (2) : 236–241.

—— 1915. Relics of Peale's museum. *Bull. Mus. Comp. Zool.* **49**: 119–148.

—— 1919. Capt. Thomas Brown's illustrations of the American ornithology of Wilson and Bonaparte. *Auk.* **46** (4) : 623–626.

—— 1921. Notes and news [obituary]. *Auk* **38** (1) : 157–158.

FEE, ANTOINE L. A. 1832. Vie de Linné, suivie de l'analyse de sa correspondance avec les principaux naturalistes de son époque. Paris, F. G. Levrault.

FELTER, HARVEY WICKS. 1927. The genesis of the American materia medica. *Bull. Lloyd Libr. of Bot., Pharm. and Materia Medica* **26**.

FELTON, SAMUEL. 1830. On the portraits of English authors on gardening . . . 2d ed. London, A & C. Black.

FERNALD, M. L. 1877. Notes on plants of Wineland. *Rhode Island Hist. Tracts* **2**.

—— 1942. Some early botanists of American Philosophical Society. *Proc. Amer. Philos. Soc.* **86** (1) : 63–71.

FIELD, HENRY. 1820. Memoirs historical and illustrative of the Botanick Garden at Chelsea. London, R. Gilbert.

FLEMING, REV. JOHN. 1823–24. Gleanings of natural history during a voyage along the coast of Scotland in 1821. *Edinb. Phil. Jour.* **10**: 97.

FOLEY, JOHN P. 1900. The Jeffersonian Cyclopedia, 607. New York and London: Funk and Wagnalls.

FORSTER, JOHANN REINHOLD. 1771. A catalogue of the animals of North America. . . . London, B. White.

—— 1772. An account of the birds sent from Hudson Bay. . . . *Phil. Trans.* **63**: 382–433.

—— 1772–1774. MS. Bird drawings made on Capt. Cook's 2d voyage round the world. Nat. Hist. Mus., London.

FOSTER, G. 1887. London marriage licenses. 1521–1869. London.

FOSTER, SIR MICHAEL. 1902. History of physiology. Cambridge.

FOTHERGILL, JOHN. 1770. Account of Peter Collinson. Royal Soc. MSS. Sims correspondence.

FOX, DR. HINGSTON. 1919. Dr. John Fothergill and his friends. London.

FOX(E), CAPT. LUKE, and CAPT. THOMAS JAMES. 1894. Voyages of Foxe and James. *Hakluyt Soc. Publ.* 2 v. 88–89.

FRANCILLON, JOHN. 1792. In add. MS. 29533. Letters by Francillon to John Leigh Philips of Manchester. Dept. of MSS, Brit. Mus.

—— 1818. Catalogue of the collection of foreign insects owned by Francillon. London, Ankionskatalog.

FRIEDMANN, HERBERT. 1934. Thomas Anburey's observations on American birds. *Auk* **51** (2) : 200–206.

—— 1946. The symbolic goldfinch; its history and significance in European devotional art. Washington, Pantheon Books.

FRIES, THEODOR MAGNUS, ed. 1908. Bref och skrifvelser af och till Carl von Linné, 1907–1922.

FUERTES, LOUIS A. 1920. Falconry, the sport of kings. *Nat. Geog. Mag.* **38**: 429–460.

FULTON, JOHN F. 1931. The rise of the experimental method. Bacon and the Royal Society. *Yale Jour. of Biol. & Med.* **3** (4) : 299–320.

GADOW, H. Oct. 26, 1907. A seventeenth century fisherman and fowler. *The Field, the Garden, the Country Gentleman's Newspaper* **110** (2861) : 765.

GALLATIN, FREDERIC, JR. 1908. Catalogue of a collection of books on ornithology in the library of Frederic Gallatin, Jr. N. Y., Privately printed.

GANONG, W. F., ed. 1907. Richard Denys Sieur de France and his attempts to settle northern New Brunswick. *Coll. N. Bruns. Hist. Soc.* **111**: 7–54.

—— 1908. The description and natural history of the coasts of North America by Nicolas Denys. Toronto, Champlain Soc. Ed. with a memoir of the author.

GARDNER, DORSEY. 1876. Wilson the ornithologist. *Scribner's Mo.* **11** (5) : 690–703.

GEE, WILSON. 1918. South Carolina botanists biography and bibliography. *Bull. Univ. of S. Car.* **72**.

GELDART, ALICE M. 1914. Sir James E. Smith and some of his friends. *Trans. Norfolk and Norwich Nat. Soc.* **9**: 645–692.

GESNER, CONRAD. 1551–1558. Historiae animalium. 4 v. Zurich.

—— 1555. Icones avium omnium quae in historia avium Conradi Gesneri describunter . . . 2 v. in 1. Tiguri.

GILL, THEODORE M. 1899. A great work proposed. *Osprey* **3** (6) : 93.

—— 1900. Correspondence of and about Audubon with Swainson. *Osprey* **5** (2) : 23.

—— 1900–1901. Swainson and his times. *Osprey* **4** (7): 104–108; **4** (8) : 120–123; 135–138; (10) : 154–156; 166–171; **5** (1) : 8–10; **5** (3) : 37–39; **5** (4) : 58–59; **5** (5) : 71–72; (9) : 136–137; **5** (10) : 152–155; **5** (11–12) : 167–172; 176.

—— 1911. General notes. Kalm's articles on the passenger pigeon. *Auk* **28** (1) : 110–111.

GLADSTONE, H. S. 1923. Seventeenth century names for some British birds. *Brit. Birds* **17** (3) : 50–54.

—— 1938. Thomas Watling, limner of Dumfries. Reprint from Trans. Dumfriesshire and Galloway, Nat. Hist. & Antiquar. Soc., Dumfries.

GLOGER, CONSTANTIN WILHELM LAMBERT. 1834. Vollständiges handbuch der naturgeschichte der vögel Europa's . . . Breslau.

GLOVER, THOMAS. 1676. Account of Virginia. *Phil. Trans.* **11**: 623–636.

GMELIN, J. 1789. Systema naturae **1**: 563. Lipsiae.

GOLDSMITH, O. 1774. A history of the earth and animated nature. London, I. Nourse.

GOODE, GEORGE BROWN. 1886. The beginnings of natural history in America. *Proc. Biol. Soc. Washington* **3**: 35–105.

—— 1886–1888. The beginnings of American science; the third century. *Proc. Biol. Soc. Washington* **4**. Educational pamphlet 52.

—— 1896. Obituary and a few facts of his career. Notes and News. *Auk*, **13**: 349.

—— 1897. Origin of national scientific and educational institutions of the United States. *Ann. Rept. Smithsonian Inst. Rept. U. S. Nat. Mus.*, pt. **2**: 265–354.

GRAY, GEORGE R. 1843. Some rectifications of Australian birds. *Annals & Mag. Nat. Hist.*, **17**: 189–194.

GRAY, DR. J. E. 1869. Birds in the Philadelphia Museum. *Annals and Mag. of Nat. Hist.* **3**: 317–319.

GREEN, J. R. 1909. A history of botany, 1860–1900; a continuation of Sache. Hist. of Botany, 1530–1860, Oxford.

GREENE, EARLE, WILLIAM GRIFFIN, EUGENE ODUM, HERBERT STODDARD, and IVAN TOMKINS. 1945. Birds of Georgia. Athens, Univ. of Georgia Pr.

GREENWAY, J., JR. 1931. A Jefferson letter of historical and ornithological interest. *Auk* **48** (2) : 175–180.

GREGORY, W. K. 1908. Linnaeus as an intermediary between ancient and modern zoology. *N. Y. Acad. Sci.* **18**: 31–32.

GREW, NEHEMIAH. 1681. Musaeum regalis societates, or a catalogue and description of the natural and artificial rarities belonging to the Royal Society and preserved at Gresham College, whereunto is subjoined the comparative anatomy of stomachs and guts. London.

—— 1687. Description of the hummingbird (from a letter written by Mr. Hamersly of Coventry). *Phil. Trans. R. Soc.* **17**: 760.

—— 1687. A query put by Dr. Grew concerning the food of the hummingbird. . . . *Phil. Trans.* **17**: 815.

GRIEVE, SYMINGTON. 1885. The great auk or gare fowl; its history, archeology and remains. London.

GRINNELL, GEORGE BIRD. 1920. Recollections of Audubon Park. *Auk* **37** (3) : 372–380.

GRONOVIUS, JOHANNES F. (with JOHN CLAYTON). 1739–1743. Flora Virginica, exhibens plantas quas v. c. Johannes Clayton in Virginia observavit atque collegit. Lugduni Batavorum, apud Cornelium Haak.

GROSART, A. B. 1876. Poems and literary prose for the first time fully collected and compared with the original, early editions and MSS. 2 v. Paisley, Alex. Garden.

GROSART, ALEXANDER B. 1876. Memoir and remains of Alexander Wilson. 2 v. Paisley, Alex. Garden.

GUDGER, E. W. 1912. George Marcgrave, the first student of American natural history. *Pop. Sci. Mo.* **81**: 250–274.

GUNTHER, ALBERT. 1899. Swainson's correspondence. *Osprey* **5** (2) : 29.

GUNTHER, ROBERT T. 1925. Early science in Oxford. *Philosophical Soc.* **4**. Oxford. Printed for subscribers.

—— 1933. The Greek herbal of Dioscorides. Oxford.

GURNEY, JOHN HENRY. 1921. Early annals of ornithology. London, Witherby.

HAGNE, HERMANN AUGUST. 1888. The pioneer painter of North American insects. *Psyche* **5** (151–152) : 134–135.

HAKLUYT, RICHARD. 1582? The principal navigations, voyages, traffiques and discoveries of the English nation . . . at any time within the compasse of these 1600 years. N. Y., E. P. Dutton [1926].

HALE, EDWARD E. 1860. Report to the Publishing Committee. *Proc. Amer. Antiquar. Soc. semi-annual meeting,* Apr. 25, 1860. P. 47.

HALKETT, SAMUEL, and JOHN LAING. 1926. Dictionary of anonymous and pseudonymous *English Literature* **4** . . . Edinburgh, Oliver and Boyd.

HALLAM, HENRY. 1886. An introduction to the literature of Europe in the 15th, 16th and 17th centuries **3** : ch. 9. London.

HALLIWELL-PHILLIPS, J. O. 1839. Catalogue of miscellaneous manuscripts. London, Royal Soc.

HALLWELL, J. O. 1841. Collection of letters illustrative of progress of science in England from Queen Liz to Charles II. London, Print. for Hist. of Sci. Society.

HAMOR, RAPHE, JR. 1615. A true discourse of the estate of Virginia . . . and the success of the affaires there till the 18 of June, 1614 . . . London, Print. by John Beale for William Welby.

HARDEN, WILLIAM. 1913. History of Savannah and South Georgia. Chicago & N. Y.

HARDY, FANNIE P. 1888. Testimony of some early voyagers on the Great Auk. *Auk* **5** : 380–384.

HARIOT, SIR THOMAS. 1585. Briefe and true report of the new found land of Virginia. London.

HARPER, FRANCIS. 1939. William Bartram's bicentennial. *Sci. Mo.* **48** : 380–384.

—— 1942. Diary of a journey through the Carolinas, Georgia and Florida from July 1765 to April 10, 1766. John Bartram. *Trans. Amer. Phil. Soc.,* n. s. **33** (1).

—— 1942. William Bartram's names of birds. *Proc. Rochester Acad. Sci.* **8** (4) : 208–221.

—— 1943. Travels in Georgia and Florida, 1773–73. A report to Dr. John Fothergill by William Bartram . . . *Trans. Amer. Philos. Soc.,* n. s. **33** (2).

HARPER, FRANCIS P. 1903. Bibliotheca Americana, priced catalogue of a remarkable collection of books . . . relating to discovery, settlement and history of the Western Hemisphere. N. Y.

HARRIS, HARRY. 1919. Historical notes on Harris' sparrow, Zonotrichia querula. *Auk* **36** : 180.

[HARRISSE, HENRY] 1866. Bibliotheca Americana velutissima. A description of works relating to America published between year 1492 and 1551. N. Y., Geo. P. Philco.

HASKELL, D. C. 1942. United States exploring expedition 1838–1842 and its publications. *N. Y. Pub. Libr. Bull.* **46.**

HASKINS, C. H. 1921. De arte venandi cum avibus of Frederick II. *Eng. Hist. Rev.* **36** : 334–355.

—— 1924. Studies in the history of mediaeval science. Cambridge, Harvard Univ. Press.

—— 1925. Rediscovery of Aristotle. *Isis* **23** : 478.

—— 1927. Renaissance of the twelfth century. Cambridge, Harvard Univ. Press.

HAWKINS, SIR JOHN. 1878. The arrival and courtesie of M. Hawkins to the distressed Frenchmen in Florida. *Hakluyt Soc.* **55** : 65.

HAWKS, FRANCIS LISTER. 1857–1858. History of North Carolina. 2 v. Fayetteville, N. C.

HAWKSWORTH, JOHN. 1773. Account of voyages undertaken by order of his present majesty. London.

HEARN, LAFCADIO. 1890. Two years in the French West Indies. N. Y., Harper and Bros.

HEARNE, S. 1795. A journey from Prince of Wales Fort in Hudson's Bay to the Northern Ocean. Birds, Chap. 10 : 398–448. London, Sold by T. Cadell, Jun. & W. Davis.

HELLMAYR, C. E. 1930. Louis Bosc, ornithologue oublié. *Alauda,* ser. 1, **2** (2) : 122–132.

HELTZEL, VIRGIL B. New light on Edward Topsell. Huntington Libr. Quart. **1** (2) : 199–202.

HEMMING, FRANCIS. 1950. Stability in zoological nomenclature. *Auk* **67** (2) : 370–374.

HENDERSON, J. 1853. Poetical works of Alexander Wilson with extended memoir of his life and writings. Belfast, Edinburgh, London.

HENNEPIN, LOUIS. 1698. A new discovery of a vast country in America extending about 4000 miles between New France and New Mexico, with a description of the Great Lakes, cataracts, rivers, plants and animals. London, M. Bentley.

HERNANDEZ, F. 1651. Rerum medicarum novae Hispaniae thesaurus. 2 v. Rome.

HERRICK, FRANCIS HOBART. 1938. Audubon the naturalist; a history of his life and time. 2 v. in 1; 2d ed. N. Y. & London, D. Appleton-Century Co.

HERVEY, SYDENHAM H. A. 1908. Biographical history of boys educated at King Edward VI free grammar school, Bury St., Edmunds, from 1550 to 1900. Bury St. Edmunds, Paul & Matthews.

—— 1914. Ladbroke and its owners. Bury St. Edmunds, Paul & Matthews.

HIGGINSON, FRANCIS. 1630. New England's plantation. London, Michaud S. Parke.

HODSON, WILLIAM WALTER. 1893. The meeting house and the manse, or the story of the independents of Sudbury.

HOLMES, MAURICE. Nov. 5, 1931. Capt. Cook's voyages. *Times Lit. Suppl.,* 866.

HOPE, SIR WILLIAM ST. JOHN. n. d. Churches of St. Nicholas. Halstead, W. H. Root.

HORN, W., and S. SCHENKLING. 1928. Index litteraturae entomologicae. Berlin-Dahlem.

HUME, EDGAR ERSKINE. 1942. Ornithologists of the United States medical corps. Thirty-six biographies. Baltimore, Johns Hopkins Press.

HUME, O. A. 1878. No title. *Stray feathers* **7** : 506-508.

HUTCHINS, THOMAS. 1772. Manuscript on American birds written at York Fort. London, Roy. Soc. of London.

HUXLEY, JULIAN. 1916. Bird watching and biological science. *Auk* **33** : 142–162.

IMLAY, GEORGE. 1793. A topographical description of the Western Territory of North America. London.

INGRAM, DAVID. 1883. Narrative. Reprinted in *Mag. Amer. Hist.* **9** : 200–208. From orig. MS. Bod. Libr. Tanner MS. 79. f. 172.

International code of zoological nomenclature. 1926. *Proc. Biol. Soc. Washington* **39** : 75–104.

IREDALE, TOM. 1925–1927. Georg Forster's drawings. *Australian Zool.* **4** : 48–53.

—— 1938. William Anderson—ornithologist. *Emu* **38** (1) : 60–62.

—— 1937. J. R. and G. Forster naturalists. *Emu* **37** : 95–199.

JACKSON, BENJAMIN DAYTON. 1881. Guide to the literature of botany, being a classified selection of botanical works . . . London, Pub. for the Index Soc. by Longmans, Green & Co.

—— 1923. Linnaeus; the story of his life adapted from the Swedish by Theodor Magnus Fries. Trans. by B. D. Jackson. London, H. F. & G. Witherby.

JAEGER, BENEDICT. 1859. The life of American insects containing a life of Sir Hans Sloane. N. Y.

JAEGER, EDMUND. 1948. Does the poor-will "hibernate"? *Condor* **50** (1) : 45–46.

—— 1949. Further observations on the hibernation of the poor-will. *Condor* **51** (3) : 105–109.

JAMES, T. E. 1932–1933. George Edwards, F. R. S., an eighteenth century naturalist. *Sci. Prog.* **37** : 486.

JARDINE, SIR WILLIAM. 1843. Ed. Naturalists' Libr. Memoir of Baron Haller, **17**: 17–63. Edinburgh, W. H. Lizars.

—— 1843. Ed. Naturalists' Libr. Memoir of Francis Willughby, **16**: 17–146. Edinburgh, W. H. Lizars.

JEFFERSON, THOMAS. 1787. Notes on the state of Virginia. London, Print. for John Stockdale.

Jeffersonian Cyclopedia. 1900. See Foley, John P.

JOHNSON, HENRY G. 1874. Lewis and Clark expedition. *Amer. Hist. Rev.* **3**: 295–403.

JOHNSTONE, JOHN. 1657. Historae naturalis de avibus. 6 pts. in 1 v. [2] De avibus. Frankfurt am Main.

JONES, Family papers. I Oct. 16, 1649–Feb. 23, 1724. MS. Washington, Libr. of Cong. Dept. Manuscripts.

JONES, CHARLES C. 1878. Dead towns of Georgia. *Ga. Hist. Soc. Coll.* **4**: 240.

JONES, LEWIS H. 1891. Capt. Roger Jones of London and Virginia. Albany.

JONES, T. CATESBY. 1934–1940. Personal letters to E. G. Allen about the Catesby family. Ithaca, N. Y., Cornell Univ.

JORDAN, DAVID STARR. 1905. A guide to the study of fishes. Hist. of Ichthyology **1**: 387–428. New York, Henry Holt & Co.

JOSSELYN, J. 1672. New England's rarities discovered: in birds, beasts, fishes, serpents and plants of that country. London, Print. for G. Widdowes.

—— 1675. An account of two voyages to New England. London, Print. for G. Widdowes.

—— 1860. New England's Rarities discovered, with introd. and notes. *Trans. Amer. Antiquarium Soc.* **4**: 137–238.

JUEL, H. O., and JOHN W. HARSHBERGER. 1929. New light on the collection of North American plants made by Peter Kalm, *Proc. Acad. Nat. Sci. Phila.* **81**: 297–303.

KALM, PEHR. 1911. A description of wild pigeons which visit southern English colonies in North America during certain years in incredible multitudes. *Auk* **28**: 53–66. Tr. by S. M. Gronberger.

KALM, PETER. 1937. Travels in North America. N. Y., Wilson-Erickson.

KAUFMANN, ALEXANDER. 1899. Thomas von Contimprés. Köln, J. P. Bachem.

KENDRICK, JAMES. 1853. Profiles of Warrington worthies. Warrington, J. Haddock & son.

KENNARD, FRED H. 1919. Obituary of Frederick Bridgham McKecknie. *Auk* **36**: 449–451.

KILLERMANN, SEBASTIAN. 1910. Die vogelkunde des Albertus Magnus. Regensberg.

KIRBY, W. F. 1888. John Abbot the Aurelian. *Can. Entomologist* **20** (12) : 230–232.

KITTREDGE, GEORGE L. 1916. Cotton Mather's scientific communication to the Royal Society. *Proc. Amer. Antiq. Soc.,* n. s. **26**: 18–57.

KOHL, JOHANN G. 1869. American discovery. Documentary history of the state of Maine. *Me. Hist. Soc. Coll.,* 2d ser. **1**: 248–289. (Expedition of Giovanni da Verrazano in 1524.) Portland.

LABAT, JEAN BAPTISTE. 1724. Nouveau voyage aux isles de l'Amérique; contenant l'histoire naturelle de ces pays, les mœurs, la religion, le gouvernement, les guerres, le commerce et les manufactures. 2 v. La Haye.

LACK, DAVID. 1944. Early references to territory in bird-life. *Condor* **46**: 108–111.

LAHONTAN, BARON DE. 1703. New voyages to North America. 2 v. London Print. for H. Bonwicke, etc.

LAUCHERT, F. 1891. Geschichte des physiologue. Strassburg.

LARSSON, HJALMAR. 1938. Carolus Linnaeus, physician and botanist. *Ann. Med. Hist.,* n.s. **10** (3) : 197–214.

LATHAM, JOHN. 1781–1785. A general synopsis of birds. 3 v. London.

—— 1790. Index ornithologicus. London.

—— 1797. The tracheae of birds. *Trans. Linn. Soc. of London* **4**: 90–128.

—— 1801. Account of the Abbey Church of Romsey. *Archaeologia* **14**.

—— 1821–1828. A general history of birds. 10 v. and 1 v. index. Winchester.

—— 1825–1835. MS. Letters. Additional MS. 29533 Presented by Dr. J. E. Gray. London, Brit. Mus. Dept. MSS.

LAUTERHORN, R. 1901. The bird-fish-and-animal book of the Strassburg Fisherman, Leonard Baldner (91666)—a manuscript. In announcements of the fisheries Association for the Prov. of Brandenburg (Mitteilungen des Fischerei—Vereins für die Provinz Brandenburg), 1901, No. 2. Reprinted also in *Naturwissenschaftliche Wochenschrift* (*The Nat. Sci. Wkly.*) **16**: 432–437.

LAVAUDEN, L. 1934. On the Partridge. *Alauda Ser.* **3** (2). In French.

LAWSON, JOHN. 1714. The history of Carolina; containing the exact description and natural history of that country. London, Print. for W. Taylor . . . and T. Baker.

LEACH, W. E. 1819. Notice of some animals from the arctic regions. *Thomson's Ann. of Philos.* **13**: 60–61.

LICHTENSTEIN, A. A. 1814–1817. Die Werke von Marcgrave und Piso über die naturgeschichte Brasiliens erläutert aus den original Abbildungen. Abhandlungen der Kgl. Akad. der Wissenshaften zu Berlin.

LEGG, JOHN. 1776. Some memoirs of the life and works of George Edwards. London.

LE MOYNE, DEMORGUES JAQUES. 1586. La clef des Champs. Blackfriars, London. Copy at Victoria and Albert Mus. London.

—— Brevis narratorio. Pt. 2 of Historia Americae. See De Bry.

LEVERKHÜN, PAUL. 1893. Ornithologists, past and present, 199–205. Chicago, World's Cong. on Ornithol. Ed. by I. Rood.

LEWES, GEORGE HENRY. 1864. Aristotle, A chapter in the history of science. London.

LEWIS, FREDERIC T. 1944. The passenger pigeon as observed by the Rev. Cotton Mather. *Auk* **61** (4) : 587–592.

—— 1945. Cotton Mather's manuscript references to the passenger pigeon. *Auk* **62** (2) : 306–307.

LEWIS, HARRISON F. 1934. Notes on some details of the explorations by Jacques Cartier in the Gulf of St. Lawrence. *Trans. R. Soc. Can.,* Sec. **2** : 117–148.

LEWIS, MERIWETHER, and W. CLARKE. 1815. Travels to the source of the Missouri River and across the American Continent to the Pacific Ocean, 1804-5-6. New ed. 3 v. London, Print. for Longman, Hurst, Rees, Orme & Brown.

LINCOLN, F. C. 1944. Chimney swifts' winter home discovered. *Auk* **61**: 604–609.

LINNAEUS, C. (Linné, C. von). 1731. MS. Methodus avium sveticarum. Carolina Rediviva Bibliotek. Upsala, Sweden, Univ. of Upsala.

—— 1788. Systema naturae. 3 v. Lipsiae.

LODWICK, CHARLES. 1692. MS. letter dated New York, Mar. 20, 1692 to Mr. Francis Lodwick and Mr. Hooker, members of the Royal Society. London, Brit. Mus., Folio 253 of Sloane MS. 3339.

LONES, THOMAS EAST. 1912. Aristotle's researches in natural science. London.

LONGOLIUS, GYBERTUS. 1544. Dialogus de avibus et earum nominibus Graecis, Latinus et Germanicis. Cologne. Ed. by Wm. Turner.

LÖNNBERG, EINAR. 1905. Peter Artedi. A bicentenary memoir written on behalf of the Swedish R. Acad. Sci. Upsala and Stockholm.

—— 1926. The ornithological collections of the Natural History Museum in Stockholm. *Auk* **43** (4): 434–446.

—— 1931. Olof Rudbeck, Jr., the first Swedish ornithologist. *Ibis,* ser. 13, **1**: 302–307.

—— 1932. Linnaei anteckningar efter Olof Rudbeck d. y:s föreläsningar om Svenska fåglar.

LORANT, STEFAN, ed. 1946. The New World; the first pictures of America; made by John White and Jacques [*sic*] Lemoyne and engraved by Theodore Debry, with contemporary narratives of the Huguenot settlement in Florida 1562–1565 and the Virginia Colony 1585–1590. N. Y., Duell, Sloan & Pearce.

LOVELL, HARVEY B., and MABEL SLACK and a brief history of Kentucky ornithology. 1949. A bibliography of Kentucky ornithology. *Ky. Ornith. Soc. Occ. Pub.* **1**. Bowling Green. Selby Smith.

LOSKIEL, GEORGE HENRY. 1794. History of the mission of the United Brethren among the Indians. 3 pts. London, Sold by John Stockdale.

LOUDON, J. C. 1838. Arboretum et fructicetum Britannicum. 8 v. London.

LOVEJOY, ARTHUR O. 1907. The place of Linnaeus in the history of science. *Popular Sci. Mo.* **71**: 498–508.

LOWELL, FRANCIS C. 1904. Horace Gray. *Proc. Amer. Acad. Arts & Sci.* **39** (22): 627–637.

LOWNES, ALBERT E. 1940. A collection of seventeenth century drawings. *Auk* **57**: 532–535.

LUCAS, F. A. 1865. The gare-fowl and its historians. *Nat. Hist. Rev.* **5**: 467–488.

—— 1888. The bird rocks of the Gulf of St. Lawrence in 1887. *Auk* **5**: 129.

—— 1908. Linnaeus and American natural history. *N. Y. Acad. of Sci. Annals* **18** (1): 52–57.

—— 1888. Great Auk notes. *Auk,* n. s. **5**: 278–283.

LUCAS, JOSEPH, tr. 1892. Pehr Kalm's account of his visit to England on his way to America in 1748. London and N. Y., Macmillan.

LUTHER, FREDERICK N. 1885. Jefferson as a naturalist. *Mag. Amer. Hist.* **13**: 379–390.

MACGILLIVRAY, WILLIAM. 1843. British quadrupeds. The Naturalists' Library **17**: 15–58. With memoir of Ulysses Aldrovandi. Edinburgh. W. H. Lizars.

MACKAY, DOUGLAS. 1938. The honourable company. A history of Hudson's Bay Company. Indianapolis. New York. Bobbs Merril.

MACLEOD, R. R. 1903. Markland or Nova Scotia, 187. Halifax.

MACNAMARA, CHARLES. 1926. Champlaine as a naturalist. *Can. Field Naturalist* **40**: 125–133.

MAIDEN, J. H. 1859. Sir Joseph Banks. London, K. Paul and Sydney. W. A. Gulick.

MARCGRAVE, GEORGE. 1648. Historie rerum naturalim Brasiliae. Leyden and Amsterdam.

MARCGRAVIUS, GEORGE. 1660. MS. Brazilianische naturgegenstände. A36 and A37. Berlin Preussische Staatsbibliotek.

MARTEN, HUMPHREY. 1750–1786. MS. A short description of the birds in a box seen at York Factory. R. Soc. of London.

MARTIN, ERNEST WHITNEY. 1914. Birds of the Latin poets. Leland Stanford Junior Univ. Publ., Univ. Ser.

MASSON, IRVINE. 1925. Three centuries of chemistry. (Founding of R. Soc. 1640–1665, ch. 3–4.) London. E. Benn, Limited.

MATHER, COTTON. 1721. The Christian philosopher: a collection of the best discoveries in nature . . . Essay xxx. Some paragraphs on the feathered kind. London.

MATHEWS, GREGORY M. 1920. Dates of ornithological works. *Austral Avian Rec.* **4** (1): 1–27.

—— 1920. Sherborn and the systematist. *Austral Avian Rec.* **4** (4–5).

—— 1921. Lichtenstein's sale catalogues. *Austral Avian Rec.* **4** (6): 139.

—— 1922. An extraordinary bird book. Ornithologia or The birds in 2 parts, by James Jennings. *Austral Avian Rec.* **4** (7): 172–175.

—— 1931. John Latham, 1740–1837: an early English ornithologist. *Ibis,* ser. 13, **1** (3): 466–475.

MATHEWS, GREGORY M., and TOM IREDALE. 1915. Table des planches enlum. of Boddaert. *Austral Avian Rec.* **3** (2): 31–51.

MATHEWS, GREGORY M., and TOM IREDALE. 1922. Captain Thomas Brown, ornithologist. *Austral Avian Rec.* **4** (7): 176–194.

MAWER, ALLEN M. A. 1920. The place-names of Northumberland and Durham. Cambridge Univ. Pr.

MAXIMILIAN, PRINCE ZU WIED. 1839–1841. Reis im Innern Nord-America, in den jahren 1832 bis 1834. 2 v. Coblenz, Rev. *Auk* **36**: 185.

McATEE, WALDO LEE. July 1911. Local names of waterfowl and other birds. Biol. Survey. Reprint. from *Forest & Stream,* 172–174, 196–197.

—— 1917. Life and writings of Professor F. E. L. Beal. *Auk* **34**: 243–264.

—— 1918. A sketch of the natural history of the District of Columbia. . . . *Bull. Biol. Soc. Washington* **1**.

—— 1924. Local names of migratory game birds. *U.S.D.A. Misc. Cir.* **13**.

—— 1946. Georgian records in John Latham's General history of birds. *Oriole* **11** (1): 1–11.

—— 1949. A Linnaean paper needing further study. Chicago, Private print.

McKECHNIE, FREDERICK BRIDGHAM. 1919. Obituary. *Auk* **36** (2): 450.

MEGENBERG, KONRAD VON. 1475. Buch der natur. Die erste naturgeschichte im Deutscher sprache. Augsburg, Johann Bämler. 1861, Stuttgart.

MEINERTZHAGEN, R. 1930. Nicoll's birds of Egypt **2**: 528. London, H. Rees, ltd.

MEISEL, MAX. 1924–1929. Bibliography of American natural history. 3 v. Pioneer Century, 1769–1865. Brooklyn, N.Y., Premier Pub. Co.

MÉNÉGAUX, DR. A., ed. 1913. Ornithological papers of R. P. Lessons contributed to Echo du monde savant. Münich, Dultz & Co.

MERRETT, CHRISTOPHER. 1667. Pinax rerum naturalium Brittanicarum. London.

MIALL, L. C. 1912. The early naturalists, their lives and works, 1530–1782. London.

MICHAELIS, ELSA, Tr. 1930. Zimmermann's Captain Cook; an account of his 3d voyage (1776–1780). Toronto, Ryerson Press.

MIKAN, J. S. 1825. Flora and fauna of Brazil. *Auk* **42**: 283.

MILLER, PHILIP. 1803–1807. The gardeners dictionary newly arranged by T. Martyn. 8 ed. revised. 4 v. London.

MILNER, J. C. 1906. Catalogue of portraits of botanists. Kew, Eng., R. Bot. Gardens.

MOREAU DE SAINT-MÉRY, MÉDÉRIC LOUIS ÉLIE. 1797–1798. Description topographique, physique, civile, politique et historique de la partie Française de l'Isle Saint-Dominique. 2 v. Phila., Chez l'Auteur.

MORITZ, JOHANN. 1660. MS. Brazilianische natur geschichte Berlin 2. Libr. Pictur. A37. Preussische Staatsbibliotek Handschriften Abteilung.

MORRELL, WILLIAM. 1792. Poem on New England. *Coll. Mass. Hist. Soc.* **1**: 125–139.

MORRIS, EDWARD E. 1899. Captain Cook's first log in the Royal navy. *Cornhill Mag.* **80** n. s. **7**: 519–532.

MORTIMER, C. 1730. An account of Mr. Mark Catesby's Essay towards the natural history of Carolina and the Bahama Islands. *Phil. Trans.* **36**: 425–434.

MORTON, CHARLES. n. d. Birds going to the moon. *Harleian Miscellany* **11**: 558.

MORTON, T. 1637. New English Canaan. Reprint, *Force's Hist. Tracts* **2**.

MULLEN, W. H. 1908. Some early British ornithologists. *Brit. Birds* **2**: 5–13.

MULLENS, W. H., and H. KIRKE SWANN. 1916. A bibliography of British ornithology from early times to 1912. London, Macmillan. Rev. by Witmer Stone. *Auk* **33**: 443.

MUMFORD, A. A. 1917. MS. letter to Sir Lazarus Fletcher dated May 23, 1917. London, Nat. Hist. Mus.

MURDOCK, BEAMISH. 1865. History of Nova Scotia **1**. Halifax.

MURPHY, HENRY. Cruse Translator. 1865. Anthology of New Netherland. N. Y., Bradford Club Series, 4.

MURRAY, DAVID. 1904. Museums, their history and their use. **1**. Glasgow.

MURRAY, J. J. 1933. Brief history of Virginia ornithology. *Raven* **4**: 2–11.

NAUMANN, JOHANN FRIEDRICH. 1895. Natur der vögel Mitteleuropas. Gera-Unterhaus, F. E. Köhler.

NEWTON, ALFRED. 1861. Abstract of Mr. John Wolley's researches in Iceland respecting the gare-fowl or great auk (*Pinguinus impennis* Linn.). *Ibis* **3**: 374–399.

—— 1876. On the assignation of a type to the Linnaean genera with special reference to the genus Strix. *Ibis* (3) **6**: 94–105.

—— 1879. [Article, no ti.] *Stray feathers* **8**: 414–415.

—— 1893–1896. A dictionary of birds. London, A. & C. Black.

—— 1926. Ornithology. Ency. Brit. 13. ed. **19–20**: 299–326.

NICCHOLS, L. NELSON. 1934. First general American bird lists by Jedediah Morse in 1789 and 1793. Paper before Amer. Ornith. Union, Chicago.

NICHOLS, JOHN. 1812–1815. Literary anecdotes of eighteenth century comprising memoirs of W. Bowyer and his friends and biographical anecdotes of writers and artists. 9 v. London.

—— 1817. Illustrations of the literary history of the eighteenth century consisting of lettters and memoirs of eminent persons. London.

NICOLLS, M. J. 1930. Birds of Egypt, by R. Meinertzhagen. 2: 528. London, Pub. under authority of Egyptian Govt., Hugh Rees, Lts.

NISSEN, CLAUS. 1935. Die ornithologische illustration; ein überblick nebst einer bibliographie shöner vogelbücher. Philobiblon **8**: 23–40; 69–89; 123–136; 169–180; 224–234; 436–443.

NUIJENS, DR. B. W. TH. 1933. Dr. Volcher Coiter, 1534–1576. Een Noord-Nederlandsche geleerde uit de 16 de EEUW. *Nederlandsche Tyds. voor Geneeskunde* **77** (4): 5383–5401.

—— 1933–1934. Doctor Volcher Coiter. Een Noord-Nederlandsche geleerde uit de 16 EEUW. *Bijdr. Geschied. Geneesk.* **13–14**: 251–269. 1 Plate.

—— 1935. De laate tien jaren von Volcher Coiter's leven. *Nederl. Tyds. voor geneesk.* **79**: 2653–2659.

OEHSER, PAUL H. 1948. Louis Jean Pierre Vieillot (1748–1831). *Auk* **65** (4): 568–576.

—— 1949. Sons of science; the story of the Smithsonian Institution and its leaders. N. Y., Henry Schuman.

OLINA, G. P. 1622. Uccelliera; overo, Discorso della natura, etc. Roma.

OLIVER, F. W. 1913. Makers of British botany. Cambridge.

ORD, GEORGE. 1813–1814. American Ornithology . . . [vol. 8 and 9 edited with a memoir of the author, by G. Ord]. See Wilson, Alexander.

—— 1817. An account of an American species of the genus Tantalus, or Ibis. *Jour. Acad. Nat. Sci. Phila.* **1**: 53–57.

—— 1817. An account of the Florida jay, Bartram. *Jour. Acad. Nat. Sci. Phila.* **1**: 345–347.

—— 1817. Observations on two species of the genus Gracula, Latham. *Jour. Acad. Nat. Sci. Phila.* **1**: 253–261.

—— 1820 [Ord, G.]. A universal geography; . . . originally compiled by William Guthrie. Birds, 1: 155–187. See Rhoads, S.

—— 1828–1829. Another edition of American Ornithology with a sketch of the author's life by George Ord.

—— 1830. Some observations on the moulting of birds. *Trans. Amer. Philos. Soc.* **3**: 292–300.

—— 1836. Observations on the cow bunting of the United States. *Mag. Nat. Hist.* **9**: 57–71.

—— 1849. Memoir of Charles Alexander Lesueur. *Amer. Jour. Sci. & Arts* (2) **8** (23): 189–216.

—— 1858. MS. Letters to Charles Waterton. Amer. Philos. Soc.

ORNSTEIN, MARTHA. 1913. The rôle of the scientific societies in the seventeenth century. Columbia Univ. Diss. 79.

OVIEDO Y VALDÉZ GANGALO, FERNANDEZ DE. 1478–1557. Sumario de la natural historia de las Indias, Toledo.

OWEN, GEORGE. 1603. Description of Pembrokeshire. London.

PAINE, THOMAS. 1791. The Rights of Man. London.

Paisley magazine, or Literary and Antiquarian Miscellany. Notices regarding Alexander Wilson, author of the Foresters and Watty and Meg. 1828: 632–635.

PALEY, WILLIAM. 1890. Natural theology; revised to harmonize with modern science, by F. Le Gros Clark. London.

PALMER, T. S. 1899. Review economic ornithology. *U. S. D. A. Yearbook*.

—— 1917. Personalia in ornithology. *Auk* **34**: 445–452.

—— 1919. Indexes to ornithological literary journals. *Auk* **36**: 630–631.

—— 1919. Where American ornithologists rest. *Auk* **36**: 631–634.

—— 1928. Notes on persons whose names appear in the nomenclature of the California birds. *Condor* **30** (5): 261–307.

—— 1931. Report of the committee on biography and bibliography. *Auk* **48** (1) 87–90.

—— 1932. Report on biography and bibliography. *Auk* **49** (1): 71–73.

—— 1933. American ornithologists' union. *Auk* **50**: 64–79.

—— 1945. The Deane collection. *Auk* **62** (1): 171.

PARKINSON, SYDNEY. 1772. Original drawings. Brit. Mus. Nat. Hist. Add. MSS. 23920–23921.

PARKMAN, FRANCIS. 1879. LaSalle and the discovery of the great west. Boston.

PATON, ALLAN. 1863. Wilson, the ornithologist (Embodying many letters hitherto unpublished), 6. London, Longman, Green & Co.

PEABODY, REV. W. B. O. 1839. Life of Alexander Wilson. *Libr. Am. Biog.* 1st series, v. 2 ed. by J. Sparks.

PEARSON, T. GILBERT, and C. S. and H. H. BRIMLEY. 1919. Birds of North Carolina. Raleigh, N. C. Geol. & Econ. Surv.

PECK, A. L. 1943. Aristotle; generation of animals, with an Eng. trans. Cambridge, Harvard Univ. Press.

PELZELN, A. V. 1873. On the birds in the Imperial collection at Vienna, obtained from the Leverian Mus. *Ibis* **3**: 14–54; 105–124.

PENARD, THOMAS E. 1924. Historical sketch of the ornithology of Surinam. Reprint. from De West-Indische Gids., 168. The Hague.

PENNANT, THOMAS. 1773. The genera of birds. Edinburgh.

—— 1784–1785. Arctic zoology. 2 v. London, Print. by Henry Hughs.

—— 1790. Indian zoology. 2d ed. London.

—— 1793. The literary life of the late Thomas Pennant by himself. London.

PENNELL, FRANCIS W. 1942. Benjamin Smith Barton as a naturalist. *Proc. Amer. Philos. Soc.* **86** (1): 108–122.

PERKINS, S. E. 1938. The Alexander Wilson memorial in Indiana. *Wilson Bull.* **50**: 13–17.

PETERS, J. L. 1934. Check-List of the birds of the world. 6 v. Cambridge.

—— 1950. Bird names in Linnaeus' Catalogue of Edwards' Natural history. *Auk* **67**: 375–377.

Philadelphia, Academy of Natural Sciences of. 1876. Guide to the museum. Ornithology. 63–69.

Philadelphia (Sunday) Press. May 3, 1896. A romance of Bartram's garden, 8.

PHILLIPS, JOHN C. 1925. Leonard Baldner, seventeenth century sportsman and naturalist. (Unrecorded copy of his book containing his portrait.) *Auk* **42** (3) : 332–341.

PICKENS, A. L., and BELLE M. 1934. Some early American bird lore. *Auk* **51** (4) : 535–536.

PICKERING, JOAN. 1948. The Sudbury Grammar School. MS. London.

PINKERTON, J. 1812. Voyages **13**. London.

PLEDGE, H. T. 1947. Science since 1500; a short history of mathematics, physics, chemistry, biology. N. Y. Phil. Libr.

PLINIUS SECUNDUS, CAIUS THE ELDER. 1601. The historie of the world, commonly called The natural historie of C. Plinius Secundus. Tr. into Eng. by P. Holland. London. (2 v. in 1.)

PLOT, ROBERT. 1677. Natural history of Oxfordshire. Oxford.

PRESCOTT, W. H. 1876. History of the conquest of Mexico. Philadelphia, J. B. Lippincott Co.

PRITZEL, GEORGE AUGUST. 1872. Thesaurus literaturae botanicae . . . Lipsiae.

PULTENEY, RICHARD. 1790. Historical and biographical sketches of the progress of botany in England **2**: 219.

PURCHAS, SAMUEL. 1617. Purchas, his pilgrimage; or Relations of the world and the religions observed in all ages and places discovered from the creation to the present. London.

PURDY, JAMES B. 1895. A relative of Alexander Wilson. *Auk* **12**: 396.

RAVEN, CHARLES E. 1942. John Ray, the naturalist; his life and works. Cambridge.

RAY, JOHN. 1678. The ornithology of F. Willughby . . . Tr. into Eng. . . . See Willughby, F.

—— 1713. Synopsis methodica avium et piscium. Ed. Wm. Derham. London.

—— 1718. Philosophical letters and those of F. Willughby. London. W. and J. Innys.

—— 1722. The wisdom of God manifested in the world of the creation. London, W. and J. Innys.

RECCHUS, NARDUS ANTONIAS. 1649. Rerum medicarum novae Hispaniae thesaurus. Roma.

—— 1651. Another ed., the work of several authors (200 birds briefly described).

REEVES, A. M. 1890. Finding of Wineland the Good. London.

REMINGTON, C. L. 1948. Brief biographies 10: John Abbot. *Lepidop. News* **1** (3) : 28–30.

RHOADS, SAMUEL N. 1894. A reprint of the North American zoology by George Ord. Haddonfield, N. J., Pub. by the ed.

—— 1908. George Ord. *Cassinia*, **12**: 4.

—— 1912. Additions to the known ornithological publications of C. S. Rafinesque. *Auk* **19**: 191–198.

—— 1912. Ornithological notes of Rafinesque in the Western Review and Misc. Mag., Lexington, Ky. *Auk* **29** (3) : 401.

—— 1918. Georgia's rarities further discovered in a 2d American portfolio of John Abbot's bird plates. *Auk* **35** (3) : 271–286.

—— 1923. Note on Bonaparte's continuation of Wilson's ornithology. *Auk* **40** (2) : 341.

RICH, OBADIAH. 1835. Bibliotheca Americana nova. London.

RICHARDSON, RICHARD. 1835. Extracts from the literary and scientific correspondence of R. Richardson of Bierly, Yorkshire . . . Yarmouth, C. Sloman.

RICHMOND, CHARLES W. 1909. A reprint of the ornithological writings of C. S. Rafinesque. *Auk* **26** (1) : 37–55.

—— 1909. [Synopsis of life of Rafinesque.] *Auk* **26** (1) : 37.

—— 1917. The earliest name for the nighthawk. *Auk* **34** (1) : 88–89.

RICHMOND, JOHN. 1781. Journal of Capt. Cook's last voyage. London.

RICKETTS, HENRY W. Legitimacy of names in Bartram's travels. *Rhodora* **46** (551) : 389–391.

RIVES, WILLIAM C. 1890. A catalogue of the birds of the Virginias. Newport, R. I.

ROBERTS, T. S. 1940. Calder's statuette of Alexander Wilson. *Flicker* **12** (4) : 39.

Royal Society of London. 1632–1727. Council minutes **2**: 324.

—— 1731. Journal book **15** (1731–1734) : 190, 292, 307.

—— 1743. Author index of the Philosophical transactions.

—— 1912. Record of the Royal Society. 3d ed. London.

RUDBECK, OLOF, JR. 1710. MS. Fågelboken. 10 Internat. Ornith. Cong., Upsala, Sweden. June 10–17, 1950.

—— 1720? MS. Svenska fåglar efter naturen. Upsala.

RUSK, RALPH LESLIE. 1923. The adventures of Gilbert Imlay. *Ind. Univ. Stud.* **57**.

RYDBERG, PER AXEL. 1905. Linnaeus and American botany. *Ann. N. Y. Acad. Sci.* **18**: 38.

RYSGAARD, G. N. 1940. Wilson's birds. *Flicker* **12** (4) : 40.

SABIN, JOSEPH. 1868. Dictionary of books relating to America from its discovery to the present time. N. Y., author.

SABINE, E. 1818. Memoir on the birds of Greenland. *Trans. Linn. Soc.* **12**: 527–529.

SACHS, JULIUS VON. 1890. History of botany (1530–1860). Tr. by H. E. F. Garnsey; rev. by I. B. Balfour. Oxford, Clarendon Pr.

SAGARD, THÉODAT G. 1632. Le grand voyage du pays des Hvrons situé en l'Amérique . . . Paris, chez Denys Moreau.

SAGE, JOHN H. 1895. Letter from John L. Gardiner to Alexander Wilson, April 30, 1810. *Auk* **12**: 359–362.

ST. ANDREW'S SOCIETY. 1923. General notes. *Auk* **40**: 575.

ST. GEORGE'S CHAPEL. 1740–1754. Parish registers. London.

ST. LUKE'S CHURCH. 1749. MS. Parish register, burials. London.

ST. PETER'S PARISH REGISTER. 1675–1685. Sudbury, Suffolk.

SALVIN, OSBERT. 1874. A visit to the principal museums of the United States, with notes on some of the birds contained therein. *Ibis*, ser. 3, **4**: 305–329.

SAVAGE, S. 1922. The discovery of some of Jaques LeMoyne's botanical drawings. *Gardener's Chron.* (3) **51**: 44.

SAWYER, F. C. 1949. Notes on some original drawings of birds used by Dr. John Latham. *Jour. Soc. Bibl. Nat. Hist.* **2** (5) : 173–180.

SCHARF, JOHN THOMAS, and THOMPSON WESTCOTT. 1884. History of Philadelphia, 1609–1884. 3 v. Phila.

SCHENK, EDWARD T., and JOHN H. McMASTERS. 1936. Procedure in taxonomy, including a reprint of the International rules of zoological nomenclature . . . Revised ed. Stanford Univ. Pr. 1948.

SCHERREN, HENRY. 1905. The first bird list of Eber & Pencer (1549) and its relation to the avium . . . Proc. 4th Internat. Ornith. Cong. London, Dulau & Co. Pub. 1907.

SCLATER, R. L. 1891. Recent advances in our knowledge of the geographical distribution of birds. *Ibis* (6), **3**: 514–557.

SCHORGER, ARLIE W. 1938. Unpublished MS. by Cotton Mather on the passenger pigeon. *Auk* **55**: 471–477.

—— 1945. Bird portraits by Peter Rendisbacher (1806–1834). *Wilson Bull.* **57** (2) : 89–91.

SCHULLIAN, DOROTHY M. Oct. 30, 1948. The Army medical library. *Antiq. Bookm., Off. Pub. Wkly.*, 777–778.

SCOTT, DAVID. 1876. The proper specific name of the song sparrow. *Amer. Naturalist* **10**: 17.

SCOTT, E. J. 1904. Index to Sloane MSS. in the British Museum. London.

SCUDDER, SAMUEL H. 1888. John Abbot, the Aurelian. *Can. Ent.* **20** (3) : 150.

—— 1889. The butterflies of Eastern United States and Canada, with special reference to New England. Excursus XX. The three pioneering students of butterflies of this country, 651–658. Cambridge. Print. for the author.

—— 1889. Butterflies of New England **1**: 651–654.

SHARPE, R. B. 1906. The history of the collections contained in the Natural history depts. of the British Museum **2** (3).

SHAW, GEORGE, and F. P. NODDER. 1789–1813. Naturalists' miscellany. 24 v. London.

SHAW, H. S. 1940. An early figure of the great auk. *Auk* **57** (1) : 112–113.

SHEEHAN, DONALD. 1941. The Manchester Literary and Philosophical Society. *Isis* **33** (4) : 519–523.

SHERARD, WILLIAM. 1722–1723. MS. Dr. Sherard's Philosophical letters **11**: 152–306.

SHERBORN, CHARLES DAVIES. 1903–1930. Index animalium. Pt. 1–14. London.

—— 1934. On the dates of Pallas'. *Zoog. Russo-Asiatica. Ibis* (13) **4**: 164–167.

SHORR, PHILIP. 1932. Science and superstition in the 18th Century; a study of the treatment of science in two encyclopedias of 1725–1750, Chandler's Cyclopedia, London, 1728, and Zedler's Universal Lexicon, Leipzig, 1732–50.

SHUFELDT, R. W. 1886. On an old portrait of Audubon painted by himself and a word about some of his early drawings. *Auk* **3** (4) : 417–420.

—— 1902. Alfred Newton, F. R. S. *Osprey* **1** (2) : 30–32.

SIMPSON, CHARLES R. n. d. St. Luke's Parish church . . . 1733–1933. London.

SINGER, CHARLES. 1928. From magic to science. N. Y., Boni and Liveright.

SLACK, MABEL, and HARVEY B. LOVELL. See Lovell, Harvey B.

SLOANE, HANS. 1707–1725. A voyage to the islands Madera, Barbados Nieves, St. Christopher's and Jamaica, with the natural history of the herbs, trees, four-footed beasts, fishes, birds, insects, reptiles . . . 2 v. London, Print. for the author.

SMITH, EDGAR F. 1924. Benjamin Smith Barton. *Papers Lancaster Co. Hist. Soc.* **28**: 59–66.

SMITH, J. 1624. The generall historie of Virginia, New-England and the Summer Isles; with the names of the adventurers, planters, and governours . . . 1548 to this present 1624. London, Print. by D. & I. H. for Michael Sparkes.

SMITH, JAMES EDWARD. 1797. The natural history of the rarer lepidopterous insects collected from observations of John Abbot. 2 v. London. Print. by T. Bensley.

—— 1821. A selection from the correspondence of Linnaeus and other naturalists **2**: 442–451.

SMITH, CAPT. JOHN. 1612. A map of Virginia with a description of the country, the commodities, the people, government and religion, 14–15. Oxford, Joseph Barnes.

SMITH, WILLIAM. 1844–49. Dictionary of Greek and Roman biography and mythology. London.

SMITHSONIAN INSTITUTION. 1901. Annual report of the Board of regents for the year ending 30 June 1897. Rpt. U. S. Nat'l Mus. II. Washington, Govt. Pr. Off.

SOUTHWELL, THOMAS. 1902. Notes and letters on the natural history of Norfolk more especially on the birds and fishes, from the MSS. of Sir Thomas Browne. London.

SPERLING, CHARLES F. D. 1861. A short history of the borough of Sudbury in the county of Suffolk; comp. from materials coll. by W. W. Hodson. Sudbury, Print. by R. B. Marten.

SPRAT, THOMAS. 1702. History of the Royal Society of London for the improving of natural knowledge. 2d. ed. corrected. London, Print. R. Chiswell.

SPRUNT, JAMES. 1916. Chronicles of the Cape Fear River, 1660–1916, 58, 584 note 21. Raleigh.

STEENDAM, JACOB. 1661. New Amsterdam, tr. by H. C. Murphy. The Hague.

STEENSTRUP, J. 1885. *Edinburgh Philosophical Jour.* **10**: 97.

STEENSTRUP, J. J. 1865. The gare-fowl and its historians. *Nat. Hist. Rev.*, 467–551.

STEIER, AUGUST. 1913. Aristotles und Plinius studien zur geschichte der zoologie. Wurzburg.

STEJNEGER, LEONARD. 1884. Analecta ornithologica. 5 pts. 2: (earliest available name of Am. titlark; 4, cardinal grosbeak). *Auk*, n. s. **1** (1) : 167–168; 171–172.

—— 1885. Analecta ornithologica. 4th ser. *Auk*, n. s. **2** (1) : 178–188.

—— 1885. Standard natural history, "Birds." Boston.

STELLUTI, F. 1625. Single sheet illustrating the external morphology of the honeybee Microscopio observabat Romae. Not seen.

STEVENS, HENRY ("of Vermont"), 1870. Bibliotheca historica. 222–226. Boston.

—— 1900. Thomas Hariot and his associates. London, Priv. print.

STEVENS, O. A. 1936. The first descriptions of North American birds. *Wilson Bull.* **48**: 203–215.

STEVENS, REV. WILLIAM BACON. 1847–1859. History of Georgia from its discovery to 1798. 2 v. N. Y. & Phila.

STONE, WITMER. 1898. Alexander Wilson and the Ipswich sparrow. *Osprey* **2** (9) : 117.

—— 1899. Some Philadelphia ornithological collections and collectors, 1784–1850. *Auk* **16** (1) : 166–177.

—— 1905. Mark Catesby, some early American ornithologists. *Bird Lore* **7**: 126.

—— 1906. A bibliography and nomenclature of the works of John James Audubon. *Auk* **23** (4) : 298–312.

—— 1906. Some unpublished letters of Alexander Wilson and John Abbot. *Auk* **23** (4) : 361–368.

—— 1913. Bird migration records of William Bartram. *Auk* **30**: 325–358.

—— 1929. Mark Catesby and the nomenclature of North American birds. *Auk* **46** (4) : 447–454.

—— 1931. Review of Phillips's catalogue of game books (American game mammals and birds, a catalogue of books 1582 to 1925). *Auk* **48** (1) : 138–139.

—— 1934. MS. Some pre-Linnaean ornithologists—Catesby, Edwards and Brisson and their place in the history of North American ornithology. Read at Amer. Ornith. Un. meeting, Chicago.

STRACHEY, WILLIAM. 1610. History of travaile into Virginia Britannia. *Hakluyt Soc. Pub.* **6**. London, 1849, p. 142.

STREET, PHILLIPS B. 1948. The Edward Harris collection of birds. *Wilson Bull.* **60** (3) : 167–184.

STRESEMANN, E. 1932. The bird collection at the Tring Museum; its development and its end. *Ornithol. Monatsberichte* **40** (3).

—— 1949. Birds collected in the North Pacific area during Capt. Cook's last voyage (1778–1779). *Ibis* **91**: 244–255.

—— 1950. Birds collected during Capt. James Cook's last expedition (1776–1780). *Auk* **67** (1) : 66–88.

STROHL, J. Conrad Gesner's zoologische werke als characteristische zeichen einer neuen betrachtungsweisse der natur. *Verhandl. Schweiz. Nat. Forsch. Gesellsch.* **115**: 440–441.

STRONG, REUBEN MYRON. 1939. A bibliography of birds: Pt. 1, Author catalogue A–J, Zoological Series, Field Mus. Nat. Hist., vol. 25, Publication 442. Pt. 2, K–Z, vol. 25, Publication 457. Pt. 3, A bibliography of birds subject index. **25** (3) : No. 581. 1946.

STRUTT, JOSEPH. 1776. A compleat view of the manners
customs arms habits etc.   3 v.   London.

SUNDEVALL, CARL. 1872. Olof Rudbeck's Fågelbog inlemnad
till K. Vetenskap's Societeten, 7.   Upsala.

SWAINSON, WILLIAM. 1818. A mansucript letter to John
Abbot penned at the bottom of one of John Abbot's letters
(that of 10 November 1818) in which Swainson gives his
receipt for birdskin preservative.   London, Linnaean Society.

—— 1840. Taxidermy with the biography of zoologists and
notices of their works, 252–259, 263–270.   London, Longman,
Orme, Brown, Green, Longmans.

—— 1900. Comments on correspondence, Osprey 5 (2) : 29–30.

SWANN, H. KIRKE. 1913. A dictionary of English and folk-
names of British birds.   London, Witherby & Co.

SWEET, JESSIE M. 1935. Sir Hans Sloane. Life and mineral
collection. Nat. Hist. Mag. [British] 1: 49–64; 2: 97–
116; 3: 145–164.

SWENK, MYRON H. 1933. A history of Nebraska ornithology:
1. The ancient period fossil birds. Neb. Bird Rev. 1 (2).

TALCOTT, WILLIAM. 1895. Surroundings and site of Raleigh's
colony. Amer. Hist. Ass'n Ann. Rpt., 47.

TAYLOR, E. C. R. 1930. Samuel Purchas. Geog. Jour. 75:
536–539.

—— 1931. Master Hore's voyage of 1536. Geog. Jour. 77:
469–470.

THACKER, T. L. 1927. Earliest recorded observations on
American birds. Can. Field Naturalist 40 (2) : 38–40.

THIEME, ULRICH, und FELIX BECKER. 1907. Jaques LeMoyne,
Allgemeines Lexikon der Bildenden Künstler 23: 31–32.
Leipzig. Verlag von Wilhelm Engelmann; New York,
G. E. Steckert & Co.

THIERY, MAURICE. 1929. Life and voyages of Capt. Cook.
London, Rev. in Geog. Rev. 75: 196–197.

THOMAS AQUINAS, SAINT. 1911–1922. The Summa theologia
of St. Thomas Aquinas (literally trans.). London, B.
Oates & Washbourne, ltd.

THOMPSON, D'ARCY WENTWORTH. 1895. A glossary of Greek
birds.   Oxford.

—— 1910. Aristotle's history of animals 8: 16, 600a; 12, 596.
Oxford. Clarendon Pr.

—— 1910. The works of Aristotle translated into English
under the editorship of J. A. Smith and W. D. Ross. 4.
Historia animalium. Oxford, Clarendon Pr.

—— 1913. Aristotle as a biologist.   Oxford.

THORNDIKE, LYNN. 1914. Roger Bacon and experimental
method in the Middle Ages. Phil. Rev. 23: 278.

—— 1915. Natural science in the Middle Ages. Pop. Sci.
Mo. 87: 271–291.

—— 1923. History of magic and experimental science. 2 v.
New York, Macmillan.

THWAITE, RUBEN GOLD, ed. 1703. Lahonton's new voyages
to N. A. 2 v. London, H. Bonwicke.

TICEHURST, CLAUDE B. 1932. History of the birds of Suffolk.
Auk 50 (2) : 241–243.

TODD, W. E. CLYDE. 1900. Requirements of a faunal list.
Osprey 4 (6) : 87–89.

TOWNSEND, C. W., Ed. 1911. Captain Cartwright and his
Labrador journal.   Boston, Dana Estes & Company.

TROTTER, SPENCER. 1907. Peter Kalm's travels. Pop. Sci.
Mo. 71: 413–419.

—— 1909. An enquiry into the history of the current
English names of North American birds. Auk 26: 346–363.

TUCKERMAN, EDWARD. 1860. New England's rarities discovered by John Josselyn, Gent., with an introduction and
notes. Archaeologia Amer., Trans. Amer. Antiq. Soc. 4:
107–238.

TRUMBULL, GURDON. 1888. Names and portraits of birds which
interest gunners, with descriptions in language understood
of the people.   N. Y. Harper & Bros.

TUFTS, R. W. 1927. Bird banding in 1798. Can. Field
Naturalist 41: 17–18.

TURGOT, E. F. 1758. Memoire instructif sur la manière de
reasembler, de preparer . . . diverse curiosites de l'histoire
naturelle.   Paris.

TURNER, WILLIAM. 1544. Avium praecipuarum quarum apud
Plinium et Artistotelem mentio est, brevis et succincta
historia.   Cologne.

TURNOR, PHILIP. 1790. Journals of Samuel Hearne and
Philip Turnor.   Rare Book Coll., Libr. Cong., Wash.

URBAN I. 1898. Symbolae Antillanae 3: 31.   Berlin.

VEGA, G. DE LA. 1633. First part of Royal Commentaries
[of Peru]. 2 v. Hakluyt Soc. Pub. 12, v. 1, 1869; 14, v.
2, 1871.

VERAZZANUS, JANUS. 1524. The voyage of John de Verraz-
zano along the coast of North America from Carolina to
Newfoundland a. d. 1524. Tr. from the original Italian
by Joseph G. Cogswell, Esq. 2d ser. 1: 37–54 (1841, N. Y.
Hist. Soc.).

VERNER, COL. WILLOUGHBY. Prehistoric man in southern Spain.
3: Country life. 36 (916) : 114–118.   London.

VIEILLOT, LOUIS JEAN PIERRE. 1807. Histoire naturelle des
oiseaux de l'Amérique septentrionale . . . 1: 1–2. Paris,
Chez Desray.

VROOMAN-SMITH, G. 1893. Scenes from life of Alexander
Wilson; his Southern trip tour. Oologist 10 (12) : 131–325.

WADE, JOHN. 1880. Alexander Wilson's schoolhouse. Oologist
5: 43.

WAYNE, ARTHUR T., and PAUL M. REA, ed. 1910. Birds of
South Carolina.   Charleston.

WEBBER, J. 1777–1779. MS. 90 drawings, some in color,
executed by J. Webber during 2d voyage of Capt. Cook
. . . Pres. by the Lord's Commissioners of the Admiralty
to the British Museum.

WEEKS, STEPHEN B. 1891. The lost colony of Roanoke.
Amer. Hist. Assn. Papers 5: 107–146.

WEISS, HARRY B., and ZIEGLER, GRACE M. 1930. Thomas Say,
early American naturalist.   Springfield, Ill.

WETMORE, ALEXANDER. 1927. Present status of the check-list
of fossil birds of North America. Auk 44 (2) : 179–183.

—— 1930. The Rabié paintings of Haitian birds (done between 1769 and 1785). . . . Auk 47 (4) : 481–486.

WETMORE, ALEXANDER, and BRADSHAW SWALES. 1931. Birds
of Haiti and the Dominican Republic. U. S. Nat. Mus.
Bull. 155.

WHITBOURNE, RICHARD A. 1620. A discourse and discovery of
Nevfovndland. . . . London.

WHITE, GILBERT. 1789. Natural history and antiquities of
Selborne in the county of Hampshire.   London.

WHITE, JOHN. 1898. Planters' plea. Amer. Colon. Tracts
Mo. 2 (3).

WILKIN, SIMON. 1835. Sir Thomas Browne's collected works.
2 v. London, H. G. Bohn.

WILLARD, S. L. 1877. Directory of United States ornithologists.   Utica, N. Y.

WILLIAMS, SAMUEL. 1794. Natural and civil history of
Vermont.   Walpole, N. H.

WILLIAMSON, JAMES A. 1929. The voyages of the Cabots and
the English discovery of North America under Henry VII
and Henry VIII.   London, Argonaut Pr.

WILLUGHBY, FRANCIS. 1678. The ornithology of Francis Willughby. 3 v., "wherein all the birds hitherto known are
accurately described." Tr. into English with many additions . . . by John Ray.   London.

WILSON, ALEXANDER. 1790. Poems. Paisley, Print. by J.
Nielson.

—— 1791. Watty and Meg; or the wife reformed. A true
tale.   Glasgow, Brash and Reid.

—— 1800–1804. The Invitation; The Rural Walk; The Solitary Tutor. *Literary Mag. Phila.* **2** (10) : 265–267; **2** (11) : 377–379; **2** (13) : 533–536.

—— 1808–1814. American ornithology or the natural history of birds of the United States. 9 v. Phila., Bradford and Inskeep.

—— 1816. Burial entry. Funeral Rec. (Burials 1803–1816, Old Swede's Church or Gloria Dei). Phila.

—— 1838. The foresters; a poem descriptive of a pedestrian journey to the falls of Niagara in the autumn of 1804. West Chester, Pa., Print. by Joseph Painter.

—— 1913. 100th anniversary of his death. *Auk* **30** (4) : 622–623.

—— 1934. Exhibit of Wilsoniana. *Carnegie Mag.* **8** (7) : 202.

—— 1941. The James Crow portrait of Alexander Wilson, by John M. McWilliam and Casey A. Wood. *Auk* **58** (2) : 236–238.

WILSON, ALEXANDER, and CHARLES L. BONAPARTE. 1831. American ornithology; or the natural history of the birds of the United States. 4 v. Edinburgh.

WILSON, GORDON. 1931. Abstract of a thesis (Ph.D.) presented at Indiana Univ. *Auk* **48** (3) : 462.

—— 1931. Alexander Wilson. MS. Univ. of Ind. Diss.

WILSON, JAMES SOUTHALL. 1906. Alexander Wilson, poet, naturalist; a study of his life. N. Y. and Washington, Neale Pub. Co.

WINSOR, JUSTIN, ed. 1884–1889. A narrative and critical history of America. 8 v. Boston.

Wisconsin Historical Collections. 1869. **6**: 220–270.

WOLLASTON, A. F. R. 1921. A life of Alfred Newton, professor of comparative anatomy, Cambridge Univ., 1866–1907. London, John Murray. Review, *Auk* **38** (4) : 612–614.

WOLLSTONECRAFT, MARY. 1787. Thoughts on the education of daughters. London.

—— 1792. Vindication of the rights of women. London.

WOOD, CASEY A. 1931. An introduction to the literature of vertebrate zoology, based chiefly on the titles in the Blacker library at McGill, The Emma Shearer Wood library of ornithology, the Bibliotheca Osleriana and other libraries of McGill University, Montreal. Oxford, Univ. Press. London, Humphrey Milford.

—— 1942. De arte venandi cum avibus of Frederick. II. Stanford Univ. Press.

WOOD, WILLIAM. 1634. New England's prospect. London, Print. by Gho. Cotes for John Bellamie.

WOTTON, EDVARDI. 1552. Ni oxoniensis de differentiis animalium, 71. Lutetiae Parisiorum.

WRIGHT, A. H. 1910–1911. Early records of the passenger pigeon. *Auk* **37** (4) : 428–443; **28**: 346–366; **23** (4) : 427–449.

—— 1912. Early records of the Carolina paroquet. *Auk* **29**: 343–363.

—— 1914–1915. Early records of the wild turkey. *Auk* **31** (3) : 334; (4) : 463; **32** (1) : 61; 207; (3) : 348.

WRIGHT, ROBERT. 1867. Memoir of James Oglethorpe. London.

WRIGHT, THOMAS. 1841. Popular treatises on science, written in Middle Ages. London.

XIMENEZ, FRANCISCO. 1615. Quatro libros de la naturaleza y virtudes de las plantas, y animales que estan recevidos en el uso de medicina en nuevo España. [Extracto de las obras del Francisco Hernandez 1888, Morelia.]

ZIMMER, JOHN TODD. 1926. Catalogue of the Edward E. Ayer ornithological library. Pts. 1–2. *Field Mus. of Nat. Hist. Pub.* 239–240. Zool. Ser. 16. 2 v. Chicago.

ZIMMERMAN, HENRY. 1930. Account of the 3rd voyage of Captain James Cook around the world 1776–1780. Translated by Elsa Michaeles and Cecil French. Toronto, Ryerson Pr.

Zoological Record—Aves. 1864–1919. London, The Zoological Society.

* For kind assistance with this index, I am indebted to my family. Numbers in italics indicate illustrations.

* 2nd edition (1815) for which George Ord wrote the zoological matter. Original title: *A New Geographical Historical and Commercial Grammar; and Present state of the several Kingdoms of the World.* Phila., Johnson and Warner.